Handbook of Tables and Graphs for the Industrial Engineer and Manager

Jerry Banks
Russell G. Heikes
Georgia Institute of Technology
Atlanta, Georgia

Reston Publishing Company, Inc.
A Prentice-Hall Company
Reston, Virginia

Library of Congress Cataloging in Publication Data

Banks, Jerry.
Handbook of tables and graphs for the industrial engineer and manager.

1. Industrial engineering—Handbooks, manuals, etc.
I. Heikes, Russell G. II. Title.
T56.23.B36 1984 519′.0212 83-11125
ISBN 0-8359-2764-4

10 9 8 7 6 5 4 3 2 1

Printed in the United States of America

To
Rose and Jake

and to
Marilyn, Brian, and Lori

Contents

VI. Quality Control 135

XI. Engineering Economy 229

XI COMPOUND INTEREST FACTORS 230

Preface

The purpose of this Handbook is to group together numerous aids used by industrial engineers and managers. These aids are normally in the form of tables, graphs, or nomographs, and make their appearance in numerous and varied publications. Heretofore, the practicing IE or manager would need many different reference sources in anticipation of solving a technical problem. Alternatively, the IE or manager may have one or more of the handbooks of industrial engineering at his or her desk. These contain IE tools, techniques, and methods, each in a separate chapter. They are generally quite voluminous (more than 100 chapters!) and are written by many different authors (as many as 125, each with his or her own style). However, the desired table for a specific need may or may not be in a particular handbook.

Our content, style, and intent are different. We have selected what we believe to be the most frequently called for tables, graphs, and nomographs (we call them "exhibits") into one volume. In each case, we have prepared a description of the methodology associated with the exhibit, discussed how the exhibit is used (perhaps "read" is a better word), and given several illustrative examples of the use of the exhibit.

With our procedure, the reader goes to the heart of the matter expeditiously, without any superfluous material. The exhibits are contained within sections, which are virtually independent of each other. In only a very few instances is the reader asked to examine a supporting section, and then generally just as an aid in selecting the appropriate methodology for solving a problem in which there may be some confusion.

Using our method, the reader is not required to wade through textbookish discussions of asides and nebulous materials. The presentations are to the point, but sufficient to give the user a basic understanding of the subject matter.

This Handbook is not simply a collection of tables. We have painstakingly attempted to describe each exhibit in sufficient detail to make it useful.

We have been consistent with the use of notation within a subject area and conventional in our approach. For example, α is used to denote the right-hand tail areas under probability functions and to denote the probability of a type I error in hypothesis testing.

In Section II, we have used upper case letters to denote random variables and lower case letters to denote realizations of these random variables. However, we have not applied this upper/lower case designation to statistics that are functions of random variables such as the sample mean and the sample variance. For the practitioner, distinguishing between random variables and realizations would create rather than alleviate confusion. The context in which a symbol is used will enable the interested reader to determine its usage.

It is our belief that the exhibits contain 95 percent of the reference material needed by practicing industrial engineers. These references are all well documented concerning their appropriate use.

We would like to express our appreciation to our colleagues at Georgia Tech, John A. White, Lynwood A. Johnson, and Russ Hunt (now of Search Technology, Inc., Norcross, Georgia); and to James L. Wolbrink, Director of Publications of the Institute of Industrial Engineers, who examined our initial listing of sections and exhibits and made valuable suggestions about the contents.

The exhibits were obtained in several ways. We have generated as many of the tables as possible by computer, because we have observed errors in typeset tables and do not desire to carry these errors forward. They creep up in publication because it is very difficult to perform inspection with 100 percent accuracy. By generating our own tables, we can avoid proofreading typeset copy. Rest assured that we have checked our computer-generated tables adequately.

We have also generated some new, and we think useful, graphs and nomographs. These will facilitate and accelerate the problem-solving process. They also enable the reader to observe many policy options right before the eye.

We have also made liberal use of the works of others. We appreciate the permission of the many publishers who have allowed us to collect such a variety of materials between two covers.

How did we decide what should be in the Handbook, how much space is allocated to each section, and what is included? Realizing that industrial engineering and management have become more and more quantitative, we have opted for that direction. We selected areas of concentration that we know are useful to manufacturing and to the service industries.

We have not allocated a specified amount of space to each exhibit and each section. We want to cover each section adequately, and no more. Just because one table requires six pages for its coverage while another requires two does not means that the first is three times as important as the second. There are cases in which extending the parameter range or offering greater precision of an exhibit were possible, but we decided that satiation had been reached and that the reader could interpolate, approximate, or even generate if need be.

Revisiting the Table of Contents at this point in time gives us a feeling similar to reaching the top of a tall mountain after a long climb. "Look what we have been through, look what's down there!" A brief run-through of the contents is in order at this point.

We begin in Section I with the basics: several sections on mathematics including logarithms, factorials, series, and trigonometric relationships. These are the foundations of modern industrial engineering.

In Section II we describe a number of discrete and continuous probability distributions. We selected three of the discrete and four of the continuous distributions for extended description. These seven distributions are frequently used in engineering statistics.

Section III describes hypothesis testing. We discuss both parametric and nonparametric tests. Closely related to hypothesis testing is sample size determination, found in Section IV. Again, we describe the procedure for parametric (normal) and nonparametric cases.

In Section V we discuss the analysis of experiments. Duncan's multiple range test and Dunnett's test are included.

The largest amount of space is given to Section VI, which concerns quality control. We discuss both attributes and variables sampling plans. We describe the use of the most popular standards (MIL and ANSI) and show how control charts are constructed.

In Section VII, we present an abbreviated table of random numbers and an abbreviated table of random normal numbers. These have application mainly in simulation, but are also used in other fields (e.g., random numbers are used in sample selection).

Section VIII describes two topics in reliability. We describe reliability testing through the use of Handbook H108. Then we relate availability to mean time between failure and mean time to repair.

Section IX describes waiting line, or queueing, models. We show how to analyze the infinite population systems with Poisson arrivals and exponential services for various numbers of servers. We also show how the finite population system can be analyzed.

In Section X we describe several procedures that can be used in procurement and inventory systems. We describe manufacturing progress, also called the learning curve, and methods which facilitate the determination of order quantities and the setting of reorder points.

Section XI contains factors for engineering economy. We have included interest rates that are representative of the wild fluctuations that have occurred over the last several years.

Section XII includes selected topics in human factors engineering. Although it is impossible to be complete in exposition, we have presented enough material to inform the reader concerning five major divisions of the field.

Finally, Section XIII is related to conversion factors. First, we have given numerous conversions between the metric and the U.S. customary system. Then we close with conversion between the decimal and other number systems. These last conversions are important in digital computing.

We feel that this Handbook will be extremely useful and a real time-saver for the practitioner. We also feel that it can have great utility in a survey course in industrial engineering, be it a short course that is part of a continuing education program or an introductory course at the university level. It could also be a most useful textbook for a set of courses in a school of technical education.

I

Basic Mathematics for Industrial Engineering

I.1 Logarithms

A. Description

Logarithms are mathematical operators used to convert any number X to the form B^Y, where Y is the logarithm of X. Any positive value can be used for B, which is referred to as the base number. The term "common log" is used for logarithms whose base number is 10, and the notation $Y = \log_{10} X$ can be used. Oftentimes, the subscript is omitted. Another frequently used base is

$$e = \sum_{k=0}^{\infty} \frac{1}{k!} = 2.71828\ldots$$

If the base number is e, then $Y = \log_e X$ is called the natural logarithm (or natural log) of X. To differentiate the natural log from other bases, particularly from $Y = \log X$ with base 10 implied, we usually write $Y = \ln X$.

Tabulation of common logs is extremely compact, as we can easily write any number X as the product of two other numbers, say V and W, where $1 \leq V < 10$, $W = 10^M$, and M is an integer. As with all logarithms, $\log_{10} X = \log_{10}(VW) = \log_{10} V + \log_{10} W$, but here we have $\log_{10} W = M$ and $0 \leq \log_{10} V < 1$. Thus, only tables of common logs for values between 1 and 10 are required. Exhibit I.1–1 contains the values used to compute the common logarithms for all numbers.

At times it is necessary to perform an inverse logarithmic operation; that is, given Y and the base B, find $X = B^Y$. This is referred to as taking the antilogarithm of Y, or antilog $Y = X$. As in the case of common logs, a table for antilogs need only be indexed on Y values between 0 and 1, with the decimal in the tabulated value moved the appropriate number of spaces. Exhibit I.1–2 gives antilogarithms for common logarithms from 0.000 to 0.999.

It may be necessary to use bases other than e or 10 (e.g., base 2 in information theory computations). It is possible to convert from logarithms of one base B to another base A by the multiplication of a constant $K = \log_A B$. That is,

$$\log_A X = \log_B X(\log_A B)$$

Conversion factors, $\log_A B$, for various values of A, for $B = 10$ and $B = e$, are as follows:

To Base A	From Base B	Conversion Factor K
10	2	0.3010
10	e	0.4343
10	3	0.4771
e	2	0.6931
e	3	1.0986
e	10	2.3026

A common use of logarithms is to reduce computational complexity. Logarithms are especially useful when large amounts of exponentiation and multiplication are required. A particular case that arises is the factorial of an integer, denoted $N!$, defined to be the product of all positive integers less than or equal to N. A table of the common logs of the factorials of the integers from 1 to 200 is provided in Exhibit I.1–3

B. Reading the Tables

Example B–1. Find the common log of 9.23. Entering Exhibit I.1–1 at the row for $X = 9.2$ and using the column headed by 3, we find $\log_{10}(9.23) = 0.9652$.

Example B–2. Find the common log of 107. Rewriting 107 as $(1.07)(10^2)$, we have $\log(107) = \log(1.07) + \log(10^2)$. Using Exhibit I.1–1, $\log(1.07) = 0.0294$, and noting that $\log(10^2) = 2\log(10) = 2.0$, we have $\log(107) = 0.0294 + 2.0 = 2.0294$.

Example B–3. Find the antilog(base 10) of 0.554. Entering Exhibit I.1–2 at the row for $Y = .55$ and using the column headed by 4, we find 3.581.

Example B–4. Find the antilog(base 10) of 4.332. We drop all numbers to the left of the decimal and look up the antilog of 0.332, finding 2.148 in Exhibit I.1–2. We then multiply by 10^M, where M equals the integer number previously dropped. In this case $M = 4$ and $10^4 = 10{,}000$. Multiplying by 2.148 gives 21,480.

Example B–5. Find the natural log of 9.23. From Example B–1, we know that $\log_{10}(9.23) = 0.9652$. Now

$$\log_e(9.23) = \log_{10}(9.23)K$$

where K is the conversion factor from base 10 to base e, found in the list of conversion factors to be 2.3026. Thus, $\log_e(9.23) = 0.9652(2.3026) = 2.2225$.

EXHIBIT I.1–1

COMMON (BASE 10) LOGARITHMS

X	.00	.01	.02	.03	.04	.05	.06	.07	.08	.09
1.0	.0000	.0043	.0086	.0128	.0170	.0212	.0253	.0294	.0334	.0374
1.1	.0414	.0453	.0492	.0531	.0569	.0607	.0645	.0682	.0719	.0755
1.2	.0792	.0828	.0864	.0899	.0934	.0969	.1004	.1038	.1072	.1106
1.3	.1139	.1173	.1206	.1239	.1271	.1303	.1335	.1367	.1399	.1430
1.4	.1461	.1492	.1523	.1553	.1584	.1614	.1644	.1673	.1703	.1732
1.5	.1761	.1790	.1818	.1847	.1875	.1903	.1931	.1959	.1987	.2014
1.6	.2041	.2068	.2095	.2122	.2148	.2175	.2201	.2227	.2253	.2279
1.7	.2304	.2330	.2355	.2380	.2405	.2430	.2455	.2480	.2504	.2529
1.8	.2553	.2577	.2601	.2625	.2648	.2672	.2695	.2718	.2742	.2765
1.9	.2788	.2810	.2833	.2856	.2878	.2900	.2923	.2945	.2967	.2989
2.0	.3010	.3032	.3054	.3075	.3096	.3118	.3139	.3160	.3181	.3201
2.1	.3222	.3243	.3263	.3284	.3304	.3324	.3345	.3365	.3385	.3404
2.2	.3424	.3444	.3464	.3483	.3502	.3522	.3541	.3560	.3579	.3598
2.3	.3617	.3636	.3655	.3674	.3692	.3711	.3729	.3747	.3766	.3784
2.4	.3802	.3820	.3838	.3856	.3874	.3892	.3909	.3927	.3945	.3962
2.5	.3979	.3997	.4014	.4031	.4048	.4065	.4082	.4099	.4116	.4133
2.6	.4150	.4166	.4183	.4200	.4216	.4232	.4249	.4265	.4281	.4298
2.7	.4314	.4330	.4346	.4362	.4378	.4393	.4409	.4425	.4440	.4456
2.8	.4472	.4487	.4502	.4518	.4533	.4548	.4564	.4579	.4594	.4609
2.9	.4624	.4639	.4654	.4669	.4683	.4698	.4713	.4728	.4742	.4757
3.0	.4771	.4786	.4800	.4814	.4829	.4843	.4857	.4871	.4886	.4900
3.1	.4914	.4928	.4942	.4955	.4969	.4983	.4997	.5011	.5024	.5038
3.2	.5051	.5065	.5079	.5092	.5105	.5119	.5132	.5145	.5159	.5172
3.3	.5185	.5198	.5211	.5224	.5237	.5250	.5263	.5276	.5289	.5302
3.4	.5315	.5328	.5340	.5353	.5366	.5378	.5391	.5403	.5416	.5428
3.5	.5441	.5453	.5465	.5478	.5490	.5502	.5514	.5527	.5539	.5551
3.6	.5563	.5575	.5587	.5599	.5611	.5623	.5635	.5647	.5658	.5670
3.7	.5682	.5694	.5705	.5717	.5729	.5740	.5752	.5763	.5775	.5786
3.8	.5798	.5809	.5821	.5832	.5843	.5855	.5866	.5877	.5888	.5899
3.9	.5911	.5922	.5933	.5944	.5955	.5966	.5977	.5988	.5999	.6010
4.0	.6021	.6031	.6042	.6053	.6064	.6075	.6085	.6096	.6107	.6117
4.1	.6128	.6138	.6149	.6160	.6170	.6180	.6191	.6201	.6212	.6222
4.2	.6232	.6243	.6253	.6263	.6274	.6284	.6294	.6304	.6314	.6325
4.3	.6335	.6345	.6355	.6365	.6375	.6385	.6395	.6405	.6415	.6425
4.4	.6435	.6444	.6454	.6464	.6474	.6484	.6493	.6503	.6513	.6522
4.5	.6532	.6542	.6551	.6561	.6571	.6580	.6590	.6599	.6609	.6618
4.6	.6628	.6637	.6646	.6656	.6665	.6675	.6684	.6693	.6702	.6712
4.7	.6721	.6730	.6739	.6749	.6758	.6767	.6776	.6785	.6794	.6803
4.8	.6812	.6821	.6830	.6839	.6848	.6857	.6866	.6875	.6884	.6893
4.9	.6902	.6911	.6920	.6928	.6937	.6946	.6955	.6964	.6972	.6981
5.0	.6990	.6998	.7007	.7016	.7024	.7033	.7042	.7050	.7059	.7067
5.1	.7076	.7084	.7093	.7101	.7110	.7118	.7126	.7135	.7143	.7152
5.2	.7160	.7168	.7177	.7185	.7193	.7202	.7210	.7218	.7226	.7235
5.3	.7243	.7251	.7259	.7267	.7275	.7284	.7292	.7300	.7308	.7316
5.4	.7324	.7332	.7340	.7348	.7356	.7364	.7372	.7380	.7388	.7396

Example B–6. Find the value of (18!). From Exhibit I.1–3, for $N = 18$ we find $\log_{10}(18!) = 15.8063$. Dropping the leading integer 15, and looking up .806 in Exhibit I.1–2 gives 6.397, which, when multiplied by 10^{15}, yields 6.397×10^{15}. Using linear interpolation, the slightly more accurate result 6.4015×10^{15} is obtained.

EXHIBIT I.1-1—CONTINUED

X	.00	.01	.02	.03	.04	.05	.06	.07	.08	.09
5.5	.7404	.7412	.7419	.7427	.7435	.7443	.7451	.7459	.7466	.7474
5.6	.7482	.7490	.7497	.7505	.7513	.7520	.7528	.7536	.7543	.7551
5.7	.7559	.7566	.7574	.7582	.7589	.7597	.7604	.7612	.7619	.7627
5.8	.7634	.7642	.7649	.7657	.7664	.7672	.7679	.7686	.7694	.7701
5.9	.7709	.7716	.7723	.7731	.7738	.7745	.7752	.7760	.7767	.7774
6.0	.7782	.7789	.7796	.7803	.7810	.7818	.7825	.7832	.7839	.7846
6.1	.7853	.7860	.7868	.7875	.7882	.7889	.7896	.7903	.7910	.7917
6.2	.7924	.7931	.7938	.7945	.7952	.7959	.7966	.7973	.7980	.7987
6.3	.7993	.8000	.8007	.8014	.8021	.8028	.8035	.8041	.8048	.8055
6.4	.8062	.8069	.8075	.8082	.8089	.8096	.8102	.8109	.8116	.8122
6.5	.8129	.8136	.8142	.8149	.8156	.8162	.8169	.8176	.8182	.8189
6.6	.8195	.8202	.8209	.8215	.8222	.8228	.8235	.8241	.8248	.8254
6.7	.8261	.8267	.8274	.8280	.8287	.8293	.8299	.8306	.8312	.8319
6.8	.8325	.8331	.8338	.8344	.8351	.8357	.8363	.8370	.8376	.8382
6.9	.8388	.8395	.8401	.8407	.8414	.8420	.8426	.8432	.8439	.8445
7.0	.8451	.8457	.8463	.8470	.8476	.8482	.8488	.8494	.8500	.8506
7.1	.8513	.8519	.8525	.8531	.8537	.8543	.8549	.8555	.8561	.8567
7.2	.8573	.8579	.8585	.8591	.8597	.8603	.8609	.8615	.8621	.8627
7.3	.8633	.8639	.8645	.8651	.8657	.8663	.8669	.8675	.8681	.8686
7.4	.8692	.8698	.8704	.8710	.8716	.8722	.8727	.8733	.8739	.8745
7.5	.8751	.8756	.8762	.8768	.8774	.8779	.8785	.8791	.8797	.8802
7.6	.8808	.8814	.8820	.8825	.8831	.8837	.8842	.8848	.8854	.8859
7.7	.8865	.8871	.8876	.8882	.8887	.8893	.8899	.8904	.8910	.8915
7.8	.8921	.8927	.8932	.8938	.8943	.8949	.8954	.8960	.8965	.8971
7.9	.8976	.8982	.8987	.8993	.8998	.9004	.9009	.9015	.9020	.9025
8.0	.9031	.9036	.9042	.9047	.9053	.9058	.9063	.9069	.9074	.9079
8.1	.9085	.9090	.9096	.9101	.9106	.9112	.9117	.9122	.9128	.9133
8.2	.9138	.9143	.9149	.9154	.9159	.9165	.9170	.9175	.9180	.9186
8.3	.9191	.9196	.9201	.9206	.9212	.9217	.9222	.9227	.9232	.9238
8.4	.9243	.9248	.9253	.9258	.9263	.9269	.9274	.9279	.9284	.9289
8.5	.9294	.9299	.9304	.9309	.9315	.9320	.9325	.9330	.9335	.9340
8.6	.9345	.9350	.9355	.9360	.9365	.9370	.9375	.9380	.9385	.9390
8.7	.9395	.9400	.9405	.9410	.9415	.9420	.9425	.9430	.9435	.9440
8.8	.9445	.9450	.9455	.9460	.9465	.9469	.9474	.9479	.9484	.9489
8.9	.9494	.9499	.9504	.9509	.9513	.9518	.9523	.9528	.9533	.9538
9.0	.9542	.9547	.9552	.9557	.9562	.9566	.9571	.9576	.9581	.9586
9.1	.9590	.9595	.9600	.9605	.9609	.9614	.9619	.9624	.9628	.9633
9.2	.9638	.9643	.9647	.9652	.9657	.9661	.9666	.9671	.9675	.9680
9.3	.9685	.9689	.9694	.9699	.9703	.9708	.9713	.9717	.9722	.9727
9.4	.9731	.9736	.9741	.9745	.9750	.9754	.9759	.9763	.9768	.9773
9.5	.9777	.9782	.9786	.9791	.9795	.9800	.9805	.9809	.9814	.9818
9.6	.9823	.9827	.9832	.9836	.9841	.9845	.9850	.9854	.9859	.9863
9.7	.9868	.9872	.9877	.9881	.9886	.9890	.9894	.9899	.9903	.9908
9.8	.9912	.9917	.9921	.9926	.9930	.9934	.9939	.9943	.9948	.9952
9.9	.9956	.9961	.9965	.9969	.9974	.9978	.9983	.9987	.9991	.9996

EXHIBIT I.1–2

COMMON (BASE 10) ANTILOGARITHMS

Y	.000	.001	.002	.003	.004	.005	.006	.007	.008	.009
.00	1.000	1.002	1.005	1.007	1.009	1.012	1.014	1.016	1.019	1.021
.01	1.023	1.026	1.028	1.030	1.033	1.035	1.038	1.040	1.042	1.045
.02	1.047	1.050	1.052	1.054	1.057	1.059	1.062	1.064	1.067	1.069
.03	1.072	1.074	1.076	1.079	1.081	1.084	1.086	1.089	1.091	1.094
.04	1.096	1.099	1.102	1.104	1.107	1.109	1.112	1.114	1.117	1.119
.05	1.122	1.125	1.127	1.130	1.132	1.135	1.138	1.140	1.143	1.146
.06	1.148	1.151	1.153	1.156	1.159	1.161	1.164	1.167	1.169	1.172
.07	1.175	1.178	1.180	1.183	1.186	1.189	1.191	1.194	1.197	1.199
.08	1.202	1.205	1.208	1.211	1.213	1.216	1.219	1.222	1.225	1.227
.09	1.230	1.233	1.236	1.239	1.242	1.245	1.247	1.250	1.253	1.256
.10	1.259	1.262	1.265	1.268	1.271	1.274	1.276	1.279	1.282	1.285
.11	1.288	1.291	1.294	1.297	1.300	1.303	1.306	1.309	1.312	1.315
.12	1.318	1.321	1.324	1.327	1.330	1.334	1.337	1.340	1.343	1.346
.13	1.349	1.352	1.355	1.358	1.361	1.365	1.368	1.371	1.374	1.377
.14	1.380	1.384	1.387	1.390	1.393	1.396	1.400	1.403	1.406	1.409
.15	1.413	1.416	1.419	1.422	1.426	1.429	1.432	1.435	1.439	1.442
.16	1.445	1.449	1.452	1.455	1.459	1.462	1.466	1.469	1.472	1.476
.17	1.479	1.483	1.486	1.489	1.493	1.496	1.500	1.503	1.507	1.510
.18	1.514	1.517	1.521	1.524	1.528	1.531	1.535	1.538	1.542	1.545
.19	1.549	1.552	1.556	1.560	1.563	1.567	1.570	1.574	1.578	1.581
.20	1.585	1.589	1.592	1.596	1.600	1.603	1.607	1.611	1.614	1.618
.21	1.622	1.626	1.629	1.633	1.637	1.641	1.644	1.648	1.652	1.656
.22	1.660	1.663	1.667	1.671	1.675	1.679	1.683	1.687	1.690	1.694
.23	1.698	1.702	1.706	1.710	1.714	1.718	1.722	1.726	1.730	1.734
.24	1.738	1.742	1.746	1.750	1.754	1.758	1.762	1.766	1.770	1.774
.25	1.778	1.782	1.786	1.791	1.795	1.799	1.803	1.807	1.811	1.816
.26	1.820	1.824	1.828	1.832	1.837	1.841	1.845	1.849	1.854	1.858
.27	1.862	1.866	1.871	1.875	1.879	1.884	1.888	1.892	1.897	1.901
.28	1.905	1.910	1.914	1.919	1.923	1.928	1.932	1.936	1.941	1.945
.29	1.950	1.954	1.959	1.963	1.968	1.972	1.977	1.982	1.986	1.991
.30	1.995	2.000	2.004	2.009	2.014	2.018	2.023	2.028	2.032	2.037
.31	2.042	2.046	2.051	2.056	2.061	2.065	2.070	2.075	2.080	2.084
.32	2.089	2.094	2.099	2.104	2.109	2.113	2.118	2.123	2.128	2.133
.33	2.138	2.143	2.148	2.153	2.158	2.163	2.168	2.173	2.178	2.183
.34	2.188	2.193	2.198	2.203	2.208	2.213	2.218	2.223	2.228	2.234
.35	2.239	2.244	2.249	2.254	2.259	2.265	2.270	2.275	2.280	2.286
.36	2.291	2.296	2.301	2.307	2.312	2.317	2.323	2.328	2.333	2.339
.37	2.344	2.350	2.355	2.360	2.366	2.371	2.377	2.382	2.388	2.393
.38	2.399	2.404	2.410	2.415	2.421	2.427	2.432	2.438	2.443	2.449
.39	2.455	2.460	2.466	2.472	2.477	2.483	2.489	2.495	2.500	2.506
.40	2.512	2.518	2.523	2.529	2.535	2.541	2.547	2.553	2.559	2.564
.41	2.570	2.576	2.582	2.588	2.594	2.600	2.606	2.612	2.618	2.624
.42	2.630	2.636	2.642	2.649	2.655	2.661	2.667	2.673	2.679	2.685
.43	2.692	2.698	2.704	2.710	2.716	2.723	2.729	2.735	2.742	2.748
.44	2.754	2.761	2.767	2.773	2.780	2.786	2.793	2.799	2.805	2.812
.45	2.818	2.825	2.831	2.838	2.844	2.851	2.858	2.864	2.871	2.877
.46	2.884	2.891	2.897	2.904	2.911	2.917	2.924	2.931	2.938	2.944
.47	2.951	2.958	2.965	2.972	2.979	2.985	2.992	2.999	3.006	3.013
.48	3.020	3.027	3.034	3.041	3.048	3.055	3.062	3.069	3.076	3.083
.49	3.090	3.097	3.105	3.112	3.119	3.126	3.133	3.141	3.148	3.155

EXHIBIT I.1-2—CONTINUED

Y	.000	.001	.002	.003	.004	.005	.006	.007	.008	.009
.50	3.162	3.170	3.177	3.184	3.192	3.199	3.206	3.214	3.221	3.228
.51	3.236	3.243	3.251	3.258	3.266	3.273	3.281	3.289	3.296	3.304
.52	3.311	3.319	3.327	3.334	3.342	3.350	3.357	3.365	3.373	3.381
.53	3.388	3.396	3.404	3.412	3.420	3.428	3.436	3.443	3.451	3.459
.54	3.467	3.475	3.483	3.491	3.499	3.508	3.516	3.524	3.532	3.540
.55	3.548	3.556	3.565	3.573	3.581	3.589	3.597	3.606	3.614	3.622
.56	3.631	3.639	3.648	3.656	3.664	3.673	3.681	3.690	3.698	3.707
.57	3.715	3.724	3.733	3.741	3.750	3.758	3.767	3.776	3.784	3.793
.58	3.802	3.811	3.819	3.828	3.837	3.846	3.855	3.864	3.873	3.882
.59	3.890	3.899	3.908	3.917	3.926	3.936	3.945	3.954	3.963	3.972
.60	3.981	3.990	3.999	4.009	4.018	4.027	4.036	4.046	4.055	4.064
.61	4.074	4.083	4.093	4.102	4.111	4.121	4.130	4.140	4.150	4.159
.62	4.169	4.178	4.188	4.198	4.207	4.217	4.227	4.236	4.246	4.256
.63	4.266	4.276	4.285	4.295	4.305	4.315	4.325	4.335	4.345	4.355
.64	4.365	4.375	4.385	4.395	4.406	4.416	4.426	4.436	4.446	4.457
.65	4.467	4.477	4.487	4.498	4.508	4.519	4.529	4.539	4.550	4.560
.66	4.571	4.581	4.592	4.603	4.613	4.624	4.634	4.645	4.656	4.667
.67	4.677	4.688	4.699	4.710	4.721	4.732	4.742	4.753	4.764	4.775
.68	4.786	4.797	4.808	4.819	4.831	4.842	4.853	4.864	4.875	4.887
.69	4.898	4.909	4.920	4.932	4.943	4.955	4.966	4.977	4.989	5.000
.70	5.012	5.023	5.035	5.047	5.058	5.070	5.082	5.093	5.105	5.117
.71	5.129	5.140	5.152	5.164	5.176	5.188	5.200	5.212	5.224	5.236
.72	5.248	5.260	5.272	5.284	5.297	5.309	5.321	5.333	5.346	5.358
.73	5.370	5.383	5.395	5.408	5.420	5.433	5.445	5.458	5.470	5.483
.74	5.495	5.508	5.521	5.534	5.546	5.559	5.572	5.585	5.598	5.610
.75	5.623	5.636	5.649	5.662	5.675	5.689	5.702	5.715	5.728	5.741
.76	5.754	5.768	5.781	5.794	5.808	5.821	5.834	5.848	5.861	5.875
.77	5.888	5.902	5.916	5.929	5.943	5.957	5.970	5.984	5.998	6.012
.78	6.026	6.039	6.053	6.067	6.081	6.095	6.109	6.124	6.138	6.152
.79	6.166	6.180	6.194	6.209	6.223	6.237	6.252	6.266	6.281	6.295
.80	6.310	6.324	6.339	6.353	6.368	6.383	6.397	6.412	6.427	6.442
.81	6.457	6.471	6.486	6.501	6.516	6.531	6.546	6.561	6.577	6.592
.82	6.607	6.622	6.637	6.653	6.668	6.683	6.699	6.714	6.730	6.745
.83	6.761	6.776	6.792	6.808	6.823	6.839	6.855	6.871	6.887	6.902
.84	6.918	6.934	6.950	6.966	6.982	6.998	7.015	7.031	7.047	7.063
.85	7.079	7.096	7.112	7.129	7.145	7.161	7.178	7.194	7.211	7.228
.86	7.244	7.261	7.278	7.295	7.311	7.328	7.345	7.362	7.379	7.396
.87	7.413	7.430	7.447	7.464	7.482	7.499	7.516	7.534	7.551	7.568
.88	7.586	7.603	7.621	7.638	7.656	7.674	7.691	7.709	7.727	7.745
.89	7.762	7.780	7.798	7.816	7.834	7.852	7.870	7.889	7.907	7.925
.90	7.943	7.962	7.980	7.998	8.017	8.035	8.054	8.072	8.091	8.110
.91	8.128	8.147	8.166	8.185	8.204	8.222	8.241	8.260	8.279	8.299
.92	8.318	8.337	8.356	8.375	8.395	8.414	8.433	8.453	8.472	8.492
.93	8.511	8.531	8.551	8.570	8.590	8.610	8.630	8.650	8.670	8.690
.94	8.710	8.730	8.750	8.770	8.790	8.810	8.831	8.851	8.872	8.892
.95	8.913	8.933	8.954	8.974	8.995	9.016	9.036	9.057	9.078	9.099
.96	9.120	9.141	9.162	9.183	9.204	9.226	9.247	9.268	9.290	9.311
.97	9.333	9.354	9.376	9.397	9.419	9.441	9.462	9.484	9.506	9.528
.98	9.550	9.572	9.594	9.616	9.638	9.661	9.683	9.705	9.727	9.750
.99	9.772	9.795	9.817	9.840	9.863	9.886	9.908	9.931	9.954	9.977

EXHIBIT I.1–3

Common (Base 10) Logarithms of Factorials

N	LOG N	N	LOG N	N	LOG N	N	LOG N	N	LOG N
1	.0000	41	49.5244	81	120.7632	121	200.9082	161	286.8803
2	.3010	42	51.1477	82	122.6770	122	202.9945	162	289.0898
3	.7782	43	52.7811	83	124.5961	123	205.0844	163	291.3020
4	1.3802	44	54.4246	84	126.5204	124	207.1779	164	293.5168
5	2.0792	45	56.0778	85	128.4498	125	209.2748	165	295.7343
6	2.8573	46	57.7406	86	130.3843	126	211.3751	166	297.9544
7	3.7024	47	59.4127	87	132.3238	127	213.4790	167	300.1771
8	4.6055	48	61.0939	88	134.2683	128	215.5862	168	302.4024
9	5.5598	49	62.7841	89	136.2177	129	217.6967	169	304.6303
10	6.5598	50	64.4831	90	138.1719	130	219.8107	170	306.8608
11	7.6012	51	66.1906	91	140.1310	131	221.9280	171	309.0938
12	8.6803	52	67.9066	92	142.0948	132	224.0485	172	311.3293
13	9.7943	53	69.6309	93	144.0632	133	226.1724	173	313.5674
14	10.9404	54	71.3633	94	146.0364	134	228.2995	174	315.8079
15	12.1165	55	73.1037	95	148.0141	135	230.4298	175	318.0509
16	13.3206	56	74.8519	96	149.9964	136	232.5634	176	320.2965
17	14.5511	57	76.6077	97	151.9831	137	234.7001	177	322.5444
18	15.8063	58	78.3712	98	153.9744	138	236.8400	178	324.7948
19	17.0851	59	80.1420	99	155.9700	139	238.9830	179	327.0477
20	18.3861	60	81.9202	100	157.9700	140	241.1291	180	329.3030
21	19.7083	61	83.7055	101	159.9743	141	243.2783	181	331.5606
22	21.0508	62	85.4979	102	161.9829	142	245.4306	182	333.8207
23	22.4125	63	87.2972	103	163.9958	143	247.5860	183	336.0832
24	23.7927	64	89.1034	104	166.0128	144	249.7443	184	338.3480
25	25.1906	65	90.9163	105	168.0340	145	251.9057	185	340.6152
26	26.6056	66	92.7359	106	170.0593	146	254.0700	186	342.8847
27	28.0370	67	94.5619	107	172.0887	147	256.2374	187	345.1565
28	29.4841	68	96.3945	108	174.1221	148	258.4076	188	347.4307
29	30.9465	69	98.2333	109	176.1595	149	260.5808	189	349.7071
30	32.4237	70	100.0784	110	178.2009	150	262.7569	190	351.9859
31	33.9150	71	101.9297	111	180.2462	151	264.9359	191	354.2669
32	35.4202	72	103.7870	112	182.2955	152	267.1177	192	356.5502
33	36.9387	73	105.6503	113	184.3485	153	269.3024	193	358.8358
34	38.4702	74	107.5196	114	186.4054	154	271.4899	194	361.1236
35	40.0142	75	109.3946	115	188.4661	155	273.6803	195	363.4136
36	41.5705	76	111.2754	116	190.5306	156	275.8734	196	365.7059
37	43.1387	77	113.1619	117	192.5988	157	278.0693	197	368.0003
38	44.7185	78	115.0540	118	194.6707	158	280.2679	198	370.2970
39	46.3096	79	116.9516	119	196.7462	159	282.4693	199	372.5959
40	47.9116	80	118.8547	120	198.8254	160	284.6735	200	374.8969

I.2 Series

A. Introduction

The need for a mathematical series arises in two situations:

1. A specified function must be expanded so that operators can be applied term by term.
2. The sum of a particular series must be identified.

Some of the more common series and their sums are given below.

B. Series of Simple Functions of Integers

$$1+2+3+\cdots+n=\sum_{i=1}^{n}(i)=n(n+1)/2$$

$$1^2+2^2+3^2+\cdots+n^2=\sum_{i=1}^{n}(i^2)=n(n+1)(2n+1)/6$$

$$1^3+2^3+3^3+\cdots+n^3=\sum_{i=1}^{n}(i^3)=n^2(n+1)^2/4$$

$$1+\frac{1}{1!}+\frac{1}{2!}+\frac{1}{3!}+\cdots=\sum_{i=0}^{\infty}\frac{1}{i!}=e=2.7182818285$$

$$1-\frac{1}{3}+\frac{1}{5}-\frac{1}{7}+\cdots=\pi/4,\text{ where }\pi=3.1415926536$$

$$1+\frac{1}{2^2}+\frac{1}{3^2}+\frac{1}{4^2}+\cdots=\pi^2/6$$

$$1-\frac{1}{2^2}+\frac{1}{3^2}-\frac{1}{4^2}+\cdots=\pi^2/12$$

$$1+\frac{1}{3^2}+\frac{1}{5^2}+\frac{1}{7^2}+\cdots=\pi^2/8$$

$$\frac{1}{2^2}+\frac{1}{4^2}+\frac{1}{6^2}+\frac{1}{8^2}+\cdots=\pi^2/24$$

$$\frac{1}{2}+\frac{1}{6}+\frac{1}{12}+\cdots=\sum_{i=1}^{\infty}\frac{1}{i(i+1)}=1$$

$$\frac{1}{6}+\frac{1}{24}+\frac{1}{60}+\cdots=\sum_{i=1}^{\infty}\frac{1}{i(i+1)(i+2)}=\frac{1}{4}$$

C. Sums of Algebraic Functions

$$1 \pm nx + \frac{n(n-1)x^2}{2!} \pm \frac{n(n-1)(n-2)x^3}{3!} + \cdots$$
$$= (1 \pm x)^n \qquad -1 < x < 1$$

$$1 \mp nx + \frac{n(n+1)x^2}{2!} \mp \frac{n(n+1)(n+2)x^3}{3!} + \cdots$$
$$= (1 \pm x)^{-n} \qquad -1 < x < 1$$

$$x^n + nx^{n-1}y + \frac{n(n-1)}{2!}x^{n-2}y^2 + \frac{n(n-1)(n-2)}{3!}x^{n-3}y^3 + \cdots$$
$$= (x+y)^n \qquad y^2 < x^2$$

$$\sum_{n=0}^{\infty} nx^n = x/(1-x)^2 \qquad 0 < x < 1$$

$$\sum_{n=0}^{\infty} n^2x^n = x(1+x)/(1-x)^3 \qquad 0 < x < 1$$

$$\sum_{n=0}^{\infty} n^3x^n = x(1+4x+x^2)/(1-x)^4 \qquad 0 < x < 1$$

$$\sum_{n=0}^{\infty} n^4x^n = x(1+11x+11x^2+x^3)/(1-x)^5 \qquad 0 < x < 1$$

D. Exponential and Logarithmic Series

$$1 + x + \frac{x^2}{2!} + \frac{x^3}{3!} + \cdots = e^x \qquad x \text{ real}$$

$$1 + x \ln a + \frac{(x \ln a)^2}{2!} + \frac{(x \ln a)^3}{3!} + \cdots = a^x \qquad x \text{ real}$$

$$x - \frac{x^2}{2} + \frac{x^3}{3} - \frac{x^4}{4} + \cdots = \ln(1+x) \qquad -1 < x < 1$$

$$2\left(\frac{1}{n} + \frac{1}{3n^3} + \frac{1}{5n^5} + \cdots\right) = \ln(n+1) - \ln(n-1) \qquad n > 1$$

$$2\left[\frac{x}{2a+x} + \frac{1}{3}\left(\frac{x}{2a+x}\right)^3 + \frac{1}{5}\left(\frac{x}{2a+x}\right)^5 + \cdots\right]$$
$$= \ln(a+x) - \ln(a) \qquad a > 0, x > -a$$

E. Trigonometric Functions

All arguments of trigonometric functions are expressed in radians. To convert degrees to radians, multiply by $180/\pi$.

$$x - \frac{x^3}{3!} + \frac{x^5}{5!} - \frac{x^7}{7!} + \cdots = \sin x \qquad x \text{ real}$$

$$1 - \frac{x^2}{2!} + \frac{x^4}{4!} - \frac{x^6}{6!} + \cdots = \cos x \qquad x \text{ real}$$

$$x + \frac{x^3}{3} + \frac{2x^5}{15} + \frac{17x^7}{315} + \cdots = \tan x \qquad x^2 < \pi^2/4$$

$$x + \sum_{n=1}^{\infty} \frac{x^{2n+1}}{2n+1} \cdot \frac{(1)(3)(5)\ldots(2n-1)}{(2)(4)(6)\ldots(2n)} = \arcsin x \qquad -1 < x < 1$$

$$x - \frac{x^3}{3} + \frac{x^5}{5} - \frac{x^7}{7} + \cdots = \arctan x \qquad -1 < x < 1$$

$$1 + \frac{x^3}{3!} + \frac{x^5}{5!} + \frac{x^7}{7!} + \cdots = \sinh x \qquad x \text{ real}$$

$$1 + \frac{x^2}{2!} + \frac{x^4}{4!} + \frac{x^6}{6!} + \cdots = \cosh x \qquad x \text{ real}$$

$$\sum_{n=0}^{\infty} x^n \sin n\omega = x \sin\omega/(1 - 2x\cos\omega + x^2) \qquad 0 < x < 1$$

$$\sum_{n=0}^{\infty} x^n \cos n\omega = (1 - x\cos\omega)/(1 - 2x\cos\omega + x^2) \qquad 0 < x < 1$$

$$\sum_{n=0}^{\infty} nx^n \sin n\omega = x(1 - x^2)\sin\omega/(1 - 2x\cos\omega + x^2)^2 \qquad 0 < x < 1$$

$$\sum_{n=0}^{\infty} nx^n \cos n\omega = \left[2x^2 - x(1 + x^2)\cos\omega\right]/(1 - 2x\cos\omega + x^2)^2 \qquad 0 < x < 1$$

I.3 Trigonometric Formulas

A. Trigonometric Functions and Relationships

A–1. Notation and Definitions

Consider the rectangular coordinate system with x- and y-axes and a circle of radius r centered at the intersection of the axes as shown below. Let θ be the angle between the positive x-axis and the line connecting the origin to any point on the circle (x, y). The angle θ can be expressed in degrees (°) or radians. Let θ be positive when measured in the counterclockwise direction, negative when measured in the clockwise direction.

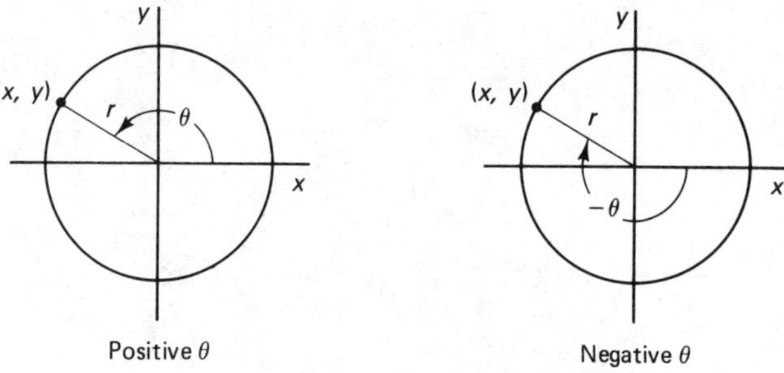

There are six real numbers associated with θ that are of fundamental importance in trigonometry. They are:

$$\text{sine}\,\theta = \sin\theta = y/r \qquad \text{cosine}\,\theta = \cos\theta = x/r$$

$$\text{tangent}\,\theta = \tan\theta = y/x \qquad \text{cotangent}\,\theta = \cot\theta = x/y$$

$$\text{secant}\,\theta = \sec\theta = r/x \qquad \text{cosecant}\,\theta = \csc\theta = r/y$$

The denominators of some of the following expressions become zero for certain values of the angles and are undefined in those cases.

A–2. Relationships of Trigonometric Functions

$$\sin\theta = 1/\csc\theta \qquad \csc\theta = 1/\sin\theta$$

$$\cos\theta = 1/\sec\theta \qquad \sec\theta = 1/\cos\theta$$

$$\tan\theta = \sin\theta/\cos\theta \qquad \cot\theta = \cos\theta/\sin\theta$$

$$\sin^2\theta + \cos^2\theta = 1$$

$$\sec^2\theta - \tan^2\theta = 1$$

$$\csc^2\theta - \cot^2\theta = 1$$

$$\sin\theta = \cos(90° - \theta) = \sin(180° - \theta)$$

$$\cos\theta = \sin(90° - \theta) = -\cos(180° - \theta)$$

$$\tan\theta = \cot(90° - \theta) = -\tan(180° - \theta)$$

A–3. Functions of Sums and Angles

$$\sin(\theta \pm \phi) = \sin\theta\cos\phi \pm \cos\theta\sin\phi$$

$$\cos(\theta \pm \phi) = \cos\theta\cos\phi \mp \sin\theta\sin\phi$$

$$\tan(\theta \pm \phi) = (\tan\theta \pm \tan\phi)/(1 \mp \tan\theta\tan\phi)$$

A–4. Functions of Multiple Angles

$$\sin 2\theta = 2\sin\theta\cos\theta$$

$$\begin{aligned}\cos 2\theta &= \cos^2\theta - \sin^2\theta \\ &= 2\cos^2\theta - 1 \\ &= 1 - 2\sin^2\theta\end{aligned}$$

$$\tan 2\theta = (2\tan\theta)/(1 - \tan^2\theta)$$

$$\sin(\theta/2) = \pm[(1 - \cos\theta)/2]^{1/2}$$

$$\cos(\theta/2) = \pm[(1 + \cos\theta)/2]^{1/2}$$

$$\tan(\theta/2) = \pm[(1 - \cos\theta)/(1 + \cos\theta)]^{1/2}$$

$$\sin 3\theta = 3\sin\theta - 4\sin^3\theta$$

$$\cos 3\theta = 4\cos^3\theta - 3\cos\theta$$

$$\sin 4\theta = 8\cos^3\theta\sin\theta - 4\cos\theta\sin\theta$$

$$\cos 4\theta = 8\cos^4\theta - 8\cos^2\theta + 1$$

A–5. Sums and Products of Trigonometric Functions

$$\sin\theta \pm \sin\phi = \{2\sin[(\theta \pm \phi)/2]\}\{\cos[(\theta \mp \phi)/2]\}$$

$$\cos\theta + \cos\phi = \{2\cos[(\theta + \phi)/2]\}\{\cos[(\theta - \phi)/2]\}$$

$$\cos\theta - \cos\phi = -\{2\sin[(\theta + \phi)/2]\}\{\sin[(\theta - \phi)/2]\}$$

$$\tan\theta + \tan\phi = [\sin(\theta + \phi)]/\cos\theta\cos\phi$$

$$\sin^2\theta - \sin^2\phi = [\sin(\theta + \phi)][\sin(\theta - \phi)]$$

$$\cos^2\theta - \cos^2\phi = -[\sin(\theta + \phi)][\sin(\theta - \phi)]$$

$$\cos^2\theta - \sin^2\phi = [\cos(\theta + \phi)][\cos(\theta - \phi)]$$

$$\sin\theta\cos\phi = \tfrac{1}{2}[\sin(\theta + \phi) + \sin(\theta - \phi)]$$

$$\cos\theta\sin\phi = \tfrac{1}{2}[\sin(\theta + \phi) - \sin(\theta - \phi)]$$

$$\cos\theta\cos\phi = \tfrac{1}{2}[\cos(\theta + \phi) + \cos(\theta - \phi)]$$

$$\sin\theta\sin\phi = -\tfrac{1}{2}[\cos(\theta + \phi) - \cos(\theta - \phi)]$$

B. Relationships Between Sides and Angles of Triangles

B–1. Right Triangles

Consider the right triangle shown below with A, B, and C as vertices (angles) and a, b, and c as the lengths of the sides. The following relationships hold.

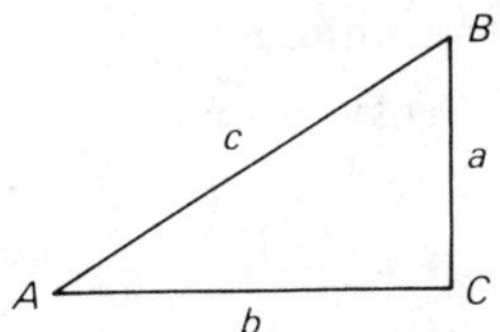

$\sin A = a/c \qquad \cos A = b/c$

$\tan A = a/b \qquad \cot A = b/a$

$\sec A = c/b \qquad \csc A = c/a$

B–2. Other Triangles

Consider any triangle ABC, not necessarily a right triangle, shown below. The following relationships hold.

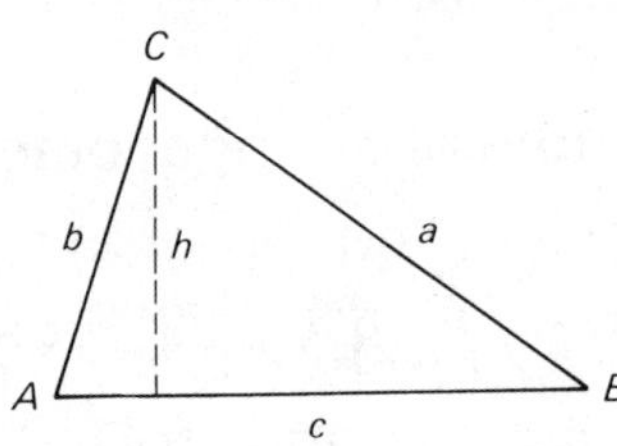

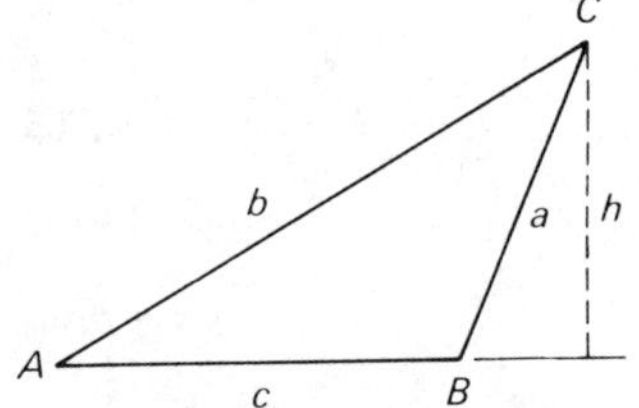

$$a/\sin A = b/\sin B = c/\sin C$$

$$a = b\cos C + c\cos B$$

$$h = c\sin A \sin B/[\sin(A + B)]$$

$$\cos A = (b^2 + c^2 - a^2)/2bc$$

$$\sin A = [2/bc][s(s - a)(s - b)(s - c)]^{1/2}$$

where

$$s = (a + b + c)/2$$

Useful Probability Distributions

II.1 Summary of Probability Distributions

A. Description

A probability distribution is a function that models the probability that a random variable, say X, takes on a particular value, x. When the range of values that X can assume is finite or countably infinite, X is said to be a *discrete random variable*, and the associated mathematical function is called the *probability mass function* (pmf). When the range of values that X can assume is an interval or a collection of intervals, X is referred to as a *continuous random variable*, and the associated mathematical function is called a *probability density function* (pdf).

The pmfs of several of the more common discrete random variables are given in Exhibit II.1–1, and the pdfs of several continuous random variables are given in Exhibit II.1–2.

Associated with each pmf is the mean, defined to be

$$\mu = \sum_{\text{all } x} xp(x)$$

EXHIBIT II.1–1

DISCRETE DISTRIBUTIONS

Distribution	Probability Function	Parameter(s)	Mean	Variance
Hypergeometric	$\dfrac{\binom{n}{x}\binom{N-n}{m-x}}{\binom{N}{n}}$; $a, a+1, a+2, \ldots, b$ $a = \max(0, n-N+m)$ $b = \min(m, n)$	$N = 1,2,\ldots$ $n = 1,2,\ldots,N$ $m = 1,2,\ldots,N$	$n\left(\frac{m}{N}\right)$	$n\left(\frac{m}{N}\right)\left(1-\frac{m}{N}\right)\left(\frac{N-n}{N-1}\right)$
Binomial	$\binom{n}{x}p(1-p)^{n-x}$; $x = 0,1,\ldots,n$	$n = 1,2,\ldots$ $0 < p < 1$	np	$np(1-p)$
Geometric	$p(1-p)^{x-1}$; $x = 1,2,\ldots$	$0 < p < 1$	$1/p$	$(1-p)/p^2$
Pascal (Negative Binomial)	$\binom{x-1}{r-1}p^r(1-p)^{x-r}$ $x = r, r+1, r+2, \ldots$	$0 < p < 1$ $r = 1,2,\ldots$	r/p	$r(1-p)/p^2$
Poisson	$\dfrac{C^x e^{-C}}{x!}$; $x = 0,1,2,\ldots$	$C > 0$	C	C
Discrete Uniform	$\dfrac{1}{b-a+1}$; $x = a, a+1, \ldots, b$	a, b integer	$\dfrac{b+a}{2}$	$\dfrac{(b-a)(b+a+2)}{12}$

EXHIBIT II.1–2

Continuous Distributions

Distribution	Probability Function	Parameter(s)	Mean	Variance
Uniform	$\frac{1}{b-a};\ a \le x \le b$	$a, b, b > a$	$\frac{b+a}{2}$	$(b-a)^2/12$
Exponential	$\lambda e^{-\lambda x};\ x > 0$	$\lambda > 0$	$1/\lambda$	$1/\lambda^2$
Gamma	$\frac{\lambda}{\Gamma(r)}(\lambda x)^{r-1}e^{-\lambda x};\ x > 0$ where $\Gamma(r) = \int_0^\infty x^{r-1}e^{-z}\,dz$	$r > 0$ $\lambda > 0$	r/λ	r/λ^2
Weibull	$\frac{\beta}{\delta}\left(\frac{x-\gamma}{\delta}\right)^{\beta-1}\exp\left\{-\left(\frac{x-\gamma}{\delta}\right)^{\beta}\right\}$ $x \ge \gamma$	$\delta > 0$ $\beta > 0$ γ	$\gamma + \delta[\Gamma(1/\beta + 1)]$, where $\Gamma(n) = \int_0^\infty x^{n-1}e^{-x}\,dx$	$\delta^2\{\Gamma(2/\beta + 1) - [\Gamma(1/\beta + 1)]^2\}$
Normal	$\frac{1}{\sigma\sqrt{2\pi}}\exp\left[-\frac{1}{2}\left(\frac{x-\mu}{\sigma}\right)^2\right] = \phi(x)$ $-\infty < \mu < \infty$	μ $\sigma > 0$	μ	σ^2
Lognormal	$\frac{1}{x\sigma_Y\sqrt{2\pi}}\exp\left\{-\frac{1}{2}\left[\frac{\ln x - \mu_Y}{\sigma_Y}\right]^2\right\}$ $x > 0$	μ_Y $\sigma_Y > 0$	$\exp[\mu_Y + \sigma_Y^2/2]$	$\exp(2\mu_Y + \sigma_Y^2)(\exp \sigma_Y^2 - 1)$
Truncated Normal	$\frac{K}{\sigma\sqrt{2\pi}}\exp\left[-\frac{1}{2}\left(\frac{x-\mu}{\sigma}\right)^2\right]$ $a \le x \le b$ $K = [\Phi(b) - \Phi(a)]^{-1}$ where $\Phi(t) = \int_{-\infty}^{t}\phi(x)\,dx$	μ $\sigma > 0$	$\mu + [\phi(a^*) - \phi(b^*)]/$ $[\Phi(b^*) - \Phi(a^*)]$ $a^* = \frac{a-\mu}{\sigma},\ b^* = \frac{b-\mu}{\sigma}$	$\sigma^2\left\{\left[1 + \frac{a^*\phi(a^*) - b^*\phi(b^*)}{\Phi(b^*) - \Phi(a^*)}\right.\right.$ $\left.\left. - \frac{\phi(a^*) - \phi(b^*)}{\Phi(b^*) - \Phi(a^*)}\right]^2\right\}$

where $p(x)$ is the pmf of the discrete random variable X. It should be noted that $P(X=x)=p(x)$. Also, for each pdf the mean is

$$\mu=\int_{\text{all } x} xf(x)\,dx$$

where $f(x)$ is the pdf of the continuous random variable X. Note also that $P(a\leq X\leq b)=\int_a^b f(x)\,dx$. We also define the variance as

$$\sigma^2=\sum_{\text{all } x}(x-\mu)^2 p(x)$$

or

$$\sigma^2=\int_{\text{all } x}(x-\mu)^2 f(x)\,dx$$

for the discrete and continuous cases, respectively. The mean and variance can provide general summary information about a pmf or pdf. The mean is a measure of central location, while the variance is a measure of dispersion.

Some pmfs and pdfs include quantities that must be assigned particular numerical values before the function can be evaluated. These are referred to as *parameters*, and may be restricted to a particular range of values. The mean and/or variance are functions of these parameters. Changing the parameters can allow a pmf or pdf to model a variety of phenomena.

Information on the means, variances, and parameters of each distribution is also included in Exhibits II.1–1 and II.1–2.

B. Discrete Distributions

B–1. Hypergeometric, Binomial, and Poisson

These distributions are discussed in Sections II.2, II.3, and II.4, respectively.

B–2. Geometric

Consider an experiment that has only two possible outcomes: either a particular event occurs, or it does not. The experiment can be repeated as many times as desired, and the probability that the event does occur remains constant at some value p. Each experiment is called a *Bernoulli trial*, or simply, trial. The random variable modeled by the geometric distribution is the number of trials until the first occurrence of the event of interest. For example, suppose the experiment is one in which containers are tested by exposure to a specified internal pressure and observed to determine whether or not they fracture. Assuming that all containers have the same probability of failure, say .05, we could use the geometric distribution to model the number of containers tested before one fails the test. In the example, a mean of $(1-p)/p = .95/.05 = 19$ containers would pass the test before a container would fail. If the sample size is fixed at some value n, the number of occurrences out of the n trials follows the binomial distribution.

B–3. Pascal (Negative Binomial)

As in B–2, concern is centered on a random variable that is a count of Bernoulli trials that have occurred. In this case, instead of the number of trials until the first occurrence of the event of interest, we are interested in the number of trials before the rth occurrence. For example, in the previous experiment we can use the Pascal distribution to find the probability of having, say, the 2nd failure occur on any particular trial, say the 10th. Then

$$P(X=10) = \binom{10-1}{2-1}(.05)^2(1-.05)^{10-2} = .015$$

A generalization of this distribution is to allow r to assume noninteger values. The distribution is then referred to as the negative binomial distribution.

B–4. Discrete Uniform

The continuous version of this distribution is more common, but when the random variable is limited to discrete equally spaced values, this model is appropriate. Each of the values has an equal probability of occurrence. The number of dots appearing on the up face of a six-sided die can be modeled with this distribution.

C. Continuous Distributions

C–1. Uniform

The uniform probability density function is used to model probabilities associated with a random variable that is equally likely to assume any real value between two limits. The parameters of this distribution are the two values defining the endpoints of the interval of values that the random variable can assume. The mean is at the midpoint between these two parameters.

The statement that a value is chosen at random from some interval means that the value will follow a uniform distribution. For example, suppose that a work sampling study is to be done. It is desired to randomly select times between, say, 1:00 and 4:00 pm at which to collect data. Since all times are to have an equal probability of being selected, the uniform probability density function is the model used to evaluate probabilities associated with these times.

C–2. Exponential and Gamma

The exponential distribution is frequently used to model the time between occurrences of an event. It is appropriate to use this model when the probability of occurrence of an event is constant for each small increment of time and is independent of the times at which events have occurred in the past. Random variables that follow this distribution have the property that the probability of failure in an interval of a specific length is independent of the starting point of that interval.

For example, assume that the time between failures of an electronic circuit follows an exponential distribution. Then the probability that the circuit fails during its first 10 hours of operation is the same as the probability that it fails during the next 10 hours after it reaches 100 hours of operation, given that it is still operating after 100 hours.

The exponential distribution is used in reliability modeling when it can be assumed that failures occur due to random shocks whose rate of occurrence is constant over time, rather than to wearing out. It can also be used to model the time between arrivals to a queueing system when it is assumed that the arrivals are independent and occur randomly at a constant rate. In this case the fact that, if the time between arrivals is exponential, the number of arrivals in a specified time follows a Poisson distribution, is quite useful.

At times, we may need to model the sum of the times of several events. If the times of each of r events are independent and follow the exponential distribution, then the sum follows a gamma distribution. A special case of the gamma distribution, obtained by requiring that the parameter r assume a positive integer value, is the *Erlang distribution*. The cumulative distribution function is defined as

$$F(x) = P(X \leq x)$$

That is, it is the probability that the random variable X assumes values less than or equal to a specified value x. For the Erlang distribution,

$$F(x)=1-\sum_{K=0}^{r-1} e^{-\lambda x}\lambda x^{K}/K!$$

Note that this is a function of the sum of Poisson probability terms with mean λx. Thus, we can use the cumulative Poisson tables to evaluate $F(x)$. In the special case where $r=1$, $F(x)=1-e^{-\lambda x}$, the same cumulative distribution frequency as for an exponential distribution.

C–3. Weibull

The Weibull distribution has been applied widely, at least partially because of its ability (through choice of parameter values) to approximate many observed phenomena. It has been particularly useful in modeling times to failure of electrical and mechanical component systems. Conveniently, the cumulative distribution function has the form

$$F(x)=1-\exp\left\{-\left(\frac{x-\gamma}{\delta}\right)^{\beta}\right\}, \qquad x\geq\gamma$$

Manipulation of the three parameters β, δ, and γ results in distributions that range from the exponential (when $\gamma=0$, $\beta=\delta=1$) to distributions that are nearly symmetric about a modal value (e.g., when $\beta=4$). The parameter β is referred to as the *shape parameter* because of this effect. The parameters γ and δ are referred to as the *location* and *scale parameters*, respectively, reflecting the nature of their influence on the distribution.

C–4. Normal

The normal distribution is one of the most widely used distributions and is discussed in detail in Section II.5.

C–5. Truncated Normal

There are cases where a random variable follows the normal distribution over a certain range, but the random variables cannot assume the full range of values from $-\infty$ to ∞. For example, consider an inventory of items that has been screened so that all items with extremely large and small measurements are removed. If the original measurements had a normal distribution, those remaining will follow the truncated normal distribution. Probabilities associated with the truncated normal can be found by using standard normal tables and multiplying by the constant

$$K=[P(a\leq Z\leq b)]^{-1}$$

where Z is the standard normal, and a and b are the points of truncation. Alternatively,

$$K = [\Phi(b) - \Phi(a)]^{-1}$$

where $\Phi(t)$ is the cumulative distribution function, i.e. $\Phi(t) = \int_{-\infty}^{t} \phi(x)\,dx$. Frequently, only one tail of the normal distribution is truncated. Then $a = -\infty$ (for truncation of the positive tail), or $b = +\infty$ (for truncation of the negative tail).

C–6. Lognormal

Associated with any lognormal random variable X is a random variable Y such that if

$$Y = \ln X$$

then Y follows a normal distribution with mean μ and variance σ^2. If we are interested in $P(X \le c)$, we can use the standard normal distribution, since

$$\begin{aligned} P(X \le c) &= P(\ln X \le \ln c) = P(Y \le \ln c) \\ &= P\left(Z \le \frac{\ln c - \mu}{\sigma}\right) \end{aligned}$$

where Z follows the standard normal distribution. Note that μ and σ are the parameters of the distribution associated with Y. If only the parameters of X are known, the two equations relating the means and variances of X and Y will have to be solved simultaneously in order to find μ and σ.

II.2 Hypergeometric Distribution

A. Description

The hypergeometric distribution has three parameters: N, the population size; n, the sample size; and m, the number of items in the population with the characteristic of interest. Evaluation of the hypergeometric distribution gives the probability that a particular number of items with the characteristic of interest will be observed in a sample taken without replacement. Hypergeometric probabilities can be found by evaluating

$$p(x) = \binom{m}{x}\binom{N-m}{n-x} \Big/ \binom{N}{n}$$

for positive integer values of x between $n - N + m$ and the smaller of m and n, where, in general,

$$\binom{i}{j} = \frac{i!}{j!(i-j)!}$$

and $i!$, read "i factorial," is

$$(i)(i-1)(i-2)\cdots(2)(1)$$

By definition, $0! = 1$.

The hypergeometric distribution is frequently used in evaluating the probability of the number of defects in a sample taken for quality monitoring purposes.

B. Reading the Tables

There are three parameters in the distribution, so that a table of $p(x)$ is extremely voluminous even for limited combinations of parameter values. The approach taken here is to make use of Exhibit I.1–3, a table of the logarithms of factorials. Letting $p(x) = (a)(b)/c$, where

$$a = \binom{m}{x}, \quad b = \binom{N-m}{n-x} \quad \text{and} \quad c = \binom{N}{n}$$

and taking logarithms (base 10 logarithms are used here, although any base will work), we have

$$\log[p(x)] = \log(a) + \log(b) - \log(c)$$

But

$$\log(a) = \log\binom{m}{x} = \log[m!/x!(m-x)!]$$

$$= \log[m!] - \log[x!] - \log[(m-x)!]$$

Similarly,

$$\log(b) = \log[(N-m)!] - \log[(n-x)!] - \log[(N-m-n+x)!]$$

and

$$\log(c) = \log[N!] - \log[n!] - \log[(N-n)!]$$

Exhibit I.1–3 can be used to evaluate the above for $\log p(x)$. Then Exhibit I.1–2 can be used to find

$$p(x) = \text{antilog}[\log p(x)]$$

At times, particularly when x and n are small, it may be more expedient to use the original form for $p(x)$ directly after dividing the numerator and denominator by common terms.

Also, as there is no closed form for the cumulative probability function, a considerable amount of computational effort will be required to find $P(X \le c)$ if c is not small. In many cases when N is not too small, the binomial approximation to the hypergeometric may provide a reasonable alternative, as shown in Section II.3.

Example B–1. Let $N = 10$, $n = 4$, $m = 5$. Find $P(X = 1)$. Following the above equations, we have

$$\begin{aligned}
\log(a) &= \log[5!] - \log[1!] - \log[(5-1)!] \\
&= 2.0792 - 0.0 - 1.3802 \\
&= 0.6990 \\
\log(b) &= \log[(10-5)!] - \log[(4-1)!] - \log[(10-5-4+1)!] \\
&= 2.0792 - 0.7782 - 0.3010 \\
&= 1.000 \\
\log(c) &= \log[10!] - \log[4!] - \log[(10-4)!] \\
&= 6.5598 - 1.3802 - 2.8573 \\
&= 2.3222 \\
\log P(X=1) &= 0.6990 + 1.0000 - 2.3222 \\
&= -0.6232 \\
P(X=1) &= \text{antilog}(-0.6232) = .238
\end{aligned}$$

Alternatively, we could have proceeded without using logarithms as follows:

$$P(X=1) = \frac{\binom{5}{1}\binom{10-5}{4-1}}{\binom{10}{4}} = \frac{\dfrac{5!}{1!(5-1)!} \cdot \dfrac{5!}{3!(5-3)!}}{\dfrac{10!}{4!(10-4)!}}$$

Making use of the fact that $i!/j! = (i)(i-1)\cdots(i-j+1)$, we can collect terms and simplify.

$$P(X=1)=\frac{5!}{4!}\frac{5!}{3!}\frac{4!}{2!}\frac{6!}{10!}$$
$$=[(5)][(5)(4)][(4)(3)]\left[\frac{1}{(10)(9)(8)(7)}\right]$$
$$=.238$$

In this case the second procedure requires less effort; but as the differences between the factorials in the numerator and denominator of $p(x)$ increase, the first procedure is preferred.

C. Using the Hypergeometric Distribution

Example C–1. A vendor supplies assemblies to a manufacturer in cases of 25 units. The manufacturer selects three units at random from each case and tests them. If any of the three tested units fails to meet specifications, all units in the case are inspected. What is the probability that a case with 5 defective units is not subjected to 100 percent inspection? Lots are not inspected if the number X of defectives in the sample is zero. Thus, we want to find $P(X=0)$ when $N=25$, $n=3$, and $m=5$. Evaluating as shown above, we have $P(X=0)=.496$.

Example C–2. Suppose that the manufacturer in Example C–1, in an attempt to improve the probability of detecting cases with large numbers of defectives, decides to increase n to 10 but to 100-percent-inspect only if more than 1 defective is found in the sample. How has the probability of not 100-percent-inspecting cases with $m=5$ defectives been affected by this change? Again, $N=25$ and $m=5$, but now $n=10$, and we want $P(X\leq 1)=P(X=0)+P(X=1)$. We find $P(X=0)=.057$ and $P(X=1)=.257$; so the new procedure has $.057+.257=.314$ probability of not 100-percent-inspecting a case with as many as 5 defectives. This is a decrease of $.496-.314=.182$. In addition, the new procedure will locate 1 of the 5 defectives 25.7 percent of the time.

II.3 Cumulative Binomial Distribution

A. Description

The binomial distribution occurs frequently in inspection sampling, although the Poisson or normal distributions are often used as approximations. The binomial is often avoided because the combinatorials that must be evaluated can become unwieldy. However, by using Exhibit II.3-1, many binomial probabilities can be determined.

The probability $p(x)$ of x occurrences of the outcome of interest in n trials is given by

$$p(x) = \begin{cases} \binom{n}{x} p^x q^{n-x}, & x = 0, 1, 2, \ldots, n \\ 0 & \text{otherwise} \end{cases}$$

where p is the probability of the occurrence of interest in one trial and $q = 1 - p$.

The probability $F(x)$ of x or fewer occurrences of the outcome of interest in n trials is given by

$$F(x) = \sum_{i=0}^{x} \binom{n}{i} p^i q^{n-i}, \quad i = 0, 1, 2, \ldots, x$$

The probability $F'(x)$ of more than x occurrences of the outcome of interest in n trials is given by

$$F'(x) = 1 - F(x)$$

The mean number $E(X)$ of occurrences of the outcome of interest in n trials is given by

$$E(X) = np$$

and the variance $V(X)$ of the number of occurrences of the outcome of interest in n trials is given by

$$V(X) = npq$$

For large values of n and small values of p ($p \leq .1$), the Poisson approximation to the binomial is quite accurate and often used in the field of quality control. Compute the mean of the Poisson distribution as $C = np$, and then follow the procedure described in Section II.4.

If p is close to $1/2$ and $n > 10$, the normal distribution is a fairly good approximation for the binomial distribution. For values of p not close to $1/2$, the value of n should be larger. In general, the approximation is fairly good as long as $np > 5$ for $p \leq 1/2$ or $nq > 5$ for $p > 1/2$. When using the normal approximation, the mean $\mu = np$ and the variance $\sigma^2 = npq$. The procedure for using the normal distribution is given in Section II.5. Like the Poisson approximation, the normal approximation to the binomial distribution is frequently used in the field of quality control.

B. Reading the Tables

The tables are indexed on p and n. The value $F(x)$ is read from Exhibit II.3–1.

Example B–1. If $p = .2$ and $n = 20$, find $F(3)$. From Exhibit II.3–1, $F(3) = .411$. Thus, the probability is .411 that 3 or fewer occurrences of the outcome of interest will occur in 20 trials.

Example B–2. If $p = .2$ and $n = 20$, find $F'(4)$. From Exhibit II.3–1, $F(4) = .630$, so $F'(4) = 1 - .630 = .370$. Hence, the probability is .370 that more than 4 occurrences of the outcome of interest will occur in 20 trials.

Example B–3. If $p = .2$ and $n = 20$, find $p(5)$. Now $p(x) = F(x) - F(x-1)$, so $p(5) = F(5) - F(4)$. From Exhibit II.3–1, $F(5) = .804$ and $F(4) = .630$. Thus, $p(5) = .804 - .630 = .174$. So the probability is .174 that there are exactly 5 occurrences of the outcome of interest in 20 trials.

Example B–4. If $p = .2$ and $n = 20$, find the probability of 6 or more outcomes of interest. The probability desired is $F'(5) = 1 - F(5)$. From Exhibit II.3–1, $F(5) = .804$, so $F'(5) = .196$.

C. Using the Tables

Example C–1. Inspection Sampling. A production process is used to manufacture semiconductor chips for microprocessors. The chips average five percent fraction defective. Every hour, a random sample of size 20 is taken from the process. If the sample contains more than one defective, the process will be stopped. Determine the probability that the process is stopped by the sampling scheme.

The desired probability is $F'(1) = 1 - F(1)$. From Exhibit II.3–1, $F(1) = .736$. Therefore, the desired probability is .264.

Example C–2. What is the upper limit of the number of defectives that can be expected to occur in 99 percent of the samples of Example C–1? From Exhibit II.3–1, $F(3) = .984$ and $F(4) = .997$. Thus, three or fewer defectives can be expected in 99 percent of the samples.

Example C–3. In Example C–1, what is the probability of 0 or 1 defectives occurring in the sample? The desired probability is given by $F(1)$. From Exhibit II.3–1, $F(1) = .736$.

Example C–4. In Example C–1, the production process might be stopped if the production quality is extremely good or if the quality is bad. When quality is good, the process is stopped to learn more about the operation so that it can be implemented on other lines. A sample of size 20 is taken, and if the sample contains zero or more than two defectives, the process will be stopped. Determine the probability that the process will be stopped by the sampling scheme.

EXHIBIT II.3–1

Cumulative Binomial Distribution

		p = Probability of Occurrence									
n	x	.05	.10	.15	.20	.25	.30	.35	.40	.45	.50
2	0	.903	.810	.722	.640	.563	.490	.423	.360	.303	.250
	1	.998	.990	.978	.960	.938	.910	.878	.840	.798	.750
3	0	.857	.729	.614	.512	.422	.343	.275	.216	.166	.125
	1	.993	.972	.939	.896	.844	.784	.718	.648	.575	.500
	2	1.000	.999	.997	.992	.984	.973	.957	.936	.909	.875
4	0	.815	.656	.522	.410	.316	.240	.179	.130	.092	.063
	1	.986	.948	.890	.819	.738	.652	.563	.475	.391	.313
	2	1.000	.996	.988	.973	.949	.916	.874	.821	.759	.687
	3		1.000	.999	.998	.996	.992	.985	.974	.959	.938
5	0	.774	.590	.444	.328	.237	.168	.116	.078	.050	.031
	1	.977	.919	.835	.737	.633	.528	.428	.337	.256	.188
	2	.999	.991	.973	.942	.896	.837	.765	.683	.593	.500
	3	1.000	1.000	.998	.993	.984	.969	.946	.913	.869	.813
	4			1.000	1.000	.999	.998	.995	.990	.982	.969
6	0	.735	.531	.377	.262	.178	.118	.075	.047	.028	.016
	1	.967	.886	.776	.655	.534	.420	.319	.233	.164	.109
	2	.998	.984	.953	.901	.831	.744	.647	.544	.442	.344
	3	1.000	.999	.994	.983	.962	.930	.883	.821	.745	.656
	4		1.000	1.000	.998	.995	.989	.978	.959	.931	.891
	5				1.000	1.000	.999	.998	.996	.992	.984
7	0	.698	.478	.321	.210	.133	.082	.049	.028	.015	.008
	1	.956	.850	.717	.577	.445	.329	.234	.159	.102	.063
	2	.996	.974	.926	.852	.756	.647	.532	.420	.316	.227
	3	1.000	.997	.988	.967	.929	.874	.800	.710	.608	.500
	4		1.000	.999	.995	.987	.971	.944	.904	.847	.773
	5			1.000	1.000	.999	.996	.991	.981	.964	.938
	6					1.000	1.000	.999	.998	.996	.992
8	0	.663	.430	.272	.168	.100	.058	.032	.017	.008	.004
	1	.943	.813	.657	.503	.367	.255	.169	.106	.063	.035
	2	.994	.962	.895	.797	.679	.552	.428	.315	.220	.145
	3	1.000	.995	.979	.944	.886	.806	.706	.594	.477	.363
	4		1.000	.997	.990	.973	.942	.894	.826	.740	.637
	5			1.000	.999	.996	.989	.975	.950	.912	.855
	6				1.000	1.000	.999	.996	.991	.982	.965
	7						1.000	1.000	.999	.998	.996
9	0	.630	.387	.232	.134	.075	.040	.021	.010	.005	.002
	1	.929	.775	.599	.436	.300	.196	.121	.071	.039	.020
	2	.992	.947	.859	.738	.601	.463	.337	.232	.150	.090
	3	.999	.992	.966	.914	.834	.730	.609	.483	.361	.254
	4	1.000	.999	.994	.980	.951	.901	.828	.733	.621	.500
	5		1.000	.999	.997	.990	.975	.946	.901	.834	.746
	6			1.000	1.000	.999	.996	.989	.975	.950	.910
	7					1.000	1.000	.999	.996	.991	.980
	8							1.000	1.000	.999	.998

EXHIBIT II.3–1—CONTINUED

		p = Probability of Occurrence									
n	x	.05	.10	.15	.20	.25	.30	.35	.40	.45	.50
10	0	.599	.349	.197	.107	.056	.028	.013	.006	.003	.001
	1	.914	.736	.544	.376	.244	.149	.086	.046	.023	.011
	2	.988	.930	.820	.678	.526	.383	.262	.167	.100	.055
	3	.999	.987	.950	.879	.776	.650	.514	.382	.266	.172
	4	1.000	.998	.990	.967	.922	.850	.751	.633	.504	.377
	5		1.000	.999	.994	.980	.953	.905	.834	.738	.623
	6			1.000	.999	.996	.989	.974	.945	.898	.828
	7				1.000	1.000	.998	.995	.988	.973	.945
	8						1.000	.999	.998	.995	.989
	9							1.000	1.000	1.000	.999
11	0	.569	.314	.167	.086	.042	.020	.009	.004	.001	.000
	1	.898	.697	.492	.322	.197	.113	.061	.030	.014	.006
	2	.985	.910	.779	.617	.455	.313	.200	.119	.065	.033
	3	.998	.981	.931	.839	.713	.570	.426	.296	.191	.113
	4	1.000	.997	.984	.950	.885	.790	.668	.533	.397	.274
	5		1.000	.997	.988	.966	.922	.851	.753	.633	.500
	6			1.000	.998	.992	.978	.950	.901	.826	.726
	7				1.000	.999	.996	.988	.971	.939	.887
	8					1.000	.999	.998	.994	.985	.967
	9						1.000	1.000	.999	.998	.994
	10								1.000	1.000	1.000
12	0	.540	.282	.142	.069	.032	.014	.006	.002	.001	.000
	1	.882	.659	.443	.275	.158	.085	.042	.020	.008	.003
	2	.980	.889	.736	.558	.391	.253	.151	.083	.042	.019
	3	.998	.974	.908	.795	.649	.493	.347	.225	.134	.073
	4	1.000	.996	.976	.927	.842	.724	.583	.438	.304	.194
	5		.999	.995	.981	.946	.882	.787	.665	.527	.387
	6		1.000	.999	.996	.986	.961	.915	.842	.739	.613
	7			1.000	.999	.997	.991	.974	.943	.888	.806
	8				1.000	1.000	.998	.994	.985	.964	.927
	9						1.000	.999	.997	.992	.981
	10							1.000	1.000	.999	.997
	11									1.000	1.000
13	0	.513	.254	.121	.055	.024	.010	.004	.001	.000	.000
	1	.865	.621	.398	.234	.127	.064	.030	.013	.005	.002
	2	.975	.866	.692	.502	.333	.202	.113	.058	.027	.011
	3	.997	.966	.882	.747	.584	.421	.278	.169	.093	.046
	4	1.000	.994	.966	.901	.794	.654	.501	.353	.228	.133
	5		.999	.992	.970	.920	.835	.716	.574	.427	.291
	6		1.000	.999	.993	.976	.938	.871	.771	.644	.500
	7			1.000	.999	.994	.982	.954	.902	.821	.709
	8				1.000	.999	.996	.987	.968	.930	.867
	9					1.000	.999	.997	.992	.980	.954
	10						1.000	1.000	.999	.996	.989
	11								1.000	.999	.998
	12									1.000	1.000

EXHIBIT II.3-1—CONTINUED

		p = Probability of Occurrence									
n	*x*	.05	.10	.15	.20	.25	.30	.35	.40	.45	.50
14	0	.488	.229	.103	.044	.018	.007	.002	.001	.000	.000
	1	.847	.585	.357	.198	.101	.047	.021	.008	.003	.001
	2	.970	.842	.648	.448	.281	.161	.084	.040	.017	.006
	3	.996	.956	.853	.698	.521	.355	.220	.124	.063	.029
	4	1.000	.991	.953	.870	.742	.584	.423	.279	.167	.090
	5		.999	.988	.956	.888	.781	.641	.486	.337	.212
	6		1.000	.998	.988	.962	.907	.816	.692	.546	.395
	7			1.000	.998	.990	.969	.925	.850	.741	.605
	8				1.000	.998	.992	.976	.942	.881	.788
	9					1.000	.998	.994	.982	.957	.910
	10						1.000	.999	.996	.989	.971
	11							1.000	.999	.998	.994
	12								1.000	1.000	.999
15	0	.463	.206	.087	.035	.013	.005	.002	.000	.000	.000
	1	.829	.549	.319	.167	.080	.035	.014	.005	.002	.000
	2	.964	.816	.604	.398	.236	.127	.062	.027	.011	.004
	3	.995	.944	.823	.648	.461	.297	.173	.091	.042	.018
	4	.999	.987	.938	.836	.686	.515	.352	.217	.120	.059
	5	1.000	.998	.983	.939	.852	.722	.564	.403	.261	.151
	6		1.000	.996	.982	.943	.869	.755	.610	.452	.304
	7			.999	.996	.983	.950	.887	.787	.654	.500
	8			1.000	.999	.996	.985	.958	.905	.818	.696
	9				1.000	.999	.996	.988	.966	.923	.849
	10					1.000	.999	.997	.991	.975	.941
	11						1.000	1.000	.998	.994	.982
	12								1.000	.999	.996
	13									1.000	1.000
16	0	.440	.185	.074	.028	.010	.003	.001	.000	.000	.000
	1	.811	.515	.284	.141	.063	.026	.010	.003	.001	.000
	2	.957	.789	.561	.352	.197	.099	.045	.018	.007	.002
	3	.993	.932	.790	.598	.405	.246	.134	.065	.028	.011
	4	.999	.983	.921	.798	.630	.450	.289	.167	.085	.038
	5	1.000	.997	.976	.918	.810	.660	.490	.329	.198	.105
	6		.999	.994	.973	.920	.825	.688	.527	.366	.227
	7		1.000	.999	.993	.973	.926	.841	.716	.563	.402
	8			1.000	.999	.993	.974	.933	.858	.744	.598
	9				1.000	.998	.993	.977	.942	.876	.773
	10					1.000	.998	.994	.981	.951	.895
	11						1.000	.999	.995	.985	.962
	12							1.000	.999	.997	.989
	13								1.000	.999	.998
	14									1.000	1.000

EXHIBIT II.3-1—CONTINUED

		p = Probability of Occurrence									
n	x	.05	.10	.15	.20	.25	.30	.35	.40	.45	.50
17	0	.418	.167	.063	.023	.008	.002	.001	.000	.000	.000
	1	.792	.482	.252	.118	.050	.019	.007	.002	.001	.000
	2	.950	.762	.520	.310	.164	.077	.033	.012	.004	.001
	3	.991	.917	.756	.549	.353	.202	.103	.046	.018	.006
	4	.999	.978	.901	.758	.574	.389	.235	.126	.060	.025
	5	1.000	.995	.968	.894	.765	.597	.420	.264	.147	.072
	6		.999	.992	.962	.893	.775	.619	.448	.290	.166
	7		1.000	.998	.989	.960	.895	.787	.641	.474	.315
	8			1.000	.997	.988	.960	.901	.801	.663	.500
	9				1.000	.997	.987	.962	.908	.817	.685
	10					.999	.997	.988	.965	.917	.834
	11					1.000	.999	.997	.989	.970	.928
	12						1.000	.999	.997	.991	.975
	13							1.000	1.000	.998	.994
	14									1.000	.999
	15										1.000
18	0	.397	.150	.054	.018	.006	.002	.000	.000	.000	.000
	1	.774	.450	.224	.099	.039	.014	.005	.001	.000	.000
	2	.942	.734	.480	.271	.135	.060	.024	.008	.003	.001
	3	.989	.902	.720	.501	.306	.165	.078	.033	.012	.004
	4	.998	.972	.879	.716	.519	.333	.189	.094	.041	.015
	5	1.000	.994	.958	.867	.717	.534	.355	.209	.108	.048
	6		.999	.988	.949	.861	.722	.549	.374	.226	.119
	7		1.000	.997	.984	.943	.859	.728	.563	.391	.240
	8			.999	.996	.981	.940	.861	.737	.578	.407
	9			1.000	.999	.995	.979	.940	.865	.747	.593
	10				1.000	.999	.994	.979	.942	.872	.760
	11					1.000	.999	.994	.980	.946	.881
	12						1.000	.999	.994	.982	.952
	13							1.000	.999	.995	.985
	14								1.000	.999	.996
	15									1.000	.999
	16										1.000

EXHIBIT II.3-1—CONTINUED

		p = Probability of Occurrence									
n	*x*	.05	.10	.15	.20	.25	.30	.35	.40	.45	.50
19	0	.377	.135	.046	.014	.004	.001	.000	.000	.000	.000
	1	.755	.420	.198	.083	.031	.010	.003	.001	.000	.000
	2	.933	.705	.441	.237	.111	.046	.017	.005	.002	.000
	3	.987	.885	.684	.455	.263	.133	.059	.023	.008	.002
	4	.998	.965	.856	.673	.465	.282	.150	.070	.028	.010
	5	1.000	.991	.946	.837	.668	.474	.297	.163	.078	.032
	6		.998	.984	.932	.825	.666	.481	.308	.173	.084
	7		1.000	.996	.977	.923	.818	.666	.488	.317	.180
	8			.999	.993	.971	.916	.815	.667	.494	.324
	9			1.000	.998	.991	.967	.913	.814	.671	.500
	10				1.000	.998	.989	.965	.912	.816	.676
	11					1.000	.997	.989	.965	.913	.820
	12						.999	.997	.988	.966	.916
	13						1.000	.999	.997	.989	.968
	14							1.000	.999	.997	.990
	15								1.000	.999	.998
	16									1.000	1.000
20	0	.358	.122	.039	.012	.003	.001	.000	.000	.000	.000
	1	.736	.392	.176	.069	.024	.008	.002	.001	.000	.000
	2	.925	.677	.405	.206	.091	.035	.012	.004	.001	.000
	3	.984	.867	.648	.411	.225	.107	.044	.016	.005	.001
	4	.997	.957	.830	.630	.415	.238	.118	.051	.019	.006
	5	1.000	.989	.933	.804	.617	.416	.245	.126	.055	.021
	6		.998	.978	.913	.786	.608	.417	.250	.130	.058
	7		1.000	.994	.968	.898	.772	.601	.416	.252	.132
	8			.999	.990	.959	.887	.762	.596	.414	.252
	9			1.000	.997	.986	.952	.878	.755	.591	.412
	10				.999	.996	.983	.947	.872	.751	.588
	11				1.000	.999	.995	.980	.943	.869	.748
	12					1.000	.999	.994	.979	.942	.868
	13						1.000	.998	.994	.979	.942
	14							1.000	.998	.994	.979
	15								1.000	.998	.994
	16									1.000	.999
	17										1.000

The desired probability can be determined in several ways. The probability that the process is *not* stopped is determined from $F(2)-F(0)$. From Exhibit II.3–1, $F(2)=.925$ and $F(0)=.358$, so $F(2)-F(0)=.567$. Therefore, the probability of stopping the process is $1-.567=.433$.

Alternatively, the probability of stopping the process is given by $p(0)+F'(2)$. From Exhibit II.3–1, $p(0)=.358$ and $F'(2)=1-F(2)=1-.925=.075$. So the probability of stopping the process is .433, as before.

II.4 Poisson Distribution

A. Description

The Poisson distribution models the probability of the number of occurrences of an event in an interval of time. It is assumed that the instantaneous rate of occurrence λ is constant over time, so that the mean rate of occurrence for any interval of time Δt is $\lambda \Delta t = C$. The variance of the number of occurrences in this time period is also equal to C. The probability function is

$$p(x)=\frac{C^x e^{-C}}{x!} \qquad x=0,1,\ldots, \qquad C>0$$

Exhibit II.4–1 gives $F(x)=\sum_{i=0}^{x} p(i)$ for various values of C and x.

The Poisson distribution is frequently used to model the number of arrivals to a queue and the number of customers serviced by a work station. It is also used as an approximation to the binomial distribution.

B. Reading the Tables

Example B–1. Find the probability of 3 or fewer occurrences in an hour when the mean rate of occurrence is 1.5 per hour. Entering Exhibit II.4–1 with $C=1.5$ and $x=3$, we find $F(3)=\sum_{i=0}^{3} p(i)=.934$.

Example B–2. Find the probability of *exactly* 3 occurrences in a one-hour period for the situation of Example B–1.

$$P(X=3)=P(X\leq 3)-P(X\leq 2)=.934-.808=.126$$

EXHIBIT II.4–1
CUMULATIVE POISSON DISTRIBUTION

	C = Mean											
x	.01	.05	.1	.2	.3	.4	.5	.6	.7	.8	.9	x
0	.990	.951	.905	.819	.741	.670	.607	.549	.497	.449	.407	0
1	1.000	.999	.995	.982	.963	.938	.910	.878	.844	.809	.772	1
2		1.000	1.000	.999	.996	.992	.986	.977	.966	.953	.937	2
3				1.000	1.000	.999	.998	.997	.994	.991	.987	3
4						1.000	1.000	1.000	.999	.999	.998	4
5									1.000	1.000	1.000	5

	C = Mean											
x	1.0	1.1	1.2	1.3	1.4	1.5	1.6	1.7	1.8	1.9	2.0	x
0	.368	.333	.301	.273	.247	.223	.202	.183	.165	.150	.135	0
1	.736	.699	.663	.627	.592	.558	.525	.493	.463	.434	.406	1
2	.920	.900	.879	.857	.833	.809	.783	.757	.731	.704	.677	2
3	.981	.974	.966	.957	.946	.934	.921	.907	.891	.875	.857	3
4	.996	.995	.992	.989	.986	.981	.976	.970	.964	.956	.947	4
5	.999	.999	.998	.998	.997	.996	.994	.992	.990	.987	.983	5
6	1.000	1.000	1.000	1.000	.999	.999	.999	.998	.997	.997	.995	6
7					1.000	1.000	1.000	1.000	.999	.999	.999	7
8									1.000	1.000	1.000	8

	C = Mean											
x	2.2	2.4	2.6	2.8	3.0	3.5	4.0	4.5	5.0	5.5	6.0	x
0	.111	.091	.074	.061	.050	.030	.018	.011	.007	.004	.002	0
1	.355	.308	.267	.231	.199	.136	.092	.061	.040	.027	.017	1
2	.623	.570	.518	.469	.423	.321	.238	.174	.125	.088	.062	2
3	.819	.779	.736	.692	.647	.537	.433	.342	.265	.202	.151	3
4	.928	.904	.877	.848	.815	.725	.629	.532	.440	.358	.285	4
5	.975	.964	.951	.935	.916	.858	.785	.703	.616	.529	.446	5
6	.993	.988	.983	.976	.966	.935	.889	.831	.762	.686	.606	6
7	.998	.997	.995	.992	.988	.973	.949	.913	.867	.809	.744	7
8	1.000	.999	.999	.998	.996	.990	.979	.960	.932	.894	.847	8
9		1.000	1.000	.999	.999	.997	.992	.983	.968	.946	.916	9
10				1.000	1.000	.999	.997	.993	.986	.975	.957	10
11						1.000	.999	.998	.995	.989	.980	11
12							1.000	.999	.998	.996	.991	12
13								1.000	.999	.998	.996	13
14									1.000	.999	.999	14
15										1.000	.999	15
16											1.000	16

EXHIBIT II.4–1—CONTINUED

	C = Mean											
x	6.5	7.0	7.5	8.0	9.0	10.0	12.0	14.0	16.0	18.0	20.0	x
0	.002	.001	.001									0
1	.011	.007	.005	.003	.001							1
2	.043	.030	.020	.014	.006	.003	.001					2
3	.112	.082	.059	.042	.021	.010	.002					3
4	.224	.173	.132	.100	.055	.029	.008	.002				4
5	.369	.301	.241	.191	.116	.067	.020	.006	.001			5
6	.527	.450	.378	.313	.207	.130	.046	.014	.004	.001		6
7	.673	.599	.525	.453	.324	.220	.090	.032	.010	.003	.001	7
8	.792	.729	.662	.593	.456	.333	.155	.062	.022	.007	.002	8
9	.877	.830	.776	.717	.587	.458	.242	.109	.043	.015	.005	9
10	.933	.901	.862	.816	.706	.583	.347	.176	.077	.030	.011	10
11	.966	.947	.921	.888	.803	.697	.462	.260	.127	.055	.021	11
12	.984	.973	.957	.936	.876	.792	.576	.358	.193	.092	.039	12
13	.993	.987	.978	.966	.926	.864	.682	.464	.275	.143	.066	13
14	.997	.994	.990	.983	.959	.917	.772	.570	.368	.208	.105	14
15	.999	.998	.995	.992	.978	.951	.844	.669	.467	.287	.157	15
16	1.000	.999	.998	.996	.989	.973	.899	.756	.566	.375	.221	16
17		1.000	.999	.998	.995	.986	.937	.827	.659	.469	.297	17
18			1.000	.999	.998	.993	.963	.883	.742	.562	.381	18
19				1.000	.999	.997	.979	.923	.812	.651	.470	19
20					1.000	.998	.988	.952	.868	.731	.559	20
21						.999	.994	.971	.911	.799	.644	21
22						1.000	.997	.983	.942	.855	.721	22
23							.999	.991	.963	.899	.787	23
24							.999	.995	.978	.932	.843	24
25							1.000	.997	.987	.955	.888	25
26								.999	.993	.972	.922	26
27								.999	.996	.983	.948	27
28								1.000	.998	.990	.966	28
29									.999	.994	.978	29
30									.999	.997	.987	30
31									1.000	.998	.992	31
32										.999	.995	32
33										1.000	.997	33
34											.999	34
35											.999	35
36											1.000	36

C. Using the Distribution

Example C–1. Queueing Application. Find the probability of 6 or more arrivals in a two-minute period when the rate of arrivals is 1.5 per minute. The mean rate of arrivals for a two-minute period is $C = \lambda\Delta t = 1.5(2) = 3.0$.

$$P(X \geq 6) = 1 - P(X \leq 5)$$

From Exhibit II.4–1 with $C = 3$ and $x = 5$, $P(X \leq 5) = .916$; thus, the solution is $1 - .916 = .084$. (Note that we would not have gotten the correct answer if we had divided the number of arrivals of interest by the length of the interval rather than multiplying the arrival rate by the length of the interval.)

Example C–2. Approximating the Binomial. A quality control sampling plan calls for taking samples of $n = 140$ from lots assembled from a continuous process. The lot is accepted if the number of defectives is less than or equal to 2. What is the probability of accepting lots from a process that has a constant probability of 1 percent of producing defectives?

We wish to find $P(X \leq 2)$, where X follows a binomial distribution with $n = 140$ and $p = .01$. Since p is small (generally, we require $p < .10$) and n is large ($n \geq 50$), the Poisson distribution is a reasonable approximation to the binomial distribution. We set the mean of the binomial distribution of interest, $np = 140(.01) = 1.4$, equal to the mean of the approximating Poisson distribution, C. Then, using Exhibit II.4–1 with $C = 1.4$, we find $P(X \leq 2) = .833$. Thus, there is approximately an 83 percent chance of acceptance.

II.5 Normal Distribution

A. Description

In many respects, the normal distribution is the basis of statistics. A random variable X is said to have a *normal distribution with mean* μ *and variance* σ^2 if it has the density function

$$f(x) = \frac{1}{\sigma\sqrt{2\pi}} \exp\left[-\frac{1}{2}\left(\frac{x-\mu}{\sigma}\right)^2\right], \qquad -\infty < x < \infty$$

where $-\infty < \mu < \infty$ and $\sigma^2 > 0$. The notation $X \sim N(\mu, \sigma^2)$ is often used to indicate that the random variable X is distributed normally with mean μ and variance σ^2. The normal distribution is symmetric about its mean μ as shown below.

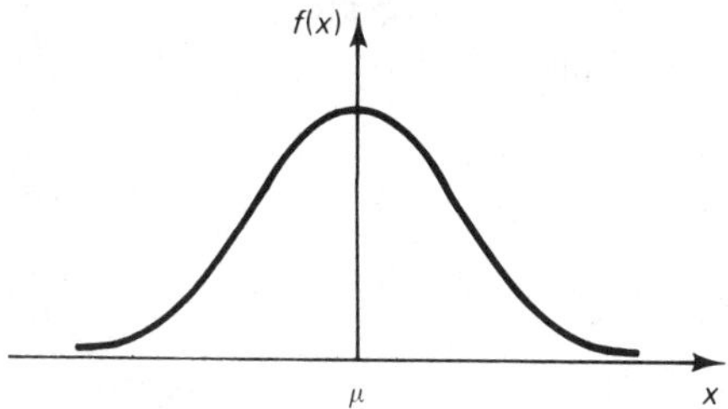

Tabulation of the cumulative density function of the normal distribution would have to be accomplished for each pair (μ, σ^2). However, a transformation of variables, $z = (x - \mu)/\sigma$, allows the tabulation to be free of μ and σ. Thus,

$$F(x) = P(X \le x) = P\left(Z \le \frac{x - \mu}{\sigma}\right) = \int_{-\infty}^{(x-\mu)/\sigma} \frac{1}{\sqrt{2\pi}} e^{-z^2/2}\, dz$$

$$= \int_{-\infty}^{(x-\mu)/\sigma} \phi(z)\, dz = \Phi\left(\frac{x - \mu}{\sigma}\right)$$

Now, $\phi(z)$ has mean zero and variance one, or $Z \sim N(0, 1)$, and Z is said to have a standard normal distribution as shown below.

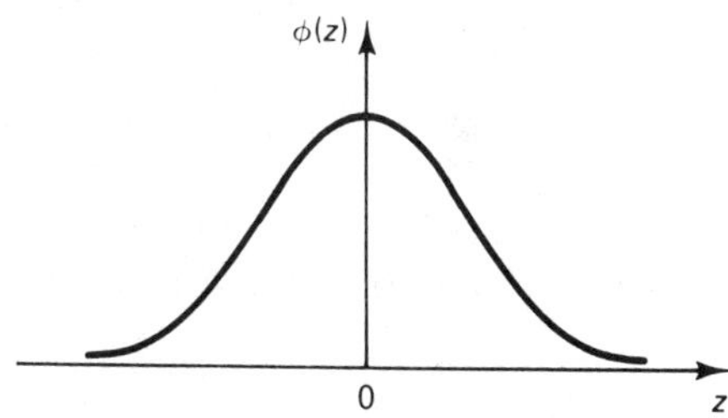

The cumulative distribution function is tabulated in Exhibit II.5–1.

Uses of the normal distribution include the following:

1. Approximating the binomial distribution.
2. Testing hypotheses on the mean(s), variance known.
3. Testing hypotheses on a proportion(s).
4. Setting a confidence interval on the mean(s), variance known.
5. Setting a confidence interval on a proportion(s).

B. Reading the Tables

Example B–1. Find the area associated with $\Phi(z)$, where $z=1$. Pictorially, the required (shaded) area is as follows, where $Z \sim N(0,1)$: From Exhibit II.5–1, $\Phi(1)=.8413$.

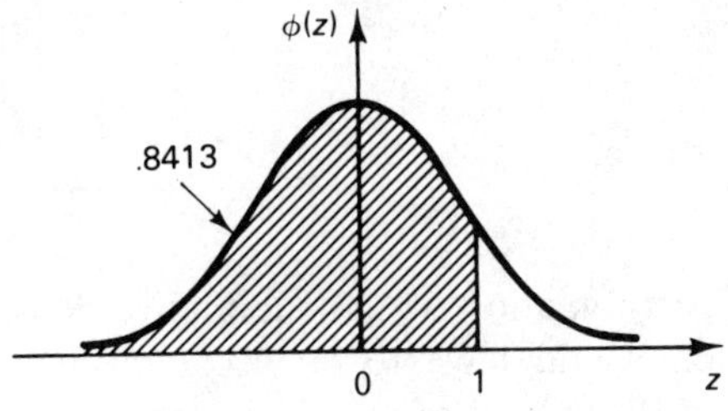

Example B–2. Find $P(Z \geq 2)$ where $Z \sim N(0,1)$. Pictorially, the required (shaded) area is as follows:

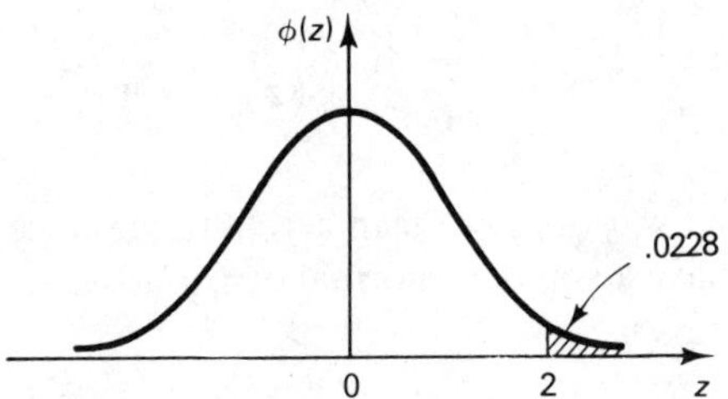

The required area is the complement of $\Phi(2)$, or $1-\Phi(2)$. From Exhibit II.5–1, $\Phi(2)=.9772$, so the required area is .0228.

Example B–3. Find $P(-1 \leq Z \leq 2)$, where $Z \sim N(0,1)$. The required area is given by $\Phi(2)-\Phi(-1)$ and is shown in the figure below.

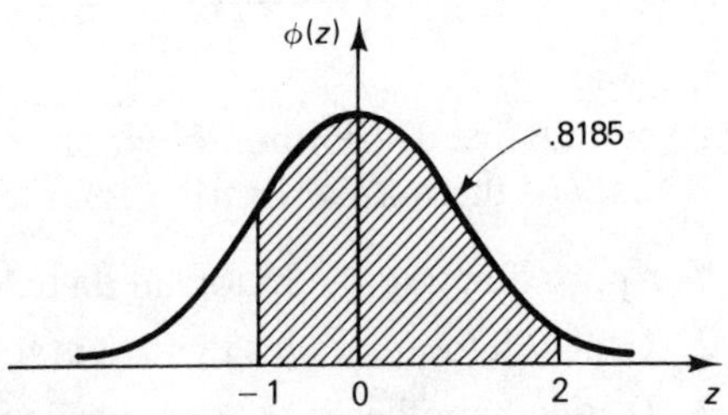

From Exhibit II.5–1, $\Phi(2)=.9772$ and $\Phi(-1)=.1587$. Thus, $P(-1 \leq Z \leq 2)$ $=.9772-.1587=.8185$.

Example B–4. Find z such that $\Phi(z) = .95$. From Exhibit II.5–1, $\Phi(1.64) = .9495$ and $\Phi(1.65) = .9505$. Thus, $z = 1.645$ satisfies the required equality. Since the normal distribution is symmetric about its mean, $\Phi(-z) = 1 - \Phi(z) = .05$, which can be verified from Exhibit II.5–1 by examining $\Phi(z)$ when $z = -1.645$.

Example B–5. The following values are useful in applied statistics and may be verified from Exhibit II.5–1:

z	$\Phi(z)$
−2.575	.005
−2.326	.010
−1.960	.025
−1.645	.050
−1.282	.100
1.282	.900
1.645	.950
1.960	.975
2.326	.990
2.575	.995

Example B–6. Determine the area that lies outside of the range $(-3 \leq z \leq 3)$. The desired area can be found from Exhibit II.5–1 by taking the complement of $\Phi(3) - \Phi(-3)$, or $1 - [.9987 - .0013] = .0024$. Thus, the probability is only about 2/1000 that a randomly selected value from a normal distribution will be more than three standard deviations from the mean.

C. Using the Tables

Example C–1. The net weight of a box of Super Soap Powder is normally distributed with a mean of 1500 grams and a variance of 100 grams, i.e., $N(1500,100)$. Determine the probability that the contents of a random box of powder weigh less than 1480 grams.

Using the notation above, $F(1480)$ represents the area from $-\infty$ to 1480 grams. The desired probability is the shaded area shown below.

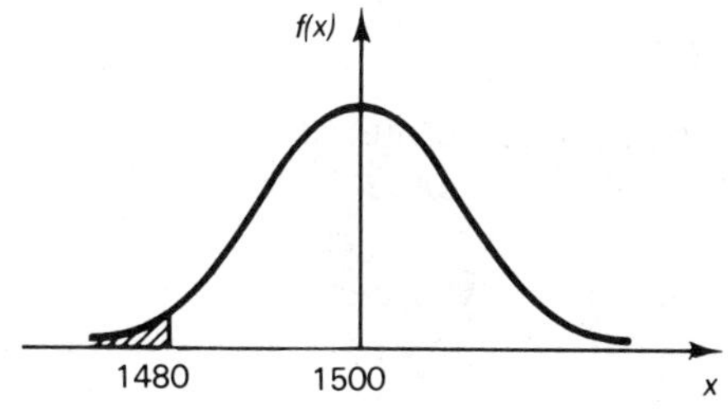

Now, $F(1480)$ can be evaluated as

$$F(1480) = \Phi\left(\frac{1480 - 1500}{10}\right) = \Phi(-2)$$

which is represented on the standard normal distribution as follows:

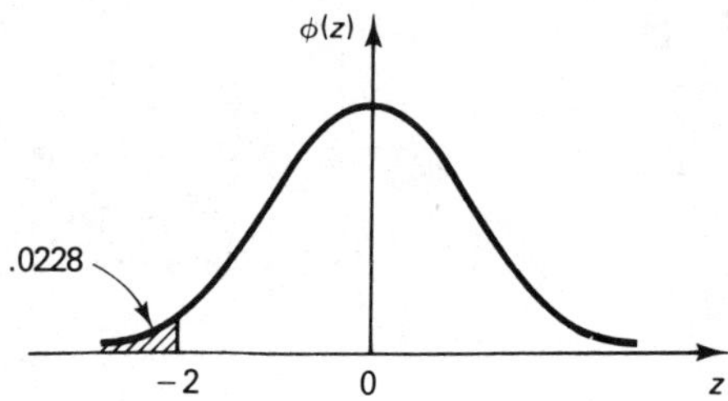

From Exhibit II.5–1, $\Phi(-2) = .0228$. Thus, the probability that the contents of a random box of powder weigh less than 1480 grams is .0228.

Example C–2. Another version of Example C–1 is the determination of the weight of soap powder such that only 5 percent of the contents selected at random will be less than that value. Then,

$$\Phi\left(\frac{x - 1500}{10}\right) = .05$$

where x is the amount that is of interest. From Exhibit II.5–1, $\Phi(-1.645) = .05$. Thus,

$$\frac{x - 1500}{10} = -1.645$$

and solving for x yields

$$x = 1483.55 \text{ grams}$$

Hence, only 5 percent of the contents of boxes selected at random weigh less than 1483.55 grams.

Example C–3. Yet another example similar to Examples C–1 and C–2 is the following: Determine the proportion of the contents of boxes that is between 1490 and 1515 grams in weight. This problem statement requires the computation of $F(1515)-F(1490)$, or

$$F(1515)-F(1490)=\Phi\left(\frac{1515-1500}{10}\right)-\Phi\left(\frac{1490-1500}{10}\right)$$
$$=\Phi(1.5)-\Phi(-1)=.9332-.1587=.7745$$

Thus, the probability is .7745 that the contents of the boxes will be between 1490 and 1515 grams.

Example C–4. Approximation to the Binomial. As p remains fixed in the binomial distribution and n grows larger, the normal distribution can be used to approximate the binomial distribution. The quantity $(X-np)/\sqrt{npq}$ has approximately an $N(0,1)$ distribution if p is close to $1/2$ and $n>10$. For other values of p, the approximation is fairly good if $np>5$ for $p\leq 1/2$ and $nq>5$ when $p>1/2$. The value of q is the complement of p, i.e., $p+q=1$.

Since the binomial distribution is discrete and the normal distribution is continuous, it is necessary to use a continuity correction in calculating probabilities. Thus, the binomial probability $P(X=x)$ would be determined from $P(x-1/2\leq X\leq x+1/2)$.

Consider the case where a random sample of 100 units is taken from a process each hour. It is known that the process produces items, 25 percent of which are defective. The probability of between a and b defectives, including a and b (where $a<b$ and a and b are integers), is given by

$$P(a-1/2\leq X\leq b+1/2)=\Phi\left[\frac{(b+1/2)-np}{\sqrt{npq}}\right]-\Phi\left[\frac{(a-1/2)-np}{\sqrt{npq}}\right]$$

With $a=21$ and $b=24$, the resulting probability is

$$P(20.5\leq X\leq 24.5)=\Phi\left[\frac{24.5-25}{\sqrt{(100)(.25)(.75)}}\right]-\Phi\left[\frac{20.5-25}{\sqrt{(100)(.25)(.75)}}\right]$$
$$=\Phi[-0.115]-\Phi[-1.039]=.4542-.1494=.3048$$

Example C–5. Tests of Hypotheses on the Mean, Variance Known. The maximum firing temperature in a Heat-Even oven used in the manufacture of semiconductor chips should not exceed 500°C. Past experience has indicated that the standard deviation of the maximum temperature is 16°C. A random sample of four Heat-Even ovens is tested, and the average maximum temperature is found to be 492°C. Should the ovens be accepted as having the appropriate maximum temperature with the confidence level $\alpha=.05$? (*Note*: α is also denoted as the probability of a type I error.)

The hypotheses are

H_0: $\mu = 500°C$

H_1: $\mu < 500°C$

The test statistic is given by

$$Z_0 = \frac{\overline{X} - \mu_0}{\sigma/\sqrt{n}}$$

with a rejection region given by $Z_0 < Z_{.05} = -1.645$. The value of $Z_{.05}$ can be obtained from Example B–5. Now

$$Z_0 = \frac{492 - 500}{16/\sqrt{4}} = -1$$

Pictorially, the distribution of $\overline{X}$ is given by

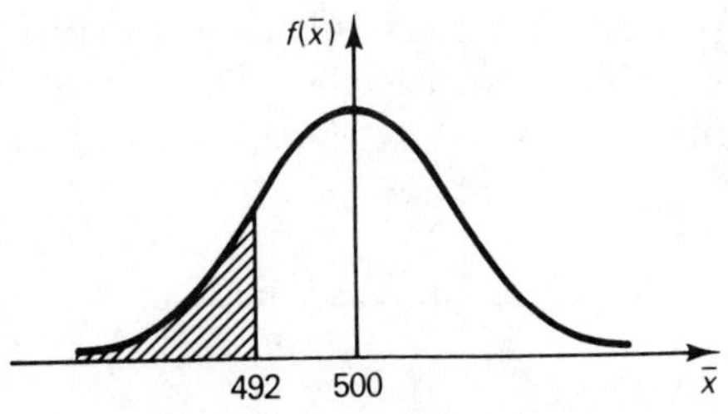

If the shaded area is less than .05, the null hypothesis, H_0, should be rejected, i.e., the sample did not come from a population whose mean is 500°C or higher. To test this hypothesis, the variable is changed to Z, resulting in the following:

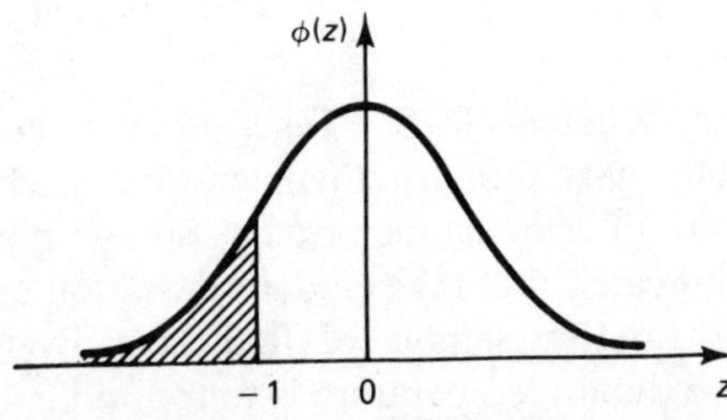

Since the value of $Z_0 > -1.645$, we fail to reject the null hypothesis.

Example C–6. Test of Hypotheses on a Proportion. An electronics firm produces semiconductors. A contract with a purchaser states that the fraction defective be no more than .10. A random sample of 200 semiconductors yields 24 defectives. Test the hypotheses

$$H_0: p = .10$$
$$H_1: p > .10$$

at $\alpha = .05$. With the expected number of defectives given by $\mu_0 = np_0 = 200(.10) = 20.0$, the test statistic would be

$$Z_0 = \frac{(X - .5) - \mu_0}{\sqrt{np_0(1 - p_0)}} = \frac{23.5 - 20.0}{\sqrt{200(.10)(.90)}} = 0.824$$

We will reject H_0 if $Z_0 > Z_{.05}$. But since $Z_{.05} = 1.645$, the null hypothesis cannot be rejected. It should be noted that if $X \leq np_0$, then the correction factor in the test statistic will be $+.5$ rather than $-.5$.

Example C–7. Confidence Interval on the Mean. Construct a 95-percent, two-sided confidence interval on the mean of the Heat-Even oven given in Example C–5 based on a sample of four with mean $\bar{X} = 492°\text{C}$.

For a two-sided test of hypotheses the confidence interval is given by

$$\bar{X} - Z_{\alpha/2}\sigma/\sqrt{n} \leq \mu \leq \bar{X} + Z_{\alpha/2}\sigma/\sqrt{n}$$

Using the data in this example yields

$$492 - 1.96(16)/\sqrt{4} \leq \mu \leq 492 + 1.96(16)/\sqrt{4}$$

or

$$476.32°\text{C} \leq \mu \leq 507.68°\text{C}$$

The complete statement of the confidence interval, with the associated probability, is

$$P(476.32°\text{C} \leq \mu \leq 507.68°\text{C}) = .95$$

Example C–8. Confidence Interval on a Proportion. The approximate $100(1 - \alpha)$ percent two-sided confidence interval on a proportion, p, is given by

$$\hat{p} - Z_{\alpha/2}\sqrt{\frac{\hat{p}(1-p)}{n}} \leq p \leq \hat{p} + Z_{\alpha/2}\sqrt{\frac{\hat{p}(1-\hat{p})}{n}}$$

EXHIBIT II.5–1

Cumulative Normal Distribution

Z	.00	.01	.02	.03	.04	.05	.06	.07	.08	.09
-3.40	.0003	.0003	.0003	.0003	.0003	.0003	.0003	.0003	.0003	.0002
-3.30	.0005	.0005	.0005	.0004	.0004	.0004	.0004	.0004	.0004	.0003
-3.20	.0007	.0007	.0006	.0006	.0006	.0006	.0006	.0005	.0005	.0005
-3.10	.0010	.0009	.0009	.0009	.0008	.0008	.0008	.0008	.0007	.0007
-3.00	.0013	.0013	.0013	.0012	.0012	.0011	.0011	.0011	.0010	.0010
-2.90	.0019	.0018	.0018	.0017	.0016	.0016	.0015	.0015	.0014	.0014
-2.80	.0026	.0025	.0024	.0023	.0023	.0022	.0021	.0021	.0020	.0019
-2.70	.0035	.0034	.0033	.0032	.0031	.0030	.0029	.0028	.0027	.0026
-2.60	.0047	.0045	.0044	.0043	.0041	.0040	.0039	.0038	.0037	.0036
-2.50	.0062	.0060	.0059	.0057	.0055	.0054	.0052	.0051	.0049	.0048
-2.40	.0082	.0080	.0078	.0075	.0073	.0071	.0069	.0068	.0066	.0064
-2.30	.0107	.0104	.0102	.0099	.0096	.0094	.0091	.0089	.0087	.0084
-2.20	.0139	.0136	.0132	.0129	.0125	.0122	.0119	.0116	.0113	.0110
-2.10	.0179	.0174	.0170	.0166	.0162	.0158	.0154	.0150	.0146	.0143
-2.00	.0228	.0222	.0217	.0212	.0207	.0202	.0197	.0192	.0188	.0183
-1.90	.0287	.0281	.0274	.0268	.0262	.0256	.0250	.0244	.0239	.0233
-1.80	.0359	.0351	.0344	.0336	.0329	.0322	.0314	.0307	.0301	.0294
-1.70	.0446	.0436	.0427	.0418	.0409	.0401	.0392	.0384	.0375	.0367
-1.60	.0548	.0537	.0526	.0516	.0505	.0495	.0485	.0475	.0465	.0455
-1.50	.0668	.0655	.0643	.0630	.0618	.0606	.0594	.0582	.0571	.0559
-1.40	.0808	.0793	.0778	.0764	.0749	.0735	.0721	.0708	.0694	.0681
-1.30	.0968	.0951	.0934	.0918	.0901	.0885	.0869	.0853	.0838	.0823
-1.20	.1151	.1131	.1112	.1093	.1075	.1056	.1038	.1020	.1003	.0985
-1.10	.1357	.1335	.1314	.1292	.1271	.1251	.1230	.1210	.1190	.1170
-1.00	.1587	.1562	.1539	.1515	.1492	.1469	.1446	.1423	.1401	.1379
-.90	.1841	.1814	.1788	.1762	.1736	.1711	.1685	.1660	.1635	.1611
-.80	.2119	.2090	.2061	.2033	.2005	.1977	.1949	.1922	.1894	.1867
-.70	.2420	.2389	.2358	.2327	.2296	.2266	.2236	.2206	.2177	.2148
-.60	.2743	.2709	.2676	.2643	.2611	.2578	.2546	.2514	.2483	.2451
-.50	.3085	.3050	.3015	.2981	.2946	.2912	.2877	.2843	.2810	.2776
-.40	.3446	.3409	.3372	.3336	.3300	.3264	.3228	.3192	.3156	.3121
-.30	.3821	.3783	.3745	.3707	.3669	.3632	.3594	.3557	.3520	.3483
-.20	.4207	.4168	.4129	.4090	.4052	.4013	.3974	.3936	.3897	.3859
-.10	.4602	.4562	.4522	.4483	.4443	.4404	.4364	.4325	.4286	.4247
-.00	.5000	.4960	.4920	.4880	.4840	.4801	.4761	.4721	.4681	.4641

The two-sided 95 percent confidence interval on the defective semiconductors in Example C–6, where $\hat{p} = 24/200 = .12$, is found from

$$.12 - 1.96\sqrt{\frac{.12(.88)}{200}} \leq p \leq .12 + 1.96\sqrt{\frac{.12(.88)}{200}}$$

EXHIBIT II.5–1—CONTINUED

z	.00	.01	.02	.03	.04	.05	.06	.07	.08	.09
.00	.5000	.5040	.5080	.5120	.5160	.5199	.5239	.5279	.5319	.5359
.10	.5398	.5438	.5478	.5517	.5557	.5596	.5636	.5675	.5714	.5753
.20	.5793	.5832	.5871	.5910	.5948	.5987	.6026	.6064	.6103	.6141
.30	.6179	.6217	.6255	.6293	.6331	.6368	.6406	.6443	.6480	.6517
.40	.6554	.6591	.6628	.6664	.6700	.6736	.6772	.6808	.6844	.6879
.50	.6915	.6950	.6985	.7019	.7054	.7088	.7123	.7157	.7190	.7224
.60	.7257	.7291	.7324	.7357	.7389	.7422	.7454	.7486	.7517	.7549
.70	.7580	.7611	.7642	.7673	.7704	.7734	.7764	.7794	.7823	.7852
.80	.7881	.7910	.7939	.7967	.7995	.8023	.8051	.8078	.8106	.8133
.90	.8159	.8186	.8212	.8238	.8264	.8289	.8315	.8340	.8365	.8389
1.00	.8413	.8438	.8461	.8485	.8508	.8531	.8554	.8577	.8599	.8621
1.10	.8643	.8665	.8686	.8708	.8729	.8749	.8770	.8790	.8810	.8830
1.20	.8849	.8869	.8888	.8907	.8925	.8944	.8962	.8980	.8997	.9015
1.30	.9032	.9049	.9066	.9082	.9099	.9115	.9131	.9147	.9162	.9177
1.40	.9192	.9207	.9222	.9236	.9251	.9265	.9279	.9292	.9306	.9319
1.50	.9332	.9345	.9357	.9370	.9382	.9394	.9406	.9418	.9429	.9441
1.60	.9452	.9463	.9474	.9484	.9495	.9505	.9515	.9525	.9535	.9545
1.70	.9554	.9564	.9573	.9582	.9591	.9599	.9608	.9616	.9625	.9633
1.80	.9641	.9649	.9656	.9664	.9671	.9678	.9686	.9693	.9699	.9706
1.90	.9713	.9719	.9726	.9732	.9738	.9744	.9750	.9756	.9761	.9767
2.00	.9772	.9778	.9783	.9788	.9793	.9798	.9803	.9808	.9812	.9817
2.10	.9821	.9826	.9830	.9834	.9838	.9842	.9846	.9850	.9854	.9857
2.20	.9861	.9864	.9868	.9871	.9875	.9878	.9881	.9884	.9887	.9890
2.30	.9893	.9896	.9898	.9901	.9904	.9906	.9909	.9911	.9913	.9916
2.40	.9918	.9920	.9922	.9925	.9927	.9929	.9931	.9932	.9934	.9936
2.50	.9938	.9940	.9941	.9943	.9945	.9946	.9948	.9949	.9951	.9952
2.60	.9953	.9955	.9956	.9957	.9959	.9960	.9961	.9962	.9963	.9964
2.70	.9965	.9966	.9967	.9968	.9969	.9970	.9971	.9972	.9973	.9974
2.80	.9974	.9975	.9976	.9977	.9977	.9978	.9979	.9979	.9980	.9981
2.90	.9981	.9982	.9982	.9983	.9984	.9984	.9985	.9985	.9986	.9986
3.00	.9987	.9987	.9987	.9988	.9988	.9989	.9989	.9989	.9990	.9990
3.10	.9990	.9991	.9991	.9991	.9992	.9992	.9992	.9992	.9993	.9993
3.20	.9993	.9993	.9994	.9994	.9994	.9994	.9994	.9995	.9995	.9995
3.30	.9995	.9995	.9995	.9996	.9996	.9996	.9996	.9996	.9996	.9997
3.40	.9997	.9997	.9997	.9997	.9997	.9997	.9997	.9997	.9997	.9998

or

$$.075 \leq p \leq .165$$

Thus,

$$P(.075 \leq p \leq .165) = .95$$

Hence, the probability is .95 that the interval (.075, .165) contains the true probability of a defective.

II.6 *t* Distribution

A. Description

Let Z be normally distributed with mean equal to zero and variance equal to one (the standard normal distribution), and let χ_ν^2 be a chi-square random variable with ν degrees of freedom, all independent. Then the random variable.

$$T = \frac{Z}{\sqrt{\chi_\nu^2/\nu}}$$

is said to follow the *t distribution with ν degrees of freedom*, denoted t_ν. The mean is given by $E(T) = 0$, and the variance by

$$V(T) = \nu/(\nu - 2) \qquad \text{for } \nu > 2$$

The t distribution is symmetrical about its mean. Historically, authors have made no distinction between T (the random variable) and t (the outcome). We will follow this precedent and use t, even though we mean T. The probability density function is shown as follows:

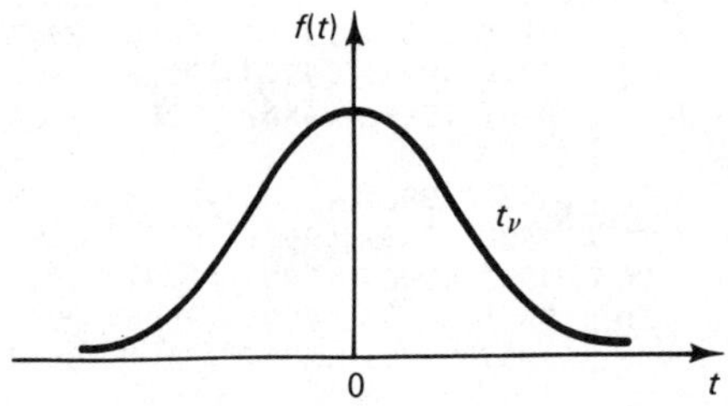

Values of t for selected percentiles are given in Exhibit II.6–1.

Uses of the t distribution include

1. Testing hypotheses on a single mean, variance unknown.
2. Testing hypotheses on two means, variances unknown.
3. Conducting a paired t test.
4. Estimating an interval on the mean, variance unknown.

B. Reading the Tables

Example B–1. For a t distribution with $\nu = 5$, find the probability α that $t > 2.0$, or $P(t > 2.0)$. From Exhibit II.6–1, the probability is approximately .05. The graphical interpretation is as follows:

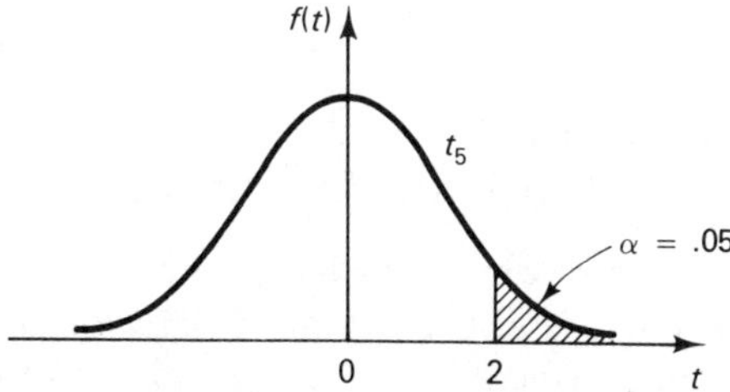

Example B–2. Find the point at which the t distribution with $\nu = 10$ has .05 of the area in the right tail. The desired value, denoted $t_{.05,10}$, is found in Exhibit II.6–1 as 1.812. The graphical interpretation is as follows:

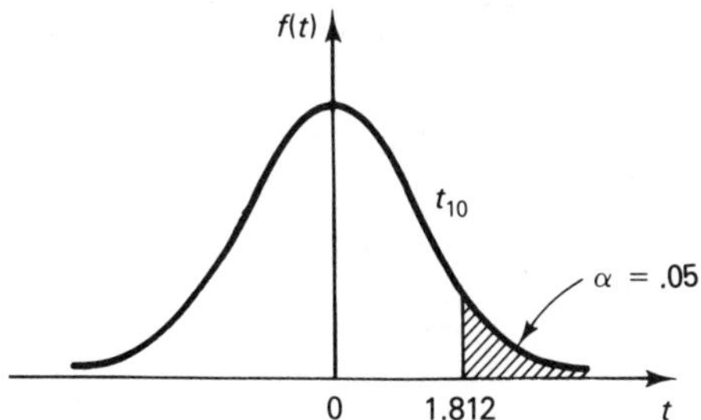

Example B–3. Find $P[-2.306 \leq t_8 \leq 2.306]$. Using the symmetry property of the t distribution, $P(t \geq 2.306) = P(t \leq -2.306)$. From Exhibit II.6–1, $P(t_8 \geq 2.306)$ is found to equal .025. Thus, the sum of the two values in the tails is .05. The complement of .05 is .95, the desired probability.

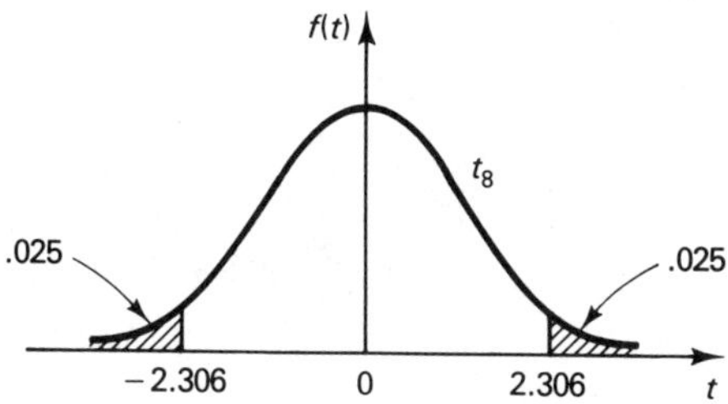

Example B–4. Find the degrees of freedom ν such that $\alpha = .025$ and $t_{.025,\nu} = 2.0$. From Exhibit II.6–1, $t_{.025,60} = 2.0$. Thus, $\nu = 60$. (Note that when $\nu = \infty$, the percentage points of the t distribution and the percentage points of the standard normal distribution are equivalent.)

C. Using the Tables

C–1. Tests of Hypotheses on a Single Mean, Variance Unknown

Consider testing hypotheses about the mean of a random variable X, where X is distributed normally with mean equal to μ and variance equal to σ^2, and where both μ and σ^2 are unknown. Assume that a random sample $X_1, X_2, \ldots, X_n$ is available. An estimator for σ^2 is S^2, the sample variance, determined from

$$S^2 = \frac{\Sigma_{i=1}^{n} X_i^2 - \dfrac{(\Sigma_{i=1}^{n} X_i)^2}{n}}{n-1}$$

There are other ways of writing S^2, such as

$$S^2 = \frac{\Sigma_{i=1}^{n}(X_i - \bar{X})^2}{n-1} = \frac{\Sigma_{i=1}^{n} X_i^2 - n\bar{X}^2}{n-1}$$

The sample standard deviation S is obtained from $\sqrt{S^2}$. The appropriate test statistic t_0 is given by

$$t_0 = \frac{\bar{X} - \mu_0}{S/\sqrt{n}}$$

where

$$\bar{X} = \frac{\Sigma_{i=1}^{n} X_i}{n}$$

It can be shown that t_0 is distributed as a t random variable with $\nu = n - 1$ degrees of freedom when the true mean is μ_0.

To test the hypotheses

$$H_0: \mu = \mu_0$$
$$H_1: \mu \neq \mu_0$$

calculate $\overline{X}$ and S from a sample taken from X, and compute t_0. Do not reject H_0 if

$$-t_{\alpha/2,\nu} \leq t_0 \leq t_{\alpha/2,\nu}$$

where $\nu = n - 1$. For the hypotheses

$$H_0: \mu = \mu_0$$
$$H_1: \mu < \mu_0$$

reject H_0 if

$$t_0 < -t_{\alpha,\nu}$$

For the hypotheses

$$H_0: \mu = \mu_0$$
$$H_1: \mu > \mu_0$$

reject H_0 if

$$t_0 > t_{\alpha,\nu}$$

Example C–1. The time to overhaul the engine in a forklift truck is a normally distributed random variable. A sample of repair times, in hours, for the last 16 overhauls is as follows:

Hours			
12.2	14.5	15.0	10.7
11.3	12.6	12.8	11.5
9.5	11.8	12.3	12.1
13.1	9.7	13.2	11.3

A standard repair time of 12.5 hours has been recommended. Test the hypotheses

$$H_0: \mu = 12.5$$
$$H_1: \mu \neq 12.5$$

with $\alpha = .05$. The values for $\bar{X}$ and S^2 are given by

$$\bar{X} = 193.6/16 = 12.1$$

and

$$S^2 = \frac{2375.94 - \dfrac{(193.6)^2}{16}}{15} = 2.225$$

With $S = \sqrt{2.225} = 1.49$,

$$t_0 = \frac{12.1 - 12.5}{1.49/\sqrt{16}} = \frac{-0.4}{0.3725} = -1.07$$

Hence, do not reject H_0, since

$$-t_{.025,15} = -2.131 \leq -1.07 \leq 2.131 = t_{.025,15}$$

C–2. Test of Hypotheses on Two Means, Variances Unknown

Assume that X_1 and X_2 are distributed normally with means μ_1 and μ_2 and variances σ_1^2 and σ_2^2, respectively.

Case 1: $\sigma_1^2 = \sigma_2^2 = \sigma^2$. Suppose that two random samples of sizes n_1 and n_2 are obtained. Denote these samples by $X_{11}, X_{12}, \ldots, X_{1n_1}$ and $X_{21}, X_{22}, \ldots, X_{2n_2}$. Compute the corrected sums of squares SS_1 and SS_2 for each sample as follows:

$$SS_1 = \sum_{i=1}^{n_1} X_{1i}^2 - \frac{(\Sigma_{i=1}^{n_1} X_{1i})^2}{n_1}$$

and

$$SS_2 = \sum_{i=1}^{n_2} X_{2i}^2 - \frac{(\Sigma_{i=1}^{n_2} X_{2i})^2}{n_2}$$

Obtain the pooled estimate of the variance S_p^2, from

$$S_p^2 = \frac{SS_1 + SS_2}{n_1 + n_2 - 2}$$

The test statistic

$$t_0 = \frac{\overline{X}_1 - \overline{X}_2}{S_p\sqrt{\dfrac{1}{n_1} + \dfrac{1}{n_2}}}$$

is distributed as a t distribution with $\nu = n_1 + n_2 - 2$ degrees of freedom when $\mu_1 = \mu_2$. To test the hypotheses

$$H_0: \mu_1 = \mu_2$$
$$H_1: \mu_1 \neq \mu_2$$

calculate $\overline{X}_1$, $\overline{X}_2$ and S_p from samples taken from X_1 and X_2, and then compute t_0. Do not reject H_0 if

$$-t_{\alpha/2,\nu} \leq t_0 \leq t_{\alpha/2,\nu}$$

For the hypotheses

$$H_0: \mu_1 = \mu_2$$
$$H_1: \mu_1 > \mu_2$$

do not reject H_0 if $t_0 < t_{\alpha,\nu}$. For the hypotheses

$$H_0: \mu_1 = \mu_2$$
$$H_1: \mu_1 < \mu_2$$

do not reject H_0 if $t_0 > -t_{\alpha,\nu}$.

Example C–2. Two machines are used to fill boxes with detergent. It is known that the amount of detergent placed in the boxes by the machine is normally distributed, and further, the variances of the two machines are approximately the same. Each month a sample of eight boxes is taken from each machine to see if the mean amount of detergent in the boxes is the same with $\alpha = .01$. The boxes are opened and the detergent is weighed. This month, the sample from the first machine had a mean of 497.3 grams and a corrected sum of squares of 60.2 grams^2. The values for the sample from the second machine were $\overline{X}_2 = 500.7$ grams and $SS_2 = 80.3$ grams^2. The hypotheses to be tested are

$$H_0: \mu_1 = \mu_2$$
$$H_1: \mu_1 \neq \mu_2$$

The value for S_p^2 is determined as

$$S_p^2 = \frac{60.2 + 80.3}{8 + 8 - 2} = 10.04$$

and

$$S_p = 3.17$$

Then, t_0 is calculated as

$$t_0 = \frac{497.3 - 500.7}{3.17\sqrt{\frac{1}{8} + \frac{1}{8}}} = \frac{-3.4}{1.585} = -2.15$$

Do not reject H_0, since

$$-t_{.005,14} = -2.977 \leq -2.145 \leq 2.977 = t_{.005,14}$$

Case 2: $\sigma_1^2 \neq \sigma_2^2$ (Behrens-Fisher Problem). Compute the statistic

$$t_0 = \frac{\bar{X}_1 - \bar{X}_2}{\sqrt{\frac{S_1^2}{n_1} + \frac{S_2^2}{n_2}}}$$

Follow the procedure as in Section C–2, except replace the degrees of freedom by

$$\nu = \frac{\left(\frac{S_1^2}{n_1} + \frac{S_2^2}{n_2}\right)}{\frac{(S_1^2/n_1)^2}{n_1 + 1} + \frac{(S_2^2/n_2)^2}{n_2 + 1}} - 2$$

Example C–3. Same as Example C–2, except that it is not known that the variances of the two machines are the same, nor can it be assumed to be the case. The relationship between the corrected sum of squares and the estimator for the variance is given by

$$S^2 = \frac{SS}{n-1}$$

Thus, S_1^2 and S_2^2 are given by

$$S_1^2 = 60.2/7 = 8.60$$

and

$$S_2^2 = 80.3/7 = 11.47$$

Then

$$t_0 = \frac{497.3 - 500.7}{\sqrt{\dfrac{8.60}{8} + \dfrac{11.47}{8}}} = \frac{-3.4}{1.58} = -2.15$$

The degrees of freedom, ν, are found as

$$\nu = \frac{\left(\dfrac{8.60}{8} + \dfrac{11.47}{8}\right)}{\dfrac{(8.60/8)^2}{9} + \dfrac{(11.47/8)^2}{9}} - 2$$

$$= \frac{1.075 + 1.434}{.128 + .228} - 2 = 5.0$$

Therefore, do not reject H_0, since

$$-t_{.005,5} = -4.032 \leq -2.152 \leq 4.032 = t_{.005,5}$$

C–3. Paired *t*-test. Test the hypotheses that

$$H_0: \mu_D = \mu_{D_0}$$
$$H_1: \mu_D \neq \mu_{D_0}$$

The test statistic is

$$t_0 = \frac{\bar{D} - \mu_{D_0}}{S_D/\sqrt{n}}$$

The test statistic is distributed as a t distribution with $\nu = n - 1$ degrees of freedom, where

$$\bar{D} = \sum_{j=1}^{n} \frac{D_j}{n}$$

and

$$S_D^2 = \frac{\Sigma_{j=1}^{n} D_j^2 - \frac{(\Sigma_{j=1}^{n} D_j)^2}{n}}{n-1}$$

and

$$D_j = X_{1j} - X_{2j}$$

For this two-sided test, H_0 would not be rejected if

$$-t_{\alpha/2,\nu} \leq t_0 \leq t_{\alpha/2,\nu}$$

Note that other hypotheses and rejection regions could be formed as in Example C–3.

Example C–4. The manufacturer of an air deflector shield claims that when this device is placed on the hood of a tractor pulling a large trailer, the fuel consumption decreases by 10 gallons on a cross country trip because of the streamlined air flow. A large trucking firm selects six tractor and trailer rigs and has the drivers record the fuel required on a trip from San Diego to Boston, both without (X_{1j}) and with (X_{2j}) the air deflector shields. The weight carried for each truck is the same on the two trips. The results are as follows:

	Fuel Consumed (Gallons)	
Truck	Without Air Deflector	With Air Deflector
1	504	497
2	500	491
3	512	509
4	536	514
5	502	492
6	516	501

The hypotheses that would put the burden of proof on the manufacturer are as follows:

$$H_0: \mu_D = 10$$

$$H_1: \mu_D > 10$$

Test these hypotheses at $\alpha = .05$. First compute the D_j values as 7, 9, 3, 22, 10, and 15, with a sum of 66. Then $\overline{D} = 66/6 = 11$. The value of S_D^2 is computed as

$$S_D^2 = \frac{940 - (66)^2/6}{5} = 44.4$$

and $S_D = 6.64$. Then,

$$t_0 = \frac{11 - 10}{6.64/\sqrt{6}} = \frac{1}{2.71} = 0.37$$

Then H_0 is rejected if $t_0 > t_{.05,5} = 2.015$. Since H_0 is not rejected, do not buy the air deflector shields.

C–3. Interval Estimation of the Mean, Variance(s) Unknown

Single Sample Case. For situations in which the variance is unknown but X is distributed normally with mean μ and variance σ^2, the two-sided interval estimator is given by

$$\overline{X} - t_{\alpha/2,\nu} S/\sqrt{n} \leq \mu \leq \overline{X} + t_{\alpha/2,\nu} S/\sqrt{n}$$

where $\nu = n - 1$. The probability that the interval contains μ is $1 - \alpha$, i.e.,

$$P\left[\overline{X} - t_{\alpha/2,\nu} S/\sqrt{n} \leq \mu \leq \overline{X} + t_{\alpha/2,\nu} S/\sqrt{n}\right] = 1 - \alpha$$

Two Sample Case, $\sigma_1^2 = \sigma_2^2$. For the two sample case, if it can reasonably be assumed that $\sigma_1^2 = \sigma_2^2$, a $100(1 - \alpha)$ percent confidence interval on the true difference in treatment means $\mu_1 - \mu_2$ is given by

$$\overline{X}_1 - \overline{X}_2 - t_{\alpha/2,\nu} S_p \sqrt{\frac{1}{n_1} + \frac{1}{n_2}} \le \mu_1 - \mu_2$$

$$\le \overline{X}_1 - \overline{X}_2 + t_{\alpha/2,\nu} S_p \sqrt{\frac{1}{n_1} + \frac{1}{n_2}}$$

where $\nu = n_1 + n_2 - 2$.

Two Sample Case, $\sigma_1^2 \neq \sigma_2^2$. For the two sample case, if $\sigma_1^2 \neq \sigma_2^2$, a $100(1-\alpha)$ percent confidence interval on the true difference in treatment means is given by

$$\overline{X}_1 - \overline{X}_2 - t_{\alpha/2,\nu} \sqrt{\frac{S_1^2}{n_1} + \frac{S_2^2}{n_2}} \le \mu_1 - \mu_2$$

$$\le \overline{X}_1 + \overline{X}_2 + t_{\alpha/2,\nu} \sqrt{\frac{S_1^2}{n_1} + \frac{S_2^2}{n_2}}$$

where ν is the degrees of freedom determined as in the Behrens-Fisher problem of Section C–2.

For all three cases, appropriate one-sided confidence intervals can be determined. Replace $\alpha/2$ by α for the desired side, and set the other side equal to positive infinity if on the right, negative infinity if on the left.

Example C–5. Consider Example C–1. To develop a 95-percent, two-sided confidence interval on μ requires the value of $t_{.025,15} = 2.131$ from Exhibit II.6–1. Then

$$P[12.1 - 2.131(1.49/4) \le \mu \le 12.1 + 2.131(1.49/4)] = .95$$

or

$$P(11.31 \le \mu \le 12.89) = .95$$

Thus, the probability that the interval (11.31, 12.89) contains the true value of μ is .95.

EXHIBIT II.6–1

t VALUES FOR GIVEN TAIL AREAS

Degrees of Freedom ν	α = Right-Hand Tail Area						
	.250	.100	.050	.025	.010	.005	.001
1	1.000	3.078	6.314	12.706	31.821	63.657	318.309
2	.816	1.886	2.920	4.303	6.965	9.925	22.327
3	.765	1.638	2.353	3.182	4.541	5.841	10.215
4	.741	1.533	2.132	2.776	3.747	4.604	7.173
5	.727	1.476	2.015	2.571	3.365	4.032	5.893
6	.718	1.440	1.943	2.447	3.143	3.707	5.208
7	.711	1.415	1.895	2.365	2.998	3.499	4.785
8	.706	1.397	1.860	2.306	2.896	3.355	4.501
9	.703	1.383	1.833	2.262	2.821	3.250	4.297
10	.700	1.372	1.812	2.228	2.764	3.169	4.144
11	.697	1.363	1.796	2.201	2.718	3.106	4.025
12	.695	1.356	1.782	2.179	2.681	3.055	3.930
13	.694	1.350	1.771	2.160	2.650	3.012	3.852
14	.692	1.345	1.761	2.145	2.624	2.977	3.787
15	.691	1.341	1.753	2.131	2.602	2.947	3.733
16	.690	1.337	1.746	2.120	2.583	2.921	3.686
17	.689	1.333	1.740	2.110	2.567	2.898	3.646
18	.688	1.330	1.734	2.101	2.552	2.878	3.610
19	.688	1.328	1.729	2.093	2.539	2.861	3.579
20	.687	1.325	1.725	2.086	2.528	2.845	3.552
21	.686	1.323	1.721	2.080	2.518	2.831	3.527
22	.686	1.321	1.717	2.074	2.508	2.819	3.505
23	.685	1.319	1.714	2.069	2.500	2.807	3.485
24	.685	1.318	1.711	2.064	2.492	2.797	3.467
25	.684	1.316	1.708	2.060	2.485	2.787	3.450
26	.684	1.315	1.706	2.056	2.479	2.779	3.435
27	.684	1.314	1.703	2.052	2.473	2.771	3.421
28	.683	1.313	1.701	2.048	2.467	2.763	3.408
29	.683	1.311	1.699	2.045	2.462	2.756	3.396
30	.683	1.310	1.697	2.042	2.457	2.750	3.385
35	.682	1.306	1.690	2.030	2.438	2.724	3.340
40	.681	1.303	1.684	2.021	2.423	2.704	3.307
50	.679	1.299	1.676	2.009	2.403	2.678	3.261
60	.679	1.296	1.671	2.000	2.390	2.660	3.232
70	.678	1.294	1.667	1.994	2.381	2.648	3.211
80	.678	1.292	1.664	1.990	2.374	2.639	3.195
90	.677	1.291	1.662	1.987	2.368	2.632	3.183
100	.677	1.290	1.660	1.984	2.364	2.626	3.174
120	.677	1.289	1.658	1.980	2.358	2.617	3.160
∞	.674	1.282	1.645	1.960	2.326	2.576	3.090

II.7 Chi-Square Distribution

A. Description

Let Z_i, $i = 1, 2, \ldots, \nu$, be independently and normally distributed random variables with means equal to zero and variances equal to one. Then the random variable

$$\chi^2 = Z_1^2 + Z_2^2 + \cdots + Z_\nu^2$$

is said to follow the *chi-square distribution with* ν *degrees of freedom*, denoted χ_ν^2. The mean and variance are given by

$$E(\chi^2) = \nu$$

and

$$V(\chi^2) = 2\nu$$

respectively. The probability function for several values of ν is shown below.

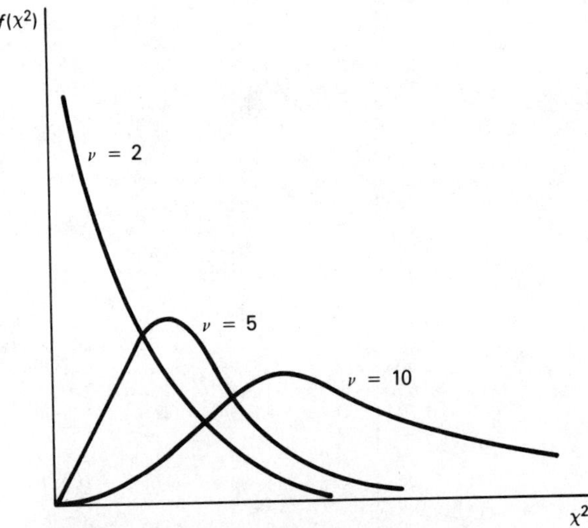

Uses of the chi-square distribution include

1. Tests of hypotheses on the variance of a normal population.
2. Interval estimation on the variance of normal population.

3. Contingency table analysis.
4. Goodness-of-fit testing.

Values of the percentile points of the χ^2 distribution are given in Exhibit II.7–1.

B. Reading the Tables

Example B–1. Find the 95 percentile point of a chi-square distributed random variable with $\nu = 10$. The desired value is 18.31, which is found at the point labeled $\chi^2_{.05,10}$ in the following figure, where the shaded area is .95.

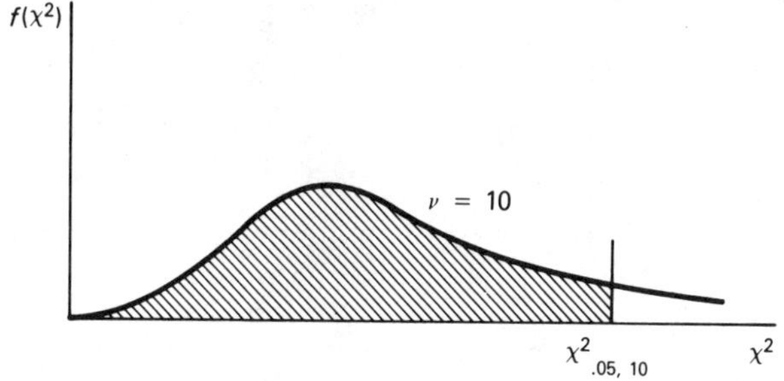

Example B–2. For a random variable with a chi-square distribution with $\nu = 7$, we wish to find the probability that the random variable is larger than 14, as shown by the shaded area in the following figure:

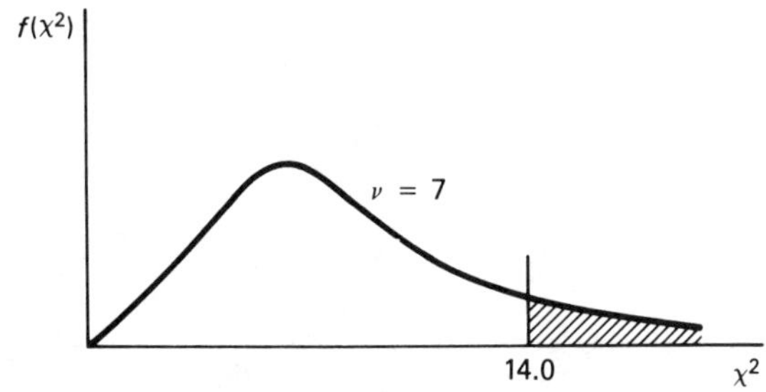

Looking in the row of Exhibit II.7–1 for $\nu = 7$, we locate the value closest to 14. The entry in the .05 column is 14.070; thus, the probability that a random variable has a value greater than 14 is slightly more than .05. Interpolation in this fashion should be used with caution since the percentile values are nonlinear, especially in the tails.

EXHIBIT II.7–1

χ^2 Values for Given Tail Areas

Degrees of Freedom ν	α = Right-Hand Tail Area											
	.999	.995	.99	.975	.95	.90	.10	.05	.025	.01	.005	.001
1	.00	.00	.00	.00	.00	.02	2.71	3.84	5.02	6.63	7.88	10.83
2	.00	.01	.02	.05	.10	.21	4.61	5.99	7.38	9.21	10.60	13.81
3	.02	.07	.11	.22	.35	.58	6.25	7.81	9.35	11.34	12.84	16.25
4	.09	.21	.30	.48	.71	1.06	7.78	9.49	11.14	13.28	14.86	18.45
5	.21	.41	.55	.83	1.15	1.61	9.24	11.07	12.83	15.09	16.75	20.50
6	.38	.68	.87	1.24	1.64	2.20	10.64	12.59	14.45	16.81	18.54	22.44
7	.60	.99	1.24	1.69	2.17	2.83	12.02	14.07	16.01	18.48	20.28	24.30
8	.86	1.34	1.65	2.18	2.73	3.49	13.36	15.51	17.53	20.09	21.95	26.11
9	1.15	1.74	2.09	2.70	3.33	4.17	14.68	16.92	19.02	21.67	23.59	27.86
10	1.48	2.16	2.56	3.25	3.94	4.87	15.99	18.31	20.48	23.21	25.19	29.57
11	1.83	2.60	3.05	3.82	4.57	5.58	17.27	19.68	21.92	24.72	26.76	31.25
12	2.22	3.07	3.57	4.40	5.23	6.30	18.55	21.03	23.34	26.22	28.30	32.90
13	2.62	3.57	4.11	5.01	5.89	7.04	19.81	22.36	24.74	27.69	29.82	34.52
14	3.05	4.07	4.66	5.63	6.57	7.79	21.06	23.68	26.12	29.14	31.32	36.12
15	3.48	4.60	5.23	6.26	7.26	8.55	22.31	25.00	27.49	30.58	32.80	37.69
16	3.94	5.14	5.81	6.91	7.96	9.31	23.54	26.30	28.85	32.00	34.27	39.25
17	4.42	5.70	6.41	7.56	8.67	10.09	24.77	27.59	30.19	33.41	35.72	40.79
18	4.91	6.26	7.01	8.23	9.39	10.86	25.99	28.87	31.53	34.81	37.16	42.31
19	5.41	6.84	7.63	8.91	10.12	11.65	27.20	30.14	32.85	36.19	38.58	43.82
20	5.92	7.43	8.26	9.59	10.85	12.44	28.41	31.41	34.17	37.57	39.99	45.31
21	6.45	8.04	8.90	10.28	11.59	13.24	29.62	32.67	35.48	38.93	41.40	46.80
22	6.98	8.64	9.54	10.98	12.34	14.04	30.81	33.92	36.78	40.29	42.79	48.24
23	7.53	9.26	10.20	11.69	13.09	14.85	32.01	35.17	38.08	41.64	44.18	49.71
24	8.08	9.89	10.86	12.40	13.85	15.66	33.20	36.42	39.36	42.98	45.56	51.16
25	8.65	10.52	11.52	13.12	14.61	16.47	34.38	37.65	40.65	44.31	46.93	52.61

EXHIBIT II.7–1—CONTINUED

Degrees of Freedom	α = Right-Hand Tail Area											
ν	.999	.995	.99	.975	.95	.90	.10	.05	.025	.01	.005	.001
26	9.2	11.2	12.2	13.8	15.4	17.3	35.6	38.9	41.9	45.6	48.3	54.0
27	9.8	11.8	12.9	14.6	16.2	18.1	36.7	40.1	43.2	47.0	49.6	55.5
28	10.4	12.5	13.6	15.3	16.9	18.9	37.9	41.3	44.5	48.3	51.0	56.9
29	11.0	13.1	14.3	16.0	17.7	19.8	39.1	42.6	45.7	49.6	52.3	58.3
30	11.6	13.8	15.0	16.8	18.5	20.6	40.3	43.8	47.0	50.9	53.7	59.7
32	12.7	15.1	16.3	18.3	20.1	22.3	42.6	46.2	49.5	53.5	56.4	62.6
34	13.9	16.5	17.8	19.8	21.7	23.9	44.9	48.6	52.0	56.1	59.0	65.3
36	15.2	17.9	19.2	21.3	23.3	25.6	47.2	51.0	54.5	58.6	61.6	68.1
38	16.5	19.3	20.7	22.9	24.9	27.3	49.5	53.4	56.9	61.2	64.2	70.8
40	17.8	20.7	22.1	24.4	26.5	29.1	51.8	55.8	59.3	63.7	66.8	73.5
42	19.2	22.1	23.6	26.0	28.1	30.8	54.1	58.1	61.8	66.2	69.4	76.2
44	20.5	23.5	25.1	27.6	29.8	32.5	56.4	60.5	64.2	68.7	71.9	78.8
46	21.9	25.0	26.6	29.2	31.4	34.2	58.6	62.8	66.6	71.2	74.5	81.5
48	23.2	26.5	28.2	30.7	33.1	36.0	60.9	65.2	69.0	73.7	77.0	84.1
50	24.6	28.0	29.7	32.3	34.8	37.7	63.2	67.5	71.4	76.2	79.5	86.7
55	28.1	31.7	33.5	36.4	39.0	42.1	68.8	73.3	77.4	82.3	85.8	93.2
60	31.7	35.5	37.5	40.5	43.2	46.5	74.4	79.1	83.3	88.4	92.0	99.7
65	35.3	39.4	41.4	44.6	47.4	50.9	80.0	84.8	89.2	94.4	98.1	106.1
70	39.0	43.2	45.4	48.8	51.7	55.3	85.5	90.5	95.0	100.4	104.2	112.4
75	42.7	47.2	49.5	52.9	56.1	59.8	91.1	96.2	100.8	106.4	110.3	118.7
80	46.5	51.1	53.5	57.1	60.4	64.3	96.6	101.9	106.6	112.3	116.3	124.9
85	50.3	55.1	57.6	61.4	64.7	68.8	102.1	107.5	112.4	118.3	122.4	131.1
90	54.1	59.2	61.7	65.6	69.1	73.3	107.6	113.1	118.1	124.1	128.3	137.3
95	58.0	63.2	65.9	69.9	73.5	77.8	113.0	118.7	123.9	130.0	134.3	143.4
100	61.9	67.3	70.0	74.2	77.9	82.4	118.5	124.3	129.6	135.8	140.2	149.5

Example B–3. Find $P(7 \leq \chi^2_{18} \leq 26)$. This is represented by the shaded area in the following figure:

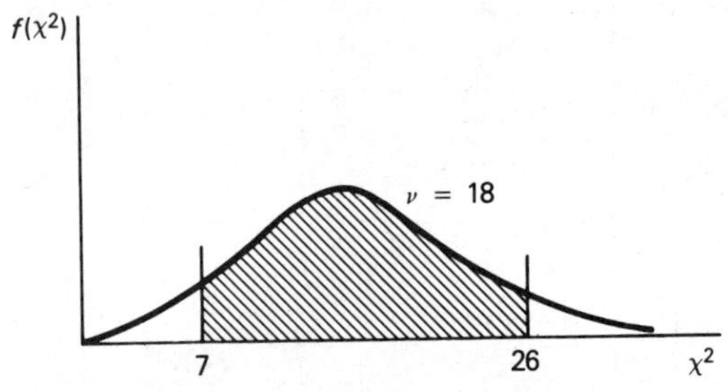

Using Exhibit II.7–1, we find that $P(\chi^2_{18} > 25.99) = .10$ and $P(\chi^2_{18} > 7.01) = .99$. Since $P(7.01 < \chi^2_{18} < 25.99) = P(\chi^2_{18} > 7.01) - P(\chi^2_{18} > 25.99)$, the shaded area is approximately $.99 - .10 = .89$.

C. Using the Tables

Example C–1. Test of Hypotheses on the Variance of a Normal Population. Data are collected on the time to overhaul the engine in a forklift truck. The time is assumed to follow a normal distribution. Sixteen repair times are recorded, and the sample variance is computed to be $S^2 = 2.22$. Industry standards state that the repair time variance for fully trained personnel should not exceed 2.0. Based on the data collected, is there statistical evidence that the variance of the repair time exceeds the standard? We test the hypotheses

$$H_0: \sigma^2 = 2.0$$

$$H_1: \sigma^2 > 2.0$$

The test statistic used is

$$\chi^2_0 = (n-1)S^2/\sigma^2_0 = (16-1)(2.22)/2.0 = 16.65$$

H_0 is rejected if $\chi^2_0 > \chi^2_{\alpha,\nu}$, where $\nu = n - 1$. Using $\alpha = .05$ and $\nu = 15$ in Exhibit II.7–1, we find $\chi^2_{.05,15} = 25.00$. Thus, the null hypothesis is not rejected.

Example C–2. Interval Estimation of the Variance of a Normal Population. A $100(1-\alpha)$ percent confidence interval can be found from

$$\frac{(n-1)S^2}{\chi^2_{\alpha/2,\nu}} \leq \sigma^2 \leq \frac{(n-1)S^2}{\chi^2_{1-\alpha/2,\nu}}$$

Suppose that a 90-percent confidence interval on the true variance of the repair times in Example C–1 is desired. From Exhibit II.7–1 with $\nu = 15$ and $\alpha/2 = .05$, we find $\chi^2_{.05,15} = 25.00$ and $\chi^2_{.95,15} = 7.26$. Thus, the confidence interval is

$$\frac{15(2.22)}{25.00} \leq \sigma^2 \leq \frac{15(2.22)}{7.26}$$

$$1.332 \leq \sigma^2 \leq 4.587$$

II.8 *F* Distribution

A. Description

Consider two independent random samples of size n_1 and n_2 taken from two normal populations, with variances σ_1^2 and σ_2^2. If S_1^2 and S_2^2 are the sample variances, then the ratio

$$F = \frac{S_1^2/\sigma_1^2}{S_2^2/\sigma_2^2}$$

has an F distribution with $\nu_1 = n_1 - 1$ and $\nu_2 = n_2 - 1$ degrees of freedom. The sample variances are calculated from

$$S^2 = \frac{\sum_{i=1}^{n} X_i^2 - n\overline{X}^2}{n-1}$$

where

$$\overline{X} = \frac{\sum_{i=1}^{n} X_i}{n}$$

The F random variable is nonnegative, and the distribution is skewed generally to the right, as shown below.

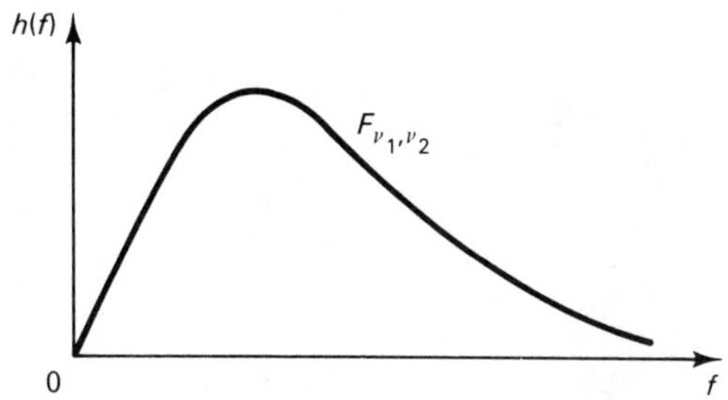

The F distribution is used when

1. Testing hypotheses on the variances of two normal distributions.
2. Developing a confidence interval on the ratio of the variance of two normal distributions.

B. Reading the Tables

The tables appearing as Exhibit II.8–1 are indexed by degrees of freedom, for the numerator ν_1 along the horizontal axis, and for the denominator ν_2 along the vertical axis. For each combination of degrees of freedom and for the most frequently needed values of α, the area in the right-hand tail is given. The value read from the tables is F_{α,ν_1,ν_2}.

Example B–1. From Exhibit II.8–1, $F_{.025,8,7} = 4.90$. Graphically, this result is shown as follows:

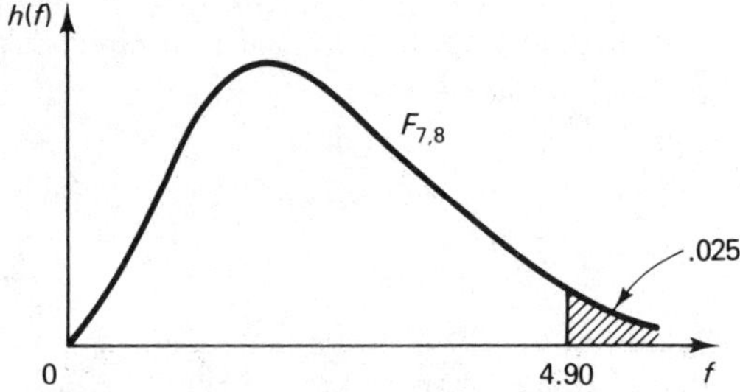

Example B–2. Determine $F_{.975,7,8}$. This value is not contained in Exhibit II.8–1 directly. However, the following relationship holds:

$$F_{1-\alpha,\nu_1,\nu_2} = \frac{1}{F_{\alpha,\nu_2,\nu_1}}$$

Thus,

$$F_{.975,7,8} = \frac{1}{F_{.025,8,7}} = \frac{1}{4.90} = 0.2041$$

Graphically, the result is

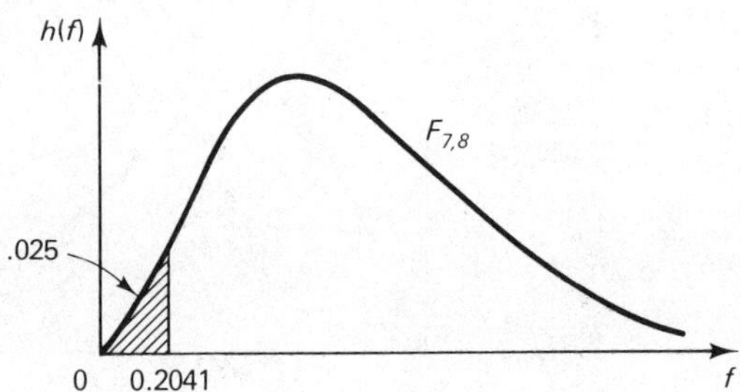

Example B-3. The probability

$$P\left[F_{1-\alpha/2,\nu_1,\nu_2} \leq F \leq F_{\alpha/2,\nu_1,\nu_2}\right]$$

can be graphically shown as

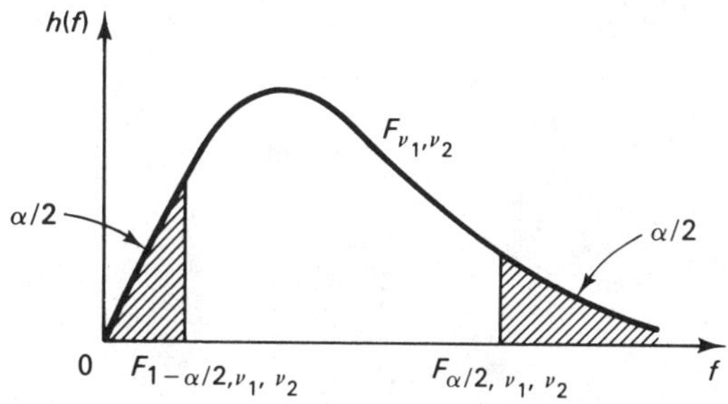

Thus, when $\alpha = .05$, $\nu_1 = 20$, and $\nu_2 = 30$,

$$P[0.426 \leq F \leq 2.20] = .95$$

where $F_{.025,20,30}$ is found in Exhibit II.8–1 as 2.20 and $F_{.975,20,30} = 1/F_{.025,30,20}$. Now, $F_{.025,30,20}$ is found in Exhibit II.8–1 as 2.35, so $F_{.975,20,30} = 1/2.35 = 0.426$.

C. Using the Distribution

C–1. Tests of Hypotheses on the Variances of Two Normal Distributions

Example C–1. Oven 1 and Oven 2 are used to cure silicon chips in a semiconductor manufacturing facility. The baking temperatures of the ovens are normally distributed. Suppose it is desired to test the hypotheses

$$H_0: \sigma_1^2 = \sigma_2^2$$

$$H_1: \sigma_1^2 \neq \sigma_2^2$$

Two samples of sizes $n_1 = n_2 = 16$ yield $S_1^2 = 34.14$ degrees^2 and $S_2^2 = 47.32$ degrees^2. Should the null hypothesis be rejected at $\alpha = .05$?

The test statistic

$$F_0 = S_1^2/S_2^2$$

is distributed as F, with $\nu_1 = 15$ and $\nu_2 = 15$ degrees of freedom if the null hypothesis $H_0: \sigma_1^2 = \sigma_2^2$ is true. Therefore, H_0 would be rejected if

$$F_0 > F_{\alpha/2,\nu_1,\nu_2}$$

EXHIBIT II.8–1

F VALUES FOR GIVEN TAIL AREAS

		ν_1 = Degrees of Freedom for Numerator								
ν_2	α	1	2	3	4	5	6	7	8	9
1	.100	39.9	49.5	53.6	55.8	57.2	58.2	58.9	59.4	59.9
	.050	161.4	199.5	215.7	224.6	230.2	234.0	236.8	238.9	240.5
	.025	647.8	799.5	864.2	899.6	921.8	937.1	948.2	956.7	963.3
	.010	4052.2	4999.5	5403.4	5624.6	5763.6	5859.0	5928.4	5981.1	6022.5
	.001	40600.	20000.	21600.	22500.	23100.	23400.	23700.	23900.	24100.
2	.100	8.53	9.00	9.16	9.24	9.29	9.33	9.35	9.37	9.38
	.050	18.51	19.00	19.16	19.25	19.30	19.33	19.35	19.37	19.38
	.025	38.51	39.00	39.17	39.25	39.30	39.33	39.36	39.37	39.39
	.010	98.50	99.00	99.17	99.25	99.30	99.33	99.36	99.37	99.39
	.001	998.50	999.00	999.17	999.25	999.30	999.33	999.36	999.37	999.39
3	.100	5.54	5.46	5.39	5.34	5.31	5.28	5.27	5.25	5.24
	.050	10.13	9.55	9.28	9.12	9.01	8.94	8.89	8.85	8.81
	.025	17.44	16.04	15.44	15.10	14.88	14.73	14.62	14.54	14.47
	.010	34.12	30.82	29.46	28.71	28.24	27.91	27.67	27.49	27.35
	.001	167.03	148.50	141.11	137.10	134.58	132.85	131.58	130.62	129.86
4	.100	4.54	4.32	4.19	4.11	4.05	4.01	3.98	3.95	3.94
	.050	7.71	6.94	6.59	6.39	6.26	6.16	6.09	6.04	6.00
	.025	12.22	10.65	9.98	9.60	9.36	9.20	9.07	8.98	8.90
	.010	21.20	18.00	16.69	15.98	15.52	15.21	14.98	14.80	14.66
	.001	74.14	61.25	56.18	53.44	51.71	50.53	49.66	49.00	48.47
5	.100	4.06	3.78	3.62	3.52	3.45	3.40	3.37	3.34	3.32
	.050	6.61	5.79	5.41	5.19	5.05	4.95	4.88	4.82	4.77
	.025	10.01	8.43	7.76	7.39	7.15	6.98	6.85	6.76	6.68
	.010	16.26	13.27	12.06	11.39	10.97	10.67	10.46	10.29	10.16
	.001	47.18	37.12	33.20	31.09	29.75	28.83	28.16	27.65	27.24
6	.100	3.78	3.46	3.29	3.18	3.11	3.05	3.01	2.98	2.96
	.050	5.99	5.14	4.76	4.53	4.39	4.28	4.21	4.15	4.10
	.025	8.81	7.26	6.60	6.23	5.99	5.82	5.70	5.60	5.52
	.010	13.75	10.92	9.78	9.15	8.75	8.47	8.26	8.10	7.98
	.001	35.51	27.00	23.70	21.92	20.80	20.03	19.46	19.03	18.69
7	.100	3.59	3.26	3.07	2.96	2.88	2.83	2.78	2.75	2.72
	.050	5.59	4.74	4.35	4.12	3.97	3.87	3.79	3.73	3.68
	.025	8.07	6.54	5.89	5.52	5.29	5.12	4.99	4.90	4.82
	.010	12.25	9.55	8.45	7.85	7.46	7.19	6.99	6.84	6.72
	.001	29.25	21.69	18.77	17.20	16.21	15.52	15.02	14.63	14.33
8	.100	3.46	3.11	2.92	2.81	2.73	2.67	2.62	2.59	2.56
	.050	5.32	4.46	4.07	3.84	3.69	3.58	3.50	3.44	3.39
	.025	7.57	6.06	5.42	5.05	4.82	4.65	4.53	4.43	4.36
	.010	11.26	8.65	7.59	7.01	6.63	6.37	6.18	6.03	5.91
	.001	25.41	18.49	15.83	14.39	13.48	12.86	12.40	12.05	11.77

α = Right-Hand Tail Area

ν_2 = Degrees of Freedom for Denominator

EXHIBIT II.8–1—CONTINUED

ν_2	α	ν_1 = Degrees of Freedom for Numerator								
		10	15	20	25	30	50	75	100	∞
	.100	60.2	61.2	61.7	62.1	62.3	62.7	62.9	63.0	63.3
	.050	241.9	245.9	248.0	249.3	250.1	251.8	252.6	253.0	280.7
1	.025	968.6	984.9	993.1	998.1	1001.4	1008.1	1011.5	1013.2	1012.2
	.010	6055.8	6157.3	6208.7	6239.8	6260.6	6302.5	6323.6	6334.1	6316.5
	.001	60600.	61600.	62100.	62400.	62500.	63000.	63200.	63300.	63700.
	.100	9.39	9.42	9.44	9.45	9.46	9.47	9.48	9.48	9.49
	.050	19.40	19.43	19.45	19.46	19.46	19.48	19.48	19.49	19.51
2	.025	39.40	39.43	39.45	39.46	39.46	39.48	39.48	39.49	39.48
	.010	99.40	99.43	99.45	99.46	99.47	99.48	99.49	99.49	99.64
	.001	999.40	999.43	999.45	999.46	999.47	999.48	999.49	999.49	947.48
	.100	5.23	5.20	5.18	5.17	5.17	5.15	5.15	5.14	5.13
	.050	8.79	8.70	8.66	8.63	8.62	8.58	8.56	8.55	8.53
3	.025	14.42	14.25	14.17	14.12	14.08	14.01	13.97	13.96	13.90
	.010	27.23	26.87	26.69	26.58	26.50	26.35	26.28	26.24	26.14
	.001	129.25	127.37	126.42	125.84	125.45	124.66	124.27	124.07	124.19
	.100	3.92	3.87	3.84	3.83	3.82	3.80	3.78	3.78	3.76
	.050	5.96	5.86	5.80	5.77	5.75	5.70	5.68	5.66	5.63
4	.025	8.84	8.66	8.56	8.50	8.46	8.38	8.34	8.32	8.27
	.010	14.55	14.20	14.02	13.91	13.84	13.69	13.61	13.58	13.47
	.001	48.05	46.76	46.10	45.70	45.43	44.88	44.61	44.47	44.46
	.100	3.30	3.24	3.21	3.19	3.17	3.15	3.13	3.13	3.11
	.050	4.74	4.62	4.56	4.52	4.50	4.44	4.42	4.41	4.37
5	.025	6.62	6.43	6.33	6.27	6.23	6.14	6.10	6.08	6.02
	.010	10.05	9.72	9.55	9.45	9.38	9.24	9.17	9.13	9.04
	.001	26.92	25.91	25.39	25.08	24.87	24.44	24.22	24.12	23.98
	.100	2.94	2.87	2.84	2.81	2.80	2.77	2.75	2.75	2.72
	.050	4.06	3.94	3.87	3.83	3.81	3.75	3.73	3.71	3.67
6	.025	5.46	5.27	5.17	5.11	5.07	4.98	4.94	4.92	4.85
	.010	7.87	7.56	7.40	7.30	7.23	7.09	7.02	6.99	6.88
	.001	18.41	17.56	17.12	16.85	16.67	16.31	16.12	16.03	15.92
	.100	2.70	2.63	2.59	2.57	2.56	2.52	2.51	2.50	2.47
	.050	3.64	3.51	3.44	3.40	3.38	3.32	3.29	3.27	3.23
7	.025	4.76	4.57	4.47	4.40	4.36	4.28	4.23	4.21	4.15
	.010	6.62	6.31	6.16	6.06	5.99	5.86	5.79	5.75	5.66
	.001	14.08	13.32	12.93	12.69	12.53	12.20	12.04	11.95	11.72
	.100	2.54	2.46	2.42	2.40	2.38	2.35	2.33	2.32	2.29
	.050	3.35	3.22	3.15	3.11	3.08	3.02	2.99	2.97	2.93
8	.025	4.30	4.10	4.00	3.94	3.89	3.81	3.76	3.74	3.67
	.010	5.81	5.52	5.36	5.26	5.20	5.07	5.00	4.96	4.87
	.001	11.54	10.84	10.48	10.26	10.11	9.80	9.65	9.57	9.41

α = Right Hand Tail Area

ν_2 = Degrees of Freedom for Denominator

EXHIBIT II.8-1—CONTINUED

		ν_1 = Degrees of Freedom for Numerator								
ν_2	α	1	2	3	4	5	6	7	8	9
9	.100	3.36	3.01	2.81	2.69	2.61	2.55	2.51	2.47	2.44
	.050	5.12	4.26	3.86	3.63	3.48	3.37	3.29	3.23	3.18
	.025	7.21	5.71	5.08	4.72	4.48	4.32	4.20	4.10	4.03
	.010	10.56	8.02	6.99	6.42	6.06	5.80	5.61	5.47	5.35
	.001	22.86	16.39	13.90	12.56	11.71	11.13	10.70	10.37	10.11
10	.100	3.29	2.92	2.73	2.61	2.52	2.46	2.41	2.38	2.35
	.050	4.96	4.10	3.71	3.48	3.33	3.22	3.14	3.07	3.02
	.025	6.94	5.46	4.83	4.47	4.24	4.07	3.95	3.85	3.78
	.010	10.04	7.56	6.55	5.99	5.64	5.39	5.20	5.06	4.94
	.001	21.04	14.91	12.55	11.28	10.4	9.93	9.52	9.20	8.96
11	.100	3.23	2.86	2.66	2.54	2.45	2.39	2.34	2.30	2.27
	.050	4.84	3.98	3.59	3.36	3.20	3.09	3.01	2.95	2.90
	.025	6.72	5.26	4.63	4.28	4.04	3.88	3.76	3.66	3.59
	.010	9.65	7.21	6.22	5.67	5.32	5.07	4.89	4.74	4.63
	.001	19.69	13.81	11.56	10.35	9.58	9.05	8.66	8.35	8.12
12	.100	3.18	2.81	2.61	2.48	2.39	2.33	2.28	2.24	2.21
	.050	4.75	3.89	3.49	3.26	3.11	3.00	2.91	2.85	2.80
	.025	6.55	5.10	4.47	4.12	3.89	3.73	3.61	3.51	3.44
	.010	9.33	6.93	5.95	5.41	5.06	4.82	4.64	4.50	4.39
	.001	18.64	12.97	10.80	9.63	8.89	8.38	8.00	7.71	7.48
15	.100	3.07	2.70	2.49	2.36	2.27	2.21	2.16	2.12	2.09
	.050	4.54	3.68	3.29	3.06	2.90	2.79	2.71	2.64	2.59
	.025	6.20	4.77	4.15	3.80	3.58	3.41	3.29	3.20	3.12
	.010	8.68	6.36	5.42	4.89	4.56	4.32	4.14	4.00	3.89
	.001	16.59	11.34	9.34	8.25	7.57	7.09	6.74	6.47	6.26
18	.100	3.01	2.62	2.42	2.29	2.20	2.13	2.08	2.04	2.00
	.050	4.41	3.55	3.16	2.93	2.77	2.66	2.58	2.51	2.46
	.025	5.98	4.56	3.95	3.61	3.38	3.22	3.10	3.01	2.93
	.010	8.29	6.01	5.09	4.58	4.25	4.01	3.84	3.71	3.60
	.001	15.38	10.39	8.49	7.46	6.81	6.35	6.02	5.76	5.56
20	.100	2.97	2.59	2.38	2.25	2.16	2.09	2.04	2.00	1.96
	.050	4.35	3.49	3.10	2.87	2.71	2.60	2.51	2.45	2.39
	.025	5.87	4.46	3.86	3.51	3.29	3.13	3.01	2.91	2.84
	.010	8.10	5.85	4.94	4.43	4.10	3.87	3.70	3.56	3.46
	.001	14.82	9.95	8.10	7.10	6.46	6.02	5.69	5.44	5.24
25	.100	2.92	2.53	2.32	2.18	2.09	2.02	1.97	1.93	1.89
	.050	4.24	3.39	2.99	2.76	2.60	2.49	2.40	2.34	2.28
	.025	5.69	4.29	3.69	3.35	3.13	2.97	2.85	2.75	2.68
	.010	7.77	5.57	4.68	4.18	3.85	3.63	3.46	3.32	3.22
	.001	13.88	9.22	7.45	6.49	5.89	5.46	5.15	4.91	4.71

α = Right Hand Tail Area

ν_2 = Degrees of Freedom for Denominator

EXHIBIT II.8-1—CONTINUED

ν_2	α	10	15	20	25	30	50	75	100	∞
		ν_1 = Degrees of Freedom for Numerator								
9	.100	2.42	2.34	2.30	2.27	2.25	2.22	2.20	2.19	2.16
	.050	3.14	3.01	2.94	2.89	2.86	2.80	2.77	2.76	2.71
	.025	3.96	3.77	3.67	3.60	3.56	3.47	3.43	3.40	3.33
	.010	5.26	4.96	4.81	4.71	4.65	4.52	4.45	4.41	4.31
	.001	9.89	9.24	8.90	8.69	8.55	8.26	8.11	8.04	7.93
10	.100	2.32	2.24	2.20	2.17	2.16	2.12	2.10	2.09	2.06
	.050	2.98	2.85	2.77	2.73	2.70	2.64	2.60	2.59	2.54
	.025	3.72	3.52	3.42	3.35	3.31	3.22	3.18	3.15	3.08
	.010	4.85	4.56	4.41	4.31	4.25	4.12	4.05	4.01	3.91
	.001	8.75	8.13	7.80	7.60	7.47	7.19	7.05	6.98	6.92
11	.100	2.25	2.17	2.12	2.10	2.08	2.04	2.02	2.01	1.97
	.050	2.85	2.72	2.65	2.60	2.57	2.51	2.47	2.46	2.40
	.025	3.53	3.33	3.23	3.16	3.12	3.03	2.98	2.96	2.88
	.010	4.54	4.25	4.10	4.01	3.94	3.81	3.74	3.71	3.61
	.001	7.92	7.32	7.01	6.81	6.68	6.42	6.28	6.21	6.05
12	.100	2.19	2.10	2.06	2.03	2.01	1.97	1.95	1.94	1.90
	.050	2.75	2.62	2.54	2.50	2.47	2.40	2.37	2.35	2.30
	.025	3.37	3.18	3.07	3.01	2.96	2.87	2.82	2.80	2.73
	.010	4.30	4.01	3.86	3.76	3.70	3.57	3.50	3.47	3.36
	.001	7.29	6.71	6.40	6.22	6.09	5.83	5.70	5.63	5.48
15	.100	2.06	1.97	1.92	1.89	1.87	1.83	1.80	1.79	1.76
	.050	2.54	2.40	2.33	2.28	2.25	2.18	2.14	2.12	2.07
	.025	3.06	2.86	2.76	2.69	2.64	2.55	2.50	2.47	2.40
	.010	3.80	3.52	3.37	3.28	3.21	3.08	3.01	2.98	2.87
	.001	6.08	5.54	5.25	5.07	4.95	4.70	4.57	4.51	4.35
18	.100	1.98	1.89	1.84	1.80	1.78	1.74	1.71	1.70	1.66
	.050	2.41	2.27	2.19	2.14	2.11	2.04	2.00	1.98	1.92
	.025	2.87	2.67	2.56	2.49	2.44	2.35	2.30	2.27	2.19
	.010	3.51	3.23	3.08	2.98	2.92	2.78	2.71	2.68	2.57
	.001	5.39	4.87	4.59	4.42	4.30	4.06	3.93	3.87	3.70
20	.100	1.94	1.84	1.79	1.76	1.74	1.69	1.66	1.65	1.61
	.050	2.35	2.20	2.12	2.07	2.04	1.97	1.93	1.91	1.84
	.025	2.77	2.57	2.46	2.40	2.35	2.25	2.20	2.17	2.09
	.010	3.37	3.09	2.94	2.84	2.78	2.64	2.57	2.54	2.42
	.001	5.08	4.56	4.29	4.12	4.00	3.77	3.64	3.58	3.42
25	.100	1.87	1.77	1.72	1.68	1.66	1.61	1.58	1.56	1.52
	.050	2.24	2.09	2.01	1.96	1.92	1.84	1.80	1.78	1.71
	.025	2.61	2.41	2.30	2.23	2.18	2.08	2.02	2.00	1.91
	.010	3.13	2.85	2.70	2.60	2.54	2.40	2.33	2.29	2.17
	.001	4.56	4.06	3.79	3.63	3.52	3.28	3.15	3.09	2.92

α = Right Hand Tail Area

ν_2 = Degrees of Freedom for Denominator

EXHIBIT II.8-1—Continued

ν_2	α	ν_1 = Degrees of Freedom for Numerator								
		1	2	3	4	5	6	7	8	9
	.100	2.88	2.49	2.28	2.14	2.05	1.98	1.93	1.88	1.85
	.050	4.17	3.32	2.92	2.69	2.53	2.42	2.33	2.27	2.21
30	.025	5.57	4.18	3.59	3.25	3.03	2.87	2.75	2.65	2.57
	.010	7.56	5.39	4.51	4.02	3.70	3.47	3.30	3.17	3.07
	.001	13.29	8.77	7.05	6.12	5.53	5.12	4.82	4.58	4.39
	.100	2.84	2.44	2.23	2.09	2.00	1.93	1.87	1.83	1.79
	.050	4.08	3.23	2.84	2.61	2.45	2.34	2.25	2.18	2.12
40	.025	5.42	4.05	3.46	3.13	2.90	2.74	2.62	2.53	2.45
	.010	7.31	5.18	4.31	3.83	3.51	3.29	3.12	2.99	2.89
	.001	12.61	8.25	6.59	5.70	5.13	4.73	4.44	4.21	4.02
	.100	2.81	2.41	2.20	2.06	1.97	1.90	1.84	1.80	1.76
	.050	4.03	3.18	2.79	2.56	2.40	2.29	2.20	2.13	2.07
50	.025	5.34	3.97	3.39	3.05	2.83	2.67	2.55	2.46	2.38
	.010	7.17	5.06	4.20	3.72	3.41	3.19	3.02	2.89	2.78
	.001	12.22	7.96	6.34	5.46	4.90	4.51	4.22	4.00	3.82
	.100	2.79	2.39	2.18	2.04	1.95	1.87	1.82	1.77	1.74
	.050	4.00	3.15	2.76	2.53	2.37	2.25	2.17	2.10	2.04
60	.025	5.29	3.93	3.34	3.01	2.79	2.63	2.51	2.41	2.33
	.010	7.08	4.98	4.13	3.65	3.34	3.12	2.95	2.82	2.72
	.001	11.97	7.77	6.17	5.31	4.76	4.37	4.09	3.86	3.69
	.100	2.77	2.37	2.15	2.02	1.92	1.85	1.79	1.75	1.71
	.050	3.96	3.11	2.72	2.49	2.33	2.21	2.13	2.06	2.00
80	.025	5.22	3.86	3.28	2.95	2.73	2.57	2.45	2.35	2.28
	.010	6.96	4.88	4.04	3.56	3.26	3.04	2.87	2.74	2.64
	.001	11.67	7.54	5.97	5.12	4.58	4.20	3.92	3.70	3.53
	.100	2.76	2.36	2.15	2.01	1.91	1.84	1.78	1.74	1.70
	.050	3.95	3.10	2.71	2.47	2.32	2.20	2.11	2.04	1.99
90	.025	5.20	3.84	3.26	2.93	2.71	2.55	2.43	2.34	2.26
	.010	6.93	4.85	4.01	3.53	3.23	3.01	2.84	2.72	2.61
	.001	11.57	7.47	5.91	5.06	4.53	4.15	3.87	3.65	3.48
	.100	2.76	2.36	2.14	2.00	1.91	1.83	1.78	1.73	1.69
	.050	3.94	3.09	2.70	2.46	2.31	2.19	2.10	2.03	1.97
100	.025	5.18	3.83	3.25	2.92	2.70	2.54	2.42	2.32	2.24
	.010	6.90	4.82	3.98	3.51	3.21	2.99	2.82	2.69	2.59
	.001	11.50	7.41	5.86	5.02	4.48	4.11	3.83	3.61	3.44
	.100	2.71	2.30	2.08	1.95	1.85	1.77	1.72	1.67	1.63
	.050	3.84	3.00	2.61	2.37	2.21	2.10	2.01	1.94	1.88
∞	.025	5.02	3.69	3.12	2.79	2.57	2.41	2.29	2.19	2.11
	.010	6.64	4.61	3.77	3.32	3.02	2.80	2.64	2.51	2.41
	.001	10.81	6.85	5.43	4.61	4.15	3.78	3.50	3.29	3.12

α = Right Hand Tail Area

ν_2 = Degrees of Freedom for Denominator

EXHIBIT II.8-1—Continued

ν_2	α	10	15	20	25	30	50	75	100	∞
		ν_1 = Degrees of Freedom for Numerator								
	.100	1.82	1.72	1.67	1.63	1.61	1.55	1.52	1.51	1.46
	.050	2.16	2.01	1.93	1.88	1.84	1.76	1.72	1.70	1.62
30	.025	2.51	2.31	2.20	2.12	2.07	1.97	1.91	1.88	1.79
	.010	2.98	2.70	2.55	2.45	2.39	2.25	2.17	2.13	2.01
	.001	4.24	3.75	3.49	3.33	3.22	2.98	2.86	2.79	2.61
	.100	1.76	1.66	1.61	1.57	1.54	1.48	1.45	1.43	1.38
	.050	2.08	1.92	1.84	1.78	1.74	1.66	1.61	1.59	1.51
40	.025	2.39	2.18	2.07	1.99	1.94	1.83	1.77	1.74	1.64
	.010	2.80	2.52	2.37	2.27	2.20	2.06	1.98	1.94	1.81
	.001	3.87	3.40	3.14	2.98	2.87	2.64	2.51	2.44	2.24
	.100	1.73	1.63	1.57	1.53	1.50	1.44	1.41	1.39	1.33
	.050	2.03	1.87	1.78	1.73	1.69	1.60	1.55	1.52	1.44
50	.025	2.32	2.11	1.99	1.92	1.87	1.75	1.69	1.66	1.55
	.010	2.70	2.42	2.27	2.17	2.10	1.95	1.87	1.82	1.68
	.001	3.67	3.20	2.95	2.79	2.68	2.44	2.31	2.25	2.03
	.100	1.71	1.60	1.54	1.50	1.48	1.41	1.38	1.36	1.29
	.050	1.99	1.84	1.75	1.69	1.65	1.56	1.51	1.48	1.39
60	.025	2.27	2.06	1.94	1.87	1.82	1.70	1.63	1.60	1.48
	.010	2.63	2.35	2.20	2.10	2.03	1.88	1.79	1.75	1.60
	.001	3.54	3.08	2.83	2.67	2.55	2.32	2.19	2.12	1.89
	.100	1.68	1.57	1.51	1.47	1.44	1.38	1.34	1.32	1.24
	.050	1.95	1.79	1.70	1.64	1.60	1.51	1.45	1.43	1.32
80	.025	2.21	2.00	1.88	1.81	1.75	1.63	1.56	1.53	1.40
	.010	2.55	2.27	2.12	2.01	1.94	1.79	1.70	1.65	1.49
	.001	3.39	2.93	2.68	2.52	2.41	2.16	2.03	1.96	1.72
	.100	1.67	1.56	1.50	1.46	1.43	1.36	1.33	1.30	1.23
	.050	1.94	1.78	1.69	1.63	1.59	1.49	1.44	1.41	1.30
90	.025	2.19	1.98	1.86	1.79	1.73	1.61	1.54	1.50	1.37
	.010	2.52	2.24	2.09	1.99	1.92	1.76	1.67	1.62	1.46
	.001	3.34	2.88	2.63	2.47	2.36	2.11	1.98	1.91	1.66
	.100	1.66	1.56	1.49	1.45	1.42	1.35	1.32	1.29	1.21
	.050	1.93	1.77	1.68	1.62	1.57	1.48	1.42	1.39	1.28
100	.025	2.18	1.97	1.85	1.77	1.71	1.59	1.52	1.48	1.35
	.010	2.50	2.22	2.07	1.97	1.89	1.74	1.65	1.60	1.43
	.001	3.30	2.84	2.59	2.43	2.32	2.08	1.94	1.87	1.62
	.100	1.60	1.49	1.42	1.38	1.34	1.26	1.21	1.18	1.00
	.050	1.83	1.67	1.57	1.51	1.46	1.35	1.28	1.24	1.00
∞	.025	2.05	1.83	1.71	1.63	1.57	1.43	1.34	1.30	1.00
	.010	2.32	2.04	1.88	1.77	1.70	1.52	1.42	1.36	1.00
	.001	2.98	2.52	2.27	2.11	1.99	1.73	1.58	1.50	1.00

α = Right Hand Tail Area

ν_2 = Degrees of Freedom for Denominator

or if

$$F_0 < F_{1-\alpha/2,\nu_1,\nu_2}$$

Now,

$$F_0 = 34.14/47.32 = 0.785$$

The critical region is determined from the tables as $F_{.025,15,15} = 2.86$ and $F_{.975,15,15} = 0.350$. Therefore, the null hypothesis $H_0: \sigma_1^2 = \sigma_2^2$ should not be rejected. Graphically, the test and the result are shown as follows:

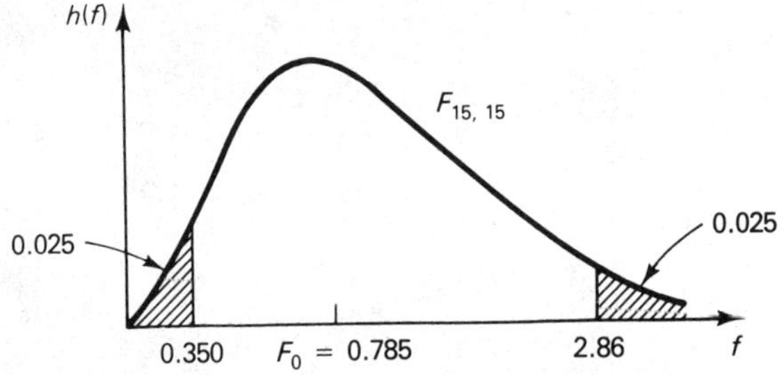

C–2. Confidence Interval on the Ratio of the Variances of Two Normal Distributions

A $100(1-\alpha)$ percent two-sided confidence interval on σ_1^2/σ_2^2 is given by

$$\frac{S_1^2}{S_2^2} F_{1-\alpha/2,\nu_1,\nu_2} \le \frac{\sigma_1^2}{\sigma_2^2} \le \frac{S_1^2}{S_2^2} F_{\alpha/2,\nu_1,\nu_2}$$

where $\nu_1 = n_1 - 1$ and $\nu_2 = n_2 - 1$.

Example C–2. A 95-percent two-sided confidence interval on the ratio of variances in Example C–1 is given by

$$(0.785)(0.350) \le \frac{\sigma_1^2}{\sigma_2^2} \le (0.785)(2.86)$$

or

$$0.275 \le \frac{\sigma_1^2}{\sigma_2^2} \le 2.245$$

Thus, the interval (0.275,2.245) contains the ratio of the variances 95 percent of the time.

III Hypothesis Testing

III.1 Summary of Normal Tests

Much of statistical inference is based on the assumption that the population under consideration has a normal distribution. Since the normal distribution has two parameters, hypothesis tests concerning such populations focus on these. Exhibit III.1–1 lists the hypotheses concerning the mean μ and variance σ^2 when considering a single population or when comparing two populations.

It is assumed that a random sample $X_1, X_2, \ldots, X_n$ from the population(s) of interest is available and that the sample mean

$$\bar{X} = \sum_{i=1}^{n} X_i / n$$

and the sample variance, computed by one of the following equations.

$$S^2 = \sum_{i=1}^{n} (X_i - \bar{X})^2/(n-1)$$

$$= \left[\sum_{i=1}^{n} X_i^2 - \frac{(\sum_{i=1}^{n} X_i)^2}{n} \right] \Big/ (n-1)$$

$$= \left(\sum_{i=1}^{n} X_i^2 - n\bar{X}^2 \right) \Big/ (n-1)$$

are computed. This allows the value of the test statistic to be determined and compared with critical values. These critical values are a function of the probability distribution of the test statistic and α, the probability of rejecting the null hypothesis when it is true. Exhibit III.1–1 also lists the test statistic, decision criteria, and the location of the critical value for each hypothesis. Examples of using each hypothesis-testing procedure can be found in the discussion associated with the exhibit from which the critical value can be obtained.

The reader is referred to Sections IV.1 through IV.4 for assistance in choosing sample sizes for statistical confidence on normal populations and for computation of the power of these tests.

If it cannot be assumed that the population has a normal distribution, it may be necessary to conduct tests on the mean using the nonparametric methods discussed in Sections III.5 or III.6.

EXHIBIT III.1–1

HYPOTHESIS TESTS FOR NORMAL DISTRIBUTIONS

Null Hypothesis	Alternative Hypothesis	Criteria for Rejection	Test Statistic	Exhibit for Critical Value
$H_0: \mu = \mu_0$ σ^2 known	$H_1: \mu \neq \mu_0$ $H_1: \mu > \mu_0$ $H_1: \mu < \mu_0$	$\|Z_0\| > Z_{\alpha/2}$ $Z_0 > Z_\alpha$ $Z_0 < -Z_\alpha$	$Z_0 = \dfrac{\overline{X} - \mu_0}{\sigma/\sqrt{n}}$	II.5–1
$H_0: \mu = \mu_0$ σ^2 unknown	$H_1: \mu \neq \mu_0$ $H_1: \mu > \mu_0$ $H_1: \mu < \mu_0$	$\|t_0\| > t_{\alpha/2,\nu}$ $t_0 > t_{\alpha,\nu}$ $t_0 < -t_{\alpha,\nu}$ $\nu = n - 1$	$t_0 = \dfrac{\overline{X} - \mu_0}{S/\sqrt{n}}$	II.6–1
$H_0: \mu_1 = \mu_2$ σ_1^2 and σ_2^2 known	$H_1: \mu_1 \neq \mu_2$ $H_1: \mu_1 > \mu_2$ $H_1: \mu_1 < \mu_2$	$\|Z_0\| > Z_{\alpha/2}$ $Z_0 > Z_\alpha$ $Z_0 < -Z_\alpha$	$Z_0 = \dfrac{\overline{X}_1 - \overline{X}_2}{\sqrt{\dfrac{\sigma_1^2}{n_1} + \dfrac{\sigma_2^2}{n_2}}}$	II.5–1
$H_0: \mu_1 = \mu_2$ $\sigma_1^2 = \sigma_2^2 = \sigma^2$ σ^2 unknown	$H_1: \mu_1 \neq \mu_2$ $H_1: \mu_1 > \mu_2$ $H_1: \mu_1 < \mu_2$	$\|t_0\| > t_{\alpha/2,\nu}$ $t_0 > t_{\alpha,\nu}$ $t_0 < -t_{\alpha,\nu}$ $\nu = n_1 + n_2 - 2$	$t_0 = \dfrac{\overline{X}_1 - \overline{X}_2}{S_p\sqrt{\dfrac{1}{n_1} + \dfrac{1}{n_2}}}$	II.6–1
$H_0: \mu_1 = \mu_2$ $\sigma_1^2 \neq \sigma_2^2$ σ^2 unknown	$H_1: \mu_1 \neq \mu_2$ $H_1: \mu_1 > \mu_2$ $H_1: \mu_1 < \mu_2$	$\|t_0\| > t_{\alpha/2,\nu}$ $t_0 > t_{\alpha,\nu}$ $t_0 < -t_{\alpha,\nu}$ $\nu = \dfrac{\left(\dfrac{S_1^2}{n_1} + \dfrac{S_2^2}{n_2}\right)^2}{\dfrac{(S_1^2/n_1)^2}{n_1+1} + \dfrac{(S_2^2/n_2)^2}{n_2+1}} - 2$	$t_0 = \dfrac{\overline{X}_1 - \overline{X}_2}{\sqrt{\dfrac{S_1^2}{n_1} + \dfrac{S_2^2}{n_2}}}$	II.6–1
$H_0: \sigma^2 = \sigma_0^2$	$H_1: \sigma^2 \neq \sigma_0^2$ $H_1: \sigma^2 > \sigma_0^2$ $H_1: \sigma^2 < \sigma_0^2$	$\chi_0^2 > \chi_{\alpha/2,\nu}^2$ or $\chi_0^2 < \chi_{1-\alpha/2,\nu}^2$ $\chi_0^2 > \chi_{\alpha,\nu}^2$ $\chi_0^2 < \chi_{1-\alpha,\nu}^2$ $\nu = n - 1$	$\chi_0^2 = \dfrac{(n-1)S^2}{\sigma_0^2}$	II.7–1
$H_0: \sigma_1^2 = \sigma_2^2$	$H_1: \sigma_1^2 \neq \sigma_2^2$ $H_1: \sigma_1^2 > \sigma_2^2$	$F_0 > F_{\alpha/2,\nu_1,\nu_2}$ or $F_0 < F_{1-\alpha/2,\nu_1,\nu_2}$ $F_0 > F_{\alpha,\nu_1,\nu_2}$ $\nu_1 = n_1 - 1$ $\nu_2 = n_2 - 1$	$F_0 = S_1^2/S_2^2$	II.8–1

III.2 Kolmogorov-Smirnov Statistic

A. Description

Suppose that on the basis of a sample of n data points we wish to test the null hypothesis that an unknown cumulative distribution function $F(y)$ is actually a particular continuous cumulative distribution function $F^*(y)$ against the alternative hypothesis that $F(y) \neq F^*(y)$. Letting $F_n(y)$ denote the sample distribution function, the following statistic, referred to as the Kolmogorov-Smirnov statistic, may be formed:

$$D_n^* = \underset{-\infty < y < \infty}{\text{maximum}} |F_n(y) - F^*(y)|$$

Thus, D_n^* is the maximum difference between the sample distribution function and the theoretical distribution function.

When the null hypothesis is true, the probability distribution of D_n^* will be the same for every possible continuous distribution function $F^*(y)$ that does not depend on the particular distribution function being investigated. Tables of the distribution of D_n^* for various values of n have been developed and published in many reference books. The two tables in this section appearing as Exhibits III.2–1 and III.2–2 pertain to the single sample case and are to be used for hypothesis testing with respect to continuous distributions only.

B. Reading the Tables

Exhibit III.2–1 provides Kolmogorov-Smirnov critical values for $\alpha = .10$, .05, and .01 for specified values of n to 35, and a constant numerator for $n > 35$. Exhibit III.2–2 provides Kolmogorov-Smirnov critical values for large sample sizes with varying values of α.

Example B–1. Kolmogorov-Smirnov Critical Values for Specified Degrees of Freedom. If $\alpha = .05$ and the sample size is 20, the critical value of D is given in Exhibit III.2–1 as $D_{\alpha,n} = D_{.05,20} = .294$. If the sample size is 100, the critical value of D is given by $D_{.05,100} = 1.36/\sqrt{n} = .136$.

Example B–2. Kolmogorov-Smirnov Critical Values for Large Sample Sizes. As $n \to \infty$, i.e., any value of $n > 35$, $D_{\alpha,n} = t/\sqrt{n}$, and Exhibit III.2–2 may be used. Since $D_{.0522,100} = 1.35/\sqrt{100} = .135$ and $D_{.0387,100} = 1.40/\sqrt{100} = .140$, by interpolation, $D_{.05,100} = .136$, as in Example B–1.

C. Using the Distribution

The steps for performing the Kolmogorov-Smirnov test are as follows:

1. Arrange the numbers in sequence from lowest to highest, $y_{(1)}, y_{(2)}, \ldots, y_{(n)}$, where $y_{(i)}$ is the number in the ith position.
2. Determine the cumulative steps that the numbers would take if they were of equal distance from each other. Call these steps i/n, where i is the position of the step.
3. Compute $(i/n) - y_{(i)}$ for every value of i. Negative values need not be computed.
4. Select the maximum value of $(i/n) - y_{(i)}$ and call this D^+.
5. Compute $y_{(i)} - (i-1)/n$ for every value of i. Negative values need not be computed.
6. Select the maximum value of $y_{(i)} - (i-1)/n$ and call this D^-.
7. Determine the maximum value of (D^+, D^-) and call this D.
8. Compare D to $D_{\alpha,n}$. If $D < D_{\alpha,n}$, do not reject the null hypothesis.

Example C–1. Using the eight steps above, test the following sequence of numbers for uniformity on the interval $(0,1)$ with $\alpha = .05$:

.77, .03, .65, .06, .42, .11, .23, .41

The following table helps to organize the procedure.

$y_{(i)}$	.03	.06	.11	.23	.41	.42	.65	.67
i/n	.125	.250	.375	.500	.625	.750	.875	1.000
$(i/n) - y_{(i)}$	.095	.190	.265	.270	.215	.330	.225	.330
$y_{(i)} - (i-1)/n$	.03	—	—	—	—	—	—	—

Step 4 requires the computation of D^+, which is seen to be .330. Step 6 results in $D^- = .03$. All other possible values are negative. Then, Step 7 requires the determination of

$$D = \text{Max}(.330, .03) = .330$$

Since $D_{.05,8} = .457 > .330$, do not reject the hypothesis of uniformity.

EXHIBIT III.2–1

Kolmogorov-Smirnov Critical Values for Specified Sample Sizes

Degrees of Freedom (n)	$D_{.10}$	$D_{.05}$	$D_{.01}$
1	.950	.975	.995
2	.776	.842	.929
3	.642	.708	.828
4	.564	.624	.733
5	.510	.565	.669
6	.470	.521	.618
7	.438	.486	.577
8	.411	.457	.543
9	.388	.432	.514
10	.368	.410	.490
11	.352	.391	.468
12	.338	.375	.450
13	.325	.361	.433
14	.314	.349	.418
15	.304	.338	.404
16	.295	.328	.392
17	.286	.318	.381
18	.278	.309	.371
19	.272	.301	.363
20	.264	.294	.356
25	.24	.27	.32
30	.22	.24	.29
35	.21	.23	.27
Over 35	$\frac{1.22}{\sqrt{n}}$	$\frac{1.36}{\sqrt{n}}$	$\frac{1.63}{\sqrt{n}}$

Source: F. J. Massey, "The Kolmogorov-Smirnov Test for Goodness of Fit," *Journal of the American Statistical Association*, Vol. 46 (1951), p. 70. Adopted with permission.

EXHIBIT III.2–2

Kolmogorov-Smirnov Critical Values for Large Sample Sizes

t	Level of Significance α	t	Level of Significance α
.30	1.0000	1.15	.1420
.35	.9997	1.20	.1122
.40	.9972	1.25	.0879
.45	.9874	1.30	.0681
.50	.9639	1.35	.0522
.55	.9228	1.40	.0397
.60	.8643	1.45	.0298
.65	.7920	1.50	.0222
.70	.7112	1.60	.0120
.75	.6272	1.70	.0062
.80	.5441	1.80	.0031
.85	.4563	1.90	.0015
.90	.3927	2.00	.0007
.95	.3275	2.10	.0003
1.00	.2700	2.20	.0001
1.05	.2202	2.30	.0001
1.10	.1777	2.40	.0000

Source: Morris H. DeGroot, *Probability and Statistics*, Addison-Wesley, Reading, Massachusetts, 1975, p. 467. Adopted with permission.

III.3 Runs Test

A. Description

A run is defined as a succession of items in the same class. There are many kinds of runs that may occur in a production setting. For example, there can be a run of defective items or a run of nondefective items. If measurements are being made, there can be runs above and below the mean, runs above and below the median, and runs up and down, to mention several types that have been analyzed extensively. For these latter types of runs, there can also be several concerns such as the number of runs that occur, the length of the runs, or the length of the longest run. The distributions of each of these have been extensively tabulated.

We will discuss two types of runs here and show how data can be analyzed for each case. Runs above and below the median are discussed first. Exhibit III.3–1 is associated with this type of run. Then, the limiting value for lengths of runs up and down is discussed. Exhibit III.3–2 is used in the analysis of this type of run.

B. Reading the Tables

B–1. Runs Above and Below the Median

Exhibit III.3–1 concerns the limiting value for the total number of runs above and below the median of a set of values. The number of runs for which the probability of an equal or smaller value is .01 and .05 are given. Thus, if there are 30 numbers below the median and 30 numbers above the median, the limiting values are 21 and 24 runs at the .01 and .05 levels, respectively. The number of runs above and below the median are counted and summed. If the total number of runs above and below the median is greater than the limiting value, there is no reason to doubt randomness on the basis of this test.

B–2. Runs Up and Down

Exhibit III.3–2 concerns the limiting values of runs up and down in a series. The shortest run for which the probability of an equal or greater run does not exceed .0032 (called the .003 point) in one instance or .0567 (called the .05 point) in the other instance is shown. These two values, .0032 and .0567, are seen to be the maximum values in their respective columns. For example, consider a series of 60 numbers, in which the longest run up and down was of length 5. The .003 and .05 limiting values are 7 and 6, respectively. Hence, there is no reason to doubt randomness on the basis of this test.

C. Using the Tables

C–1. Runs Above and Below the Median

If an even number of values is being examined, there will be an equal number above the median and below the median. If an odd number is being examined, at least one value will be at the median and the remaining cases will be above and below the median. Exceptions to these two cases occur when more than one of the values falls at the median. In this instance, the values that are at the median will have to be assigned so as to have an equal number above and below. The conservative rule of assigning values so as to increase, rather than decrease, the number of runs should be followed [Duncan, 1974].

Example C–1. A power pack is supposed to deliver a constant 1.5 volts D.C. The incoming line is always 120 volts A.C. A total of 60 measurements were taken, one per minute, after the power pack warmed up sufficiently, with the following row-wise results (1.5 has been subtracted from all measures):

.015	.012	.002	.028	.021	.033	.031	.022	.041	.045
.037	.027	.019	.023	.013	.005	−.002	−.005	.019	.036
.047	.057	.063	.059	.064	.065	.051	.043	.008	.006
.021	.025	.036	.019	.000	−.008	−.016	.008	.024	.012
−.009	−.017	.001	.013	.010	.021	.029	.033	.035	.036
.029	.037	.043	.040	.040	.020	.010	.015	.021	.026

Is there any reason to doubt the randomness of the sampled output voltages on the basis of runs above and below the median? The median value is at .0225. Using an *a* to indicate a value above the median and a *b* to indicate a value below the median, the assignments are as follows:

b b b a b a a b a a a a b a b b b b b a
a a a a a a a a b b b a a b b b b b a b
b b b b b b a a a a a a a a a b b b b a

There are nine runs above the median and nine runs below the median, for a total of 18 runs. From Exhibit III.3–1, the limiting values are 21 and 24 runs for the .01 and .05 points. Thus, there is an indication that nonrandom influences are affecting runs in the series.

Consider what would happen if the median had been at .021 instead of at .0225. There would have been four values at the median. If some were to be assigned above and some below the median, the decision would have to be made for each occurrence (of the value .021) as to whether the number of runs can be increased. The first occurrence is in the 5th position. If it is considered above the median, then there is one run of length 9. If it is below the median, three runs are formed. Hence, label it below the median, thereby increasing the number of runs.

C–2. Runs Up and Down

Prior to showing an example, it is useful to describe just what constitutes a run up and a run down. Consider the following ten values:

58 93 99 05 08 57 63 21 19 99

A "+" is assigned if the succeeding value is greater than the preceding value and a "−" is assigned if the succeeding value is less than the preceding value. (In case of a tie, go to the next value). Runs up and down begin with "no event." So the first + is between 58 and 93. The nine +'s and −'s are as follows:

+ + − + + + − − +

There are five runs. The first run is up and of length two. The second run down, and of length one, and so on.

A rule of thumb often used is that a run up or down of 7 or more indicates nonrandom influences. However, use of that rule can lead to a search for nonrandom influences when none exists [Duncan, 1974]. It all depends on the size of the sample.

Example C–2. Consider the same data as in Example C–1. In the manner described above, +'s and −'s can be assigned as follows:

− − + − + − − + + − − − + − − − − + +
+ + + − + + − − − − + + + − − − − + +
− − − + + − + + + + + − + + − − − + + +

Note that there are two less + or − assignments than numbers. One of these occurs because runs begin and end with "no event." The second "no event" occurs at the 54th position, where the same value occurs twice in succession. The longest run up or down in the series is a run up of length five, which occurs twice. In Exhibit III.3–2, the limiting values are 7 and 6 at the .003 and .05 points, respectively. Hence, there is no reason to reject the randomness of this series on the basis of length or runs.

Reference

Duncan, Acheson J. *Quality Control and Industrial Statistics*, 4th Ed. Irwin, Homewood, Illinois, 1974.

EXHIBIT III.3–1

Limiting Values for the Total Number of Runs Above and Below the Median of a Set of Values

	Probability of an Equal or Smaller Value			Probability of an Equal or Smaller Value	
Above or Below	.01	.05	Above or Below	.01	.05
10	5	6	55	43	46
11	6	7	56	44	47
12	6	8	57	45	48
13	7	9	58	46	49
14	8	10	59	46	50
15	9	11	60	47	51
16	10	11	61	48	52
17	10	12	62	49	53
18	11	13	63	50	54
19	12	14	64	51	55
20	13	15	65	52	56
21	14	16	66	53	57
22	14	17	67	54	58
23	15	17	68	54	58
24	16	18	69	55	59
25	17	19	70	56	60
26	18	20	71	57	61
27	19	21	72	58	62
28	19	22	73	59	63
29	20	23	74	60	64
30	21	24	75	61	65
31	22	25	76	62	66
32	23	25	77	63	67
33	24	26	78	64	68
34	24	27	79	64	69
35	25	28	80	65	70
36	26	29	81	66	71
37	27	30	82	67	71
38	28	31	83	68	72
39	29	32	84	69	73
40	30	33	85	70	74
41	31	34	86	71	75
42	31	35	87	72	76
43	32	35	88	73	77
44	33	36	89	74	78
45	34	37	90	74	79
46	35	38	91	75	80
47	36	39	92	76	81
48	37	40	93	77	82
49	38	41	94	78	83
50	38	42	95	79	84
51	39	43	96	80	85
52	40	44	97	81	86
53	41	45	98	82	87
54	42	45	99	83	88
			100	84	89

Source: Swed, S., and C. Eisenhart, "Tables for Testing Randomness of Grouping in a Sequence", *Annals of Math. Stat.*, Vol. XIV (1943), pp. 70–75, 83–87. Permission to reprint has been granted by the Institute of Mathematical Statistics.

EXHIBIT III.3–2

LIMITING VALUES FOR LENGTHS OF RUNS UP AND DOWN IN A SERIES OF n NUMBERS

PROBABILITY EQUAL TO OR LESS THAN .0032			PROBABILITY EQUAL TO OR LESS THAN .0567	
n	Run	Probability of an Equal or Greater Run	Run	Probability of an Equal or Greater Run
4	4	.0028	4	.0028
5	5	.0004	4	.0165
6	5	.0028	4	.0301
7	6	.0004	4	.0435
8	6	.0007	4	.0567
9	6	.0011	5	.0099
10	6	.0014	5	.0122
11	6	.0018	5	.0146
12	6	.0021	5	.0169
13	6	.0025	5	.0193
14	6	.0028	5	.0216
15	6	.0032	5	.0239
20	7	.0006	5	.0355
40	7	.0015	6	.0118
60	7	.0023	6	.0186
80	7	.0032	6	.0254
100	8	.0005	6	.0322
200	8	.0010	7	.0035
500	8	.0024	7	.0215
1000	9	.0005	7	.0428
5000	9	.0025	8	.0245

Source: Format adopted with permission from Duncan, A. J., *Quality Control and Industrial Statistics*, 4th Ed., Irwin, Homewood, Illinois, 1974. Values adopted from Olmstead, P., "Distribution of Sample Arrangements for Runs Up Down," *Annals of Math. Stat.*, Vol. XVII (1946), p. 29. Permission to reprint has been granted by the Institute of Mathematical Statistics.

III.4 Durbin-Watson Test

A. Description

Consider a series of realizations of random variables, $\varepsilon_1, \varepsilon_2, \ldots, \varepsilon_n$, that can be ordered on the basis of an external criterion, e.g., the time sequence in which the values were observed. For convenience, let the subscripts indicate this ordering. It is assumed that the series has a constant mean. The matter of interest is whether or not these sample observations indicate that serial correlation exists, i.e., that observations with a given number of intervening observations in such a series are statistically related to each other. Specifically, we look at the residuals after the least squares regression line for the model

$$Y_i = \beta_0 + \sum_{j=1}^{K} \beta_j X_{ij} + \varepsilon_i$$

has been found for the observations

$$(Y_i, X_{i1}, X_{i2}, \ldots, X_{iK}), \qquad i = 1,2,\ldots,n$$

where Y_i is the response variable at the ith point in time and X_{ij} is the value of the jth predictor variable at the ith point in time.

The Durbin-Watson test provides a means of testing the hypothesis that the observations are independent against the specific alternative that the correlation between residuals ε_i and $\varepsilon_{i+\ell}$ is ρ^{ℓ}, where $\ell = 1,2,\ldots$ and $0 < \rho < 1$ or $-1 < \rho < 0$. This type of autocorrelative structure is frequently found in real-world data from a variety of settings. In addition, the test procedure is likely to reject the hypothesis of independence for other types of autocorrelative structures.

The test procedure requires that

$$d = \sum_{i=2}^{n} (e_i - e_{i-1})^2 \Big/ \sum_{i=1}^{n} e_i^2$$

be computed, where e_i is the difference between the observed Y_i and the estimate from the regression model. If the alternative hypothesis that $\rho > 0$ is being considered, d is used as the test statistic. If the alternative hypothesis is that $\rho < 0$, then the quantity $(4 - d)$ is the test statistic. The critical values for the test statistic for Type I error probabilities of 5 percent, 2.5 percent, and 1 percent are given in Exhibits III.4–1 through III.4–3, respectively. They are tabulated as a function of the number of predictor variables in the regression equation and the number of observations in the data base.

If a two-sided test is to be conducted, both d and $(4 - d)$ must be compared to the critical values. However, the critical values must be taken from tables with stated Type I error probabilities that are one-half as large as the α desired for the two-sided test.

Note that there are two critical values that must be used for each test. If the test statistic value is less than the smaller of the two critical values, d_L, the hypothesis of no correlation is rejected. If the test statistic value is more than the larger of the critical values, d_U, there is no significant correlation. However, if the test statistic value falls between d_L and d_U, the test is said to be inconclusive.

B. Reading the Tables

Example B–1. For $n = 20$ and $K = 5$, the critical values for a one-sided test with $\alpha = .05$ are found in Exhibit III.4–1 as $d_L = 0.79$ and $d_U = 1.99$.

Example B–2. For $n = 30$ and $K = 3$, the critical values for a two-sided test with $\alpha = .05$ are found in Exhibit III.4–2 as $d_L = 1.12$ and $d_U = 1.54$. Note that the α for the two-sided test was halved when choosing the appropriate exhibit.

C. Using the Tables

A regression model to predict weekly total energy usage for a plant as a function of the number of hours of direct labor per week in each of three manufacturing areas is being developed. Data for 15 weeks is used to build a regression model, and the difference between the predicted value $\hat{Y}_i$ and the actual value Y_i for each data point is computed. Visual examination of these values shows that when these residual e_i's are ordered in the same sequence as they occurred, there tend to be runs of positive values followed by runs of negative values. As this indicates positive correlation of the residuals, the Durbin-Watson test is applied to test H_0: $\rho_\ell = 0$ versus H_1: $\rho_\ell = \rho^\ell$, where $\rho > 0$. A Type I risk of 5 percent is desired.

The test statistic d is computed from the time-ordered residuals as shown below.

Week	Y_i	$\hat{Y}_i$	e_i	e_i^2	$e_i - e_{i-1}$	$(e_i - e_{i-1})^2$
1	275	274	1	1		
2	253	250	3	9	2	4
3	261	259	2	4	−1	1
4	271	272	−1	1	−3	9
5	286	289	−3	9	2	4
6	306	309	−3	9	0	0
7	321	322	−1	1	2	4
8	291	291	0	0	1	1
9	270	268	2	4	2	4
10	243	240	3	9	1	1
11	218	215	3	9	0	0
12	244	245	−1	1	−4	16
13	234	236	−2	4	−1	1
14	275	276	−1	1	1	1
15	278	280	−2	4	−1	1
Total				66		47

EXHIBIT III.4–1

Durbin-Watson Critical Values

($\alpha = .05$)

	$K=1$		$K=2$		$K=3$		$K=4$		$K=5$	
n	d_L	d_U	d_L	d_U	d_L	d_U	d_L	d_U	d_L	d_U
15	1.08	1.36	0.95	1.54	0.82	1.75	0.69	1.97	0.56	2.21
16	1.10	1.37	0.98	1.54	0.86	1.73	0.74	1.93	0.62	2.15
17	1.13	1.38	1.02	1.54	0.90	1.71	0.78	1.90	0.67	2.10
18	1.16	1.39	1.05	1.53	0.93	1.69	0.82	1.87	0.71	2.06
19	1.18	1.40	1.08	1.53	0.97	1.68	0.86	1.85	0.75	2.02
20	1.20	1.41	1.10	1.54	1.00	1.68	0.90	1.83	0.79	1.99
21	1.22	1.42	1.13	1.54	1.03	1.67	0.93	1.81	0.83	1.96
22	1.24	1.43	1.15	1.54	1.05	1.66	0.96	1.80	0.86	1.94
23	1.26	1.44	1.17	1.54	1.08	1.66	0.99	1.79	0.90	1.92
24	1.27	1.45	1.19	1.55	1.10	1.66	1.01	1.78	0.93	1.90
25	1.29	1.45	1.21	1.55	1.12	1.66	1.04	1.77	0.95	1.89
26	1.30	1.46	1.22	1.55	1.14	1.65	1.06	1.76	0.98	1.88
27	1.32	1.47	1.24	1.56	1.16	1.65	1.08	1.76	1.01	1.86
28	1.33	1.48	1.26	1.56	1.18	1.65	1.10	1.75	1.03	1.85
29	1.34	1.48	1.27	1.56	1.20	1.65	1.12	1.74	1.05	1.84
30	1.35	1.49	1.28	1.57	1.21	1.65	1.14	1.74	1.07	1.83
31	1.36	1.50	1.30	1.57	1.23	1.65	1.16	1.74	1.09	1.83
32	1.37	1.50	1.31	1.57	1.24	1.65	1.18	1.73	1.11	1.82
33	1.38	1.51	1.32	1.58	1.26	1.65	1.19	1.73	1.13	1.81
34	1.39	1.51	1.33	1.58	1.27	1.65	1.21	1.73	1.15	1.81
35	1.40	1.52	1.34	1.58	1.28	1.65	1.22	1.73	1.16	1.80
36	1.41	1.52	1.35	1.59	1.29	1.65	1.24	1.73	1.18	1.80
37	1.42	1.53	1.36	1.59	1.31	1.66	1.25	1.72	1.19	1.80
38	1.43	1.54	1.37	1.59	1.32	1.66	1.26	1.72	1.21	1.79
39	1.43	1.54	1.38	1.60	1.33	1.66	1.27	1.72	1.22	1.79
40	1.44	1.54	1.39	1.60	1.34	1.66	1.29	1.72	1.23	1.79
45	1.48	1.57	1.43	1.62	1.38	1.67	1.34	1.72	1.29	1.78
50	1.50	1.59	1.46	1.63	1.42	1.67	1.38	1.72	1.34	1.77
55	1.53	1.60	1.49	1.64	1.45	1.68	1.41	1.72	1.38	1.77
60	1.55	1.62	1.51	1.65	1.48	1.69	1.44	1.73	1.41	1.77
65	1.57	1.63	1.54	1.66	1.50	1.70	1.47	1.73	1.44	1.77
70	1.58	1.64	1.55	1.67	1.52	1.70	1.49	1.74	1.46	1.77
75	1.60	1.65	1.57	1.68	1.54	1.71	1.51	1.74	1.49	1.77
80	1.61	1.66	1.59	1.69	1.56	1.72	1.53	1.74	1.51	1.77
85	1.62	1.67	1.60	1.70	1.57	1.72	1.55	1.75	1.52	1.77
90	1.63	1.68	1.61	1.70	1.59	1.73	1.57	1.75	1.54	1.78
95	1.64	1.69	1.62	1.71	1.60	1.73	1.58	1.75	1.56	1.78
100	1.65	1.69	1.63	1.72	1.61	1.74	1.59	1.76	1.57	1.78

Source: Durbin, J., and G. S. Watson, "Testing for Serial Correlation in Least Squares Regression, II," *Biometrika*, Vol. 38 (1951), p. 173. Reproduced with permission of the Biometrika Trustees.

EXHIBIT III.4–2

DURBIN-WATSON CRITICAL VALUES

($\alpha = .025$)

	$K=1$		$K=2$		$K=3$		$K=4$		$K=5$	
n	d_L	d_U	d_L	d_U	d_L	d_U	d_L	d_U	d_L	d_U
15	0.95	1.23	0.83	1.40	0.71	1.61	0.59	1.84	0.48	2.09
16	0.98	1.24	0.86	1.40	0.75	1.59	0.64	1.80	0.53	2.03
17	1.01	1.25	0.90	1.40	0.79	1.58	0.68	1.77	0.57	1.98
18	1.03	1.26	0.93	1.40	0.82	1.56	0.72	1.74	0.62	1.93
19	1.06	1.28	0.96	1.41	0.86	1.55	0.76	1.72	0.66	1.90
20	1.08	1.28	0.99	1.41	0.89	1.55	0.79	1.70	0.70	1.87
21	1.10	1.30	1.01	1.41	0.92	1.54	0.83	1.69	0.73	1.84
22	1.12	1.31	1.04	1.42	0.95	1.54	0.86	1.68	0.77	1.82
23	1.14	1.32	1.06	1.42	0.97	1.54	0.89	1.67	0.80	1.80
24	1.16	1.33	1.08	1.43	1.00	1.54	0.91	1.66	0.83	1.79
25	1.18	1.34	1.10	1.43	1.02	1.54	0.94	1.65	0.86	1.77
26	1.19	1.35	1.12	1.44	1.04	1.54	0.96	1.65	0.88	1.76
27	1.21	1.36	1.13	1.44	1.06	1.54	0.99	1.64	0.91	1.75
28	1.22	1.37	1.15	1.45	1.08	1.54	1.01	1.64	0.93	1.74
29	1.24	1.38	1.17	1.45	1.10	1.54	1.03	1.63	0.96	1.73
30	1.25	1.38	1.18	1.46	1.12	1.54	1.05	1.63	0.98	1.73
31	1.26	1.39	1.20	1.47	1.13	1.55	1.07	1.63	1.00	1.72
32	1.27	1.40	1.21	1.47	1.15	1.55	1.08	1.63	1.02	1.71
33	1.28	1.41	1.22	1.48	1.16	1.55	1.10	1.63	1.04	1.71
34	1.29	1.41	1.24	1.48	1.17	1.55	1.12	1.63	1.06	1.70
35	1.30	1.42	1.25	1.48	1.19	1.55	1.13	1.63	1.07	1.70
36	1.31	1.43	1.26	1.49	1.20	1.56	1.15	1.63	1.09	1.70
37	1.32	1.43	1.27	1.49	1.21	1.56	1.16	1.62	1.10	1.70
38	1.33	1.44	1.28	1.50	1.23	1.56	1.17	1.62	1.12	1.70
39	1.34	1.44	1.29	1.50	1.24	1.56	1.19	1.63	1.13	1.69
40	1.35	1.45	1.30	1.51	1.25	1.57	1.20	1.63	1.15	1.69
45	1.39	1.48	1.34	1.53	1.30	1.58	1.25	1.63	1.21	1.69
50	1.42	1.50	1.38	1.54	1.34	1.59	1.30	1.64	1.26	1.69
55	1.45	1.52	1.41	1.56	1.37	1.60	1.33	1.64	1.30	1.69
60	1.47	1.54	1.44	1.57	1.40	1.61	1.37	1.65	1.33	1.69
65	1.49	1.55	1.46	1.59	1.43	1.62	1.40	1.66	1.36	1.69
70	1.51	1.57	1.48	1.60	1.45	1.63	1.42	1.66	1.39	1.70
75	1.53	1.58	1.50	1.61	1.47	1.64	1.45	1.67	1.42	1.70
80	1.54	1.59	1.52	1.62	1.49	1.65	1.47	1.67	1.44	1.70
85	1.56	1.60	1.53	1.63	1.51	1.65	1.49	1.68	1.46	1.71
90	1.57	1.61	1.55	1.64	1.53	1.66	1.50	1.69	1.48	1.71
95	1.58	1.62	1.56	1.65	1.54	1.67	1.52	1.69	1.50	1.71
100	1.59	1.63	1.57	1.65	1.55	1.67	1.53	1.70	1.51	1.72

Source: Durbin, J., and G. S. Watson, "Testing for Serial Correlation in Least Squares Regression, II," *Biometrika*, Vol. 38 (1951) p. 174. Reproduced with permission of the Biometrika Trustees.

EXHIBIT III.4–3

Durbin-Watson Critical Values

($\alpha = .01$)

	$K=1$		$K=2$		$K=3$		$K=4$		$K=5$	
n	d_L	d_U	d_L	d_U	d_L	d_U	d_L	d_U	d_L	d_U
15	0.81	1.07	0.70	1.25	0.59	1.46	0.49	1.70	0.39	1.96
16	0.84	1.09	0.74	1.25	0.63	1.44	0.53	1.66	0.44	1.90
17	0.87	1.10	0.77	1.25	0.67	1.43	0.57	1.63	0.48	1.85
18	0.90	1.12	0.80	1.26	0.71	1.42	0.61	1.60	0.52	1.80
19	0.93	1.13	0.83	1.26	0.74	1.41	0.65	1.58	0.56	1.77
20	0.95	1.15	0.86	1.27	0.77	1.41	0.68	1.57	0.60	1.74
21	0.97	1.16	0.89	1.27	0.80	1.41	0.72	1.55	0.63	1.71
22	1.00	1.17	0.91	1.28	0.83	1.40	0.75	1.54	0.66	1.69
23	1.02	1.19	0.94	1.29	0.86	1.40	0.77	1.53	0.70	1.67
24	1.04	1.20	0.96	1.30	0.88	1.41	0.80	1.53	0.72	1.66
25	1.05	1.21	0.98	1.30	0.90	1.41	0.83	1.52	0.75	1.65
26	1.07	1.22	1.00	1.31	0.93	1.41	0.85	1.52	0.78	1.64
27	1.09	1.23	1.02	1.32	0.95	1.41	0.88	1.51	0.81	1.63
28	1.10	1.24	1.04	1.32	0.97	1.41	0.90	1.51	0.83	1.62
29	1.12	1.25	1.05	1.33	0.99	1.42	0.92	1.51	0.85	1.61
30	1.13	1.26	1.07	1.34	1.01	1.42	0.94	1.51	0.88	1.61
31	1.15	1.27	1.08	1.34	1.02	1.42	0.96	1.51	0.90	1.60
32	1.16	1.28	1.10	1.35	1.04	1.43	0.98	1.51	0.92	1.60
33	1.17	1.29	1.11	1.36	1.05	1.43	1.00	1.51	0.94	1.59
34	1.18	1.30	1.13	1.36	1.07	1.43	1.01	1.51	0.95	1.59
35	1.19	1.31	1.14	1.37	1.08	1.44	1.03	1.51	0.97	1.59
36	1.21	1.32	1.15	1.38	1.10	1.44	1.04	1.51	0.99	1.59
37	1.22	1.32	1.16	1.38	1.11	1.45	1.06	1.51	1.00	1.59
38	1.23	1.33	1.18	1.39	1.12	1.45	1.07	1.52	1.02	1.58
39	1.24	1.34	1.19	1.39	1.14	1.45	1.09	1.52	1.03	1.58
40	1.25	1.34	1.20	1.40	1.15	1.46	1.10	1.52	1.05	1.58
45	1.29	1.38	1.24	1.42	1.20	1.48	1.16	1.53	1.11	1.58
50	1.32	1.40	1.28	1.45	1.24	1.49	1.20	1.54	1.16	1.59
55	1.36	1.43	1.32	1.47	1.28	1.51	1.25	1.55	1.21	1.59
60	1.38	1.45	1.35	1.48	1.32	1.52	1.28	1.56	1.25	1.60
65	1.41	1.47	1.38	1.50	1.35	1.53	1.31	1.57	1.28	1.61
70	1.43	1.49	1.40	1.52	1.37	1.55	1.34	1.58	1.31	1.61
75	1.45	1.50	1.42	1.53	1.39	1.56	1.37	1.59	1.34	1.62
80	1.47	1.52	1.44	1.54	1.42	1.57	1.39	1.60	1.36	1.62
85	1.48	1.53	1.46	1.55	1.43	1.58	1.41	1.60	1.39	1.63
90	1.50	1.54	1.47	1.56	1.45	1.59	1.43	1.61	1.41	1.64
95	1.51	1.55	1.49	1.57	1.47	1.60	1.45	1.62	1.42	1.64
100	1.52	1.56	1.50	1.58	1.48	1.60	1.46	1.63	1.44	1.65

Source: Durbin, J., and G. S. Watson, "Testing for Serial Correlation in Least Squares Regression, II," *Biometrika*, Vol. 38 (1951), p. 175. Reproduced with permission of the Biometrika Trustees.

The test statistic is

$$d = 47/66 = 0.71$$

The critical values in Exhibit III.4–1 with $K = 3$ and $n = 15$ are $d_L = 0.82$ and $d_U = 1.75$. Since the test statistic value of $0.71 < 0.82 = d_L$, the hypothesis is rejected, and it is concluded that the residuals exhibit positive autocorrelation.

III.5 Wilcoxon Two-Sample Test

A. Description

The Wilcoxon two-sample test procedure is used to test the hypothesis that the means of two populations are equal based on independent random samples from the two populations. It does not require assumptions about the form of the distribution of the populations. Hence, it is an alternative to tests on the means of two populations presented in Section III.1 when normality cannot be assumed. However, it should not be used if normality can be assumed, as it is not as powerful a test.

The procedure for carrying out the test, where n_1 is the size of the sample from one population, n_2 is the size of the sample from the second population, and $n_1 \leq n_2$, is

1. Arrange all $n_1 + n_2$ observations in ascending order.
2. Assign ranks to each observation based on the position of the observation in the ordered set. (If two or more observations have the same value, assign each the average value of the ranks that would have been assigned had the observations differed).
3. Compute the sum of the ranks of the observations that were in the first population. Call this R_1.
4. Compute $R_2 = n_1(n_1 + n_2 + 1) - R_1$.

If the means of the two populations are the same, the values of R_1 and R_2 should not differ greatly. For specified values of n_1 and n_2, this is equivalent to R_1 and R_2 both having values that are not too small. Exhibits III.5–1 and III.5–2 provide critical values, R^*_α, for $\alpha = .05$ and .01, respectively. If *either* R_1 or R_2 is less than R^*_α, the hypothesis of equality of means is rejected.

The tables include critical values for $2 \le n_1 \le 15$ and $4 \le n_2 \le 28$. For larger sample sizes, the value of

$$Z_0 = \frac{R_1 - \mu_R}{\sigma_R}$$

where

$$\mu_R = n_1(n_1 + n_2 + 1)/2$$
$$\sigma_R^2 = n_1 n_2 (n_1 + n_2 + 1)/12$$

is computed. The hypothesis is rejected if $|Z_0|$ is greater than $Z_{\alpha/2}$, where $Z_{\alpha/2}$ is the point of the standardized normal distribution at which $100(\alpha/2)$ percent of the area is in the right-hand tail. Procedures for determining areas under a normal distribution are discussed in Section II.5.

B. Using the Tables

Example B–1. The mean response times to calls for emergency care of two different units of a service organization are being studied. The actual response times, measured to the nearest 0.05 minute, are monitored for each unit during a one-week period. The values are as follows:

Unit A	Unit B
3.40	4.25
3.35	2.90
2.95	3.00
3.15	3.15
3.20	
3.40	

As the assumption of normality of the distribution of response time is not supported, we choose to apply the Wilcoxon two-sample test in order to test the equality of the means of the two units. Assume $\alpha = .01$.

First, we order the combined observations and assign ranks.

Unit	B	A	B	B	A	A	A	A	A	B
Ordered Observations	29.0	29.5	30.0	31.5	31.5	32.0	33.4	34.0	34.0	42.5
Rank	1	2	3	4.5	4.5	6	7	8.5	8.5	10

Then we compute the sum of ranks for Unit B. (It has the smaller sample size.)

$$R_1 = 1 + 3 + 4.5 + 10 = 18.5$$

Then

$$R_2 = 4(4+6+1) - 18.5 = 25.5$$

Since $R_1 < R_2$, we will compare R_1 with the critical value from Exhibit III.5–2. For $n_1 = 4$, $n_2 = 6$, we find $R^*_{.01} = 11$. Since R_1 is greater than R^*_α, we do not reject the hypothesis and conclude that there is not sufficient evidence to state that the mean response times differ.

Example B–2. Suppose that 14 additional data points on Unit A and 20 additional points for Unit B are observed so that $n_1 = 14+6 = 20$ and $n_2 = 20+4 = 24$. After ordering and ranking, we find that $R_1 = 312$. Since

EXHIBIT III.5–1

Two-Sample Test Critical Values

($\alpha = .05$)

n_2 \ n_1	2	3	4	5	6	7	8	9	10	11	12	13	14	15
4			10											
5		6	11	17										
6		7	12	18	26									
7		7	13	20	27	36								
8	3	8	14	21	29	38	49							
9	3	8	15	22	31	40	51	63						
10	3	9	15	23	32	42	53	65	78					
11	4	9	16	24	34	44	55	68	81	96				
12	4	10	17	26	35	46	58	71	85	99	115			
13	4	10	18	27	37	48	60	73	88	103	119	137		
14	4	11	19	28	38	50	63	76	91	106	123	141	160	
15	4	11	20	29	40	52	65	79	94	110	127	145	164	185
16	4	12	21	31	42	54	67	82	97	114	131	150	169	
17	5	12	21	32	43	56	70	84	100	117	135	154		
18	5	13	22	33	45	58	72	87	103	121	139			
19	5	13	23	34	46	60	74	90	107	124				
20	5	14	24	35	48	62	77	93	110					
21	6	14	25	37	50	64	79	95						
22	6	15	26	38	51	66	82							
23	6	15	27	39	53	68								
24	6	16	28	40	55									
25	6	16	28	42										
26	7	17	29											
27	7	17												
28	7													

Note: n_1 and n_2 are the numbers of cases in the two groups. If the groups are unequal in size, n_1 refers to the smaller.

Source: C. White, "The Use of Ranks in a Test of Significance for Comparing Two Treatments," *Biometrics* 8 (1952): 33–41. With permission from the Biometric Society.

n_1 and n_2 exceed the values in Exhibit III.5–2, we compute

$$\mu_R = 20(20+24+1)/2 = 450$$
$$\sigma_R^2 = (20)(24)(20+24+1)/12 = 1800$$
$$\sigma_R = 42.43$$

and

$$Z_0 = \frac{312-450}{42.43} = -3.25$$

From Exhibit II.5–1, for $\alpha = .05$, we find $Z_{\alpha/2} = 1.96$. Since $|-3.25| > 1.96$, we reject the hypothesis that the means are equal.

EXHIBIT III.5–2

TWO-SAMPLE TEST CRITICAL VALUES

($\alpha = .01$)

n_2 \ n_1	2	3	4	5	6	7	8	9	10	11	12	13	14	15
5				15										
6			10	16	23									
7			10	17	24	32								
8			11	17	25	34	43							
9		6	11	18	26	35	45	56						
10		6	12	19	27	37	47	58	71					
11		6	12	20	28	38	49	61	74	87				
12		7	13	21	30	40	51	63	76	90	106			
13		7	14	22	31	41	53	65	79	93	109	125		
14		7	14	22	32	43	54	67	81	96	112	129	147	
15		8	15	23	33	44	56	70	84	99	115	133	151	171
16		8	15	24	34	46	58	72	86	102	119	137	155	
17		8	16	25	36	47	60	74	89	105	122	140		
18		8	16	26	37	49	62	76	92	108	125			
19	3	9	17	27	38	50	64	78	94	111				
20	3	9	18	28	39	52	66	81	97					
21	3	9	18	29	40	53	68	83						
22	3	10	19	29	42	55	70							
23	3	10	19	30	43	57								
24	3	10	20	31	44									
25	3	11	20	32										
26	3	11	21											
27	4	11												
28	4													

Note: n_1 and n_2 are the numbers of cases in the two groups. If the groups are unequal in size, n_1 refers to the smaller.

Source: C. White, "The Use of Ranks in a Test of Significance for Comparing Two Treatments," *Biometrics* 8 (1952): 33–41. With permission from the Biometric Society.

III.6 Wilcoxon Signed-Rank Test

A. Description

The signed-rank test is used to investigate whether the medians of two populations are equal. If it is assumed that the populations are symmetric, this is equivalent to testing if the means are equal. The test is based on samples from the two populations that are paired (as opposed to being independent, as assumed in Section III.5). No assumptions are made about the form of the distributions of the populations. Thus, this test is an alternative to tests discussed in Section III.1. However, if normality can be assumed, the tests in Section III.1 should be used, as they are more powerful.

The procedure is accomplished by the following steps:

1. Let the paired observations be denoted by $(X_{1j}, X_{2j}), j = 1, 2, \ldots, n$.
2. Compute $D_j = X_{1j} - X_{2j}$, for $j = 1, 2, \ldots, n$.
3. Arrange the D_j's in ascending order of their *absolute* values.
4. Assign ranks to each observation based on its position in the ordered observations.
5. Give each rank the sign (+ or −) of the D_j with which it is associated.
6. Compute P, the sum of the ranks with positive values.
7. Compute N, the sum of the absolute values of the ranks with negative values.
8. Let R be the smaller of P and N.

When R is less than the critical values, R^*_α, provided in Exhibit III.6–1, the hypothesis of equality of medians is rejected. Critical values for $\alpha = .01$, .02, .05, and .10 for $n = 4$ to 50 are given. If $n > 50$, the value of

$$Z_0 = \frac{R - \mu_R}{\sigma_R}$$

where

$$\mu_R = n(n+1)/4$$

and

$$\sigma_R^2 = n(n+1)(2n+1)/24$$

is computed. The hypothesis is rejected if Z_0 is less than $-Z_{\alpha/2}$, where $Z_{\alpha/2}$ is the point of the standardized normal distribution at which $100(\alpha/2)$ percent of the area is in the right-hand tail. Procedures for determining areas under a normal distribution are discussed in Section II.5.

B. Using the Tables

Example B–1. An inventor claims to have developed a product that will improve gasoline consumption of internal combustion engines. To test this claim, with $\alpha = .05$, ten engines are chosen at random, and each is tested with and without the device under identical conditions. The results are:

Car	Miles Per Gallon		Differences
	With Device	Without Device	
1	21.6	20.8	0.8
2	23.5	22.2	1.3
3	19.3	20.0	−0.7
4	20.3	20.5	−0.2
5	19.9	19.4	0.5
6	22.4	22.0	0.4
7	22.2	21.9	0.3
8	23.1	24.1	−1.0
9	21.8	20.7	1.1
10	21.3	20.4	0.9

Arranging the differences in order of absolute magnitudes along with their signed ranks gives:

Ordered Differences	Signed Rank
−0.2	−1
0.3	2
0.4	3
0.5	4
−0.7	−5
0.8	6
0.9	7
−1.0	−8
1.1	9
1.3	10

The sum of the ranks with positive values gives

$$P = 2 + 3 + 4 + 6 + 7 + 9 + 10 = 41$$

EXHIBIT III.6–1

SIGNED-RANK CRITICAL VALUES

Sample Size n	$R^*_{.10}$	$R^*_{.05}$	$R^*_{.02}$	$R^*_{.01}$
4	0	0	0	0
5	0	0	0	0
6	2	0	0	0
7	3	2	0	0
8	5	3	1	0
9	8	5	3	1
10	10	8	5	3
11	13	10	7	5
12	17	13	9	7
13	21	17	12	9
14	25	21	15	12
15	30	25	19	15
16	35	29	23	19
17	41	34	27	23
18	47	40	32	27
19	53	46	37	32
20	60	52	43	37
21	67	58	49	42
22	75	65	55	48
23	83	73	62	54
24	91	81	69	61
25	100	89	76	68
26	110	98	84	75
27	119	107	92	83
28	130	116	101	91
29	140	126	110	100
30	151	137	120	109
31	163	147	130	118
32	175	159	140	128
33	187	170	151	138
34	200	182	162	148
35	213	195	173	159
36	227	208	185	171
37	241	221	198	182
38	256	235	211	194
39	271	249	224	207
40	286	264	238	220
41	302	279	252	233
42	319	294	266	247
43	336	310	281	261
44	353	327	296	276
45	371	343	312	291
46	389	361	328	307
47	407	378	345	322
48	426	396	362	339
49	446	415	379	355
50	466	434	397	373

Source: McCornack, R. L., "Extended Tables of the Wilcoxon Match Pair Sign Rank Statistic," *Journal of the American Statistical Association*, Vol. 60 (1965), p. 866. Reproduced with permission.

and summing those with negative values gives

$$N = 1 + 5 + 8 = 14$$

Since $N < P$, we have $R = N = 14$. From Exhibit III.6–1 with $n = 10$ and $\alpha = .05$, we find the critical value $R^*_{.05} = 8$. As R is greater than 8, we do not have sufficient evidence to conclude that the device has any effect on the gasoline consumption of internal combustion engines.

Example B–2. Suppose the previous test is extended to include 100 engines. Applying the above procedures, we find $N = 2104$ and $P = 2946$, giving $R = N = 2104$. Since $n > 50$, we cannot obtain critical values from Exhibit III.6–1. Thus, we compute

$$\mu_R = (100)(101)/4 = 2525$$

$$\sigma_R^2 = (100)(101)(200 + 1)/24 = 84{,}587.5$$

$$\sigma_R = 290.84$$

and

$$Z_0 = \frac{2104 - 2525}{290.84} = -1.45$$

For $\alpha = .05$, $Z_{.05/2} = 1.96$. Since -1.45 is not less than $-Z_{\alpha/2} = -1.96$, we cannot conclude that the device has a significant effect on gasoline consumption.

IV

Sample Size Determination

IV.1 Tests on the Mean of a Normal Population

A. Description

A–1. Introduction

When testing hypotheses, the decision criterion is established through selection of the probability of rejecting the null hypothesis when it is true. This is called a Type I error, and its probability is denoted by α. A second type of error that should also be of concern is when the null hypothesis is accepted when it is false. This is termed a Type II error, and its probability is denoted by β. For a given test, a mathematical relationship exists between α, β, and the sample size n. When any two of these three quantities are specified, the third can be determined. The values of α, β, and n are frequently specified in one of the following ways:

1. For given values of n and α, the value of β is determined. This allows the analyst to evaluate the risk of a Type II error for a test that is proposed or has been conducted.
2. For given values of α and β, the required sample size is found, usually in the planning stage, so that a test with appropriate risk levels can be conducted.

The probability of accepting the null hypothesis depends on the extent to which the hypothesis and the true situation differ. Thus, when specifying β, it is also necessary to specify the amount of difference associated with β.

The hypothesis tests considered in this section concern the mean of a normal population. Thus, β is a function of the difference between the hypothesized mean μ_0 and the true mean, say μ_1. Exhibits IV.1–1 through IV.1–8 display the relationship between n and β (for various differences between the hypothesized and true means) for selected values of α.

A–2. Tests with Variance Known

When the variance σ^2 of the population being tested is known, the standard normal distribution is used to compute the error probabilities. The difference between the means, $\mu_1 - \mu_0$, can also be standardized by dividing by the standard deviation σ. The relationship between α, β, and n is shown in Exhibits IV.1–1 through IV.1–4 as a function of this standardized difference,

$$d = |\mu_1 - \mu_0|/\sigma$$

Exhibits IV.1–1 and IV.1–3 are provided for one-sided tests with $\alpha = .05$ and $\alpha = .01$, respectively. Exhibits IV.1–2 and IV.1–4 are for two-sided tests with $\alpha = .05$ and $\alpha = .01$, respectively. An exhibit for a one-sided test can be used for a two-sided test by doubling the α value, or that for a two-sided test can be used for a one-sided test by halving the α value. Also, for the lower tail tests we require $\mu_1 < \mu_0$, and for upper tail tests $\mu_1 > \mu_0$.

A–3. Tests with Variance Unknown

When the variance of the population being tested is not known, but is estimated from the sample, this additional source of variation will require larger sample sizes to achieve a given α and β than in the case when the variance is known. The standardized difference between the means is

$$d = |\mu_1 - \mu_0|/\sigma$$

as in the variance-known case. However, here the true value of σ is unknown, and it is necessary to define d conditionally on the value of σ. This can be accomplished by defining the differences between μ_1 and μ_0 in terms of a multiple of σ. Alternatively, a workable approach is to use whatever available sample estimate of σ there is in place of σ in the equation for d.

Similarly to the variance-known case, Exhibits IV.1–5 and IV.1–7 are supplied for $\alpha = .05$ and .01 for the one-sided cases, and Exhibits IV.1–6 and IV.1–8 for the two-sided cases. The one- (two-) sided exhibits can be used for two- (one-) sided tests by doubling (halving) the α values. For example, Exhibit IV.1–7, which has $\alpha = .01$ for a one-sided test, can be used for a two-sided test with $\alpha = .02$. Similarly, Exhibit IV.1–6 for a two-sided test with $\alpha = .05$ can be used for a one-sided test with $\alpha = .025$. The restrictions on the relationship between μ_1 and μ_0 for one-sided tests still hold.

B. Reading the Charts

Example B–1. The sample size required for conducting a one-sided test on the mean of a normal population with variance known, with $\alpha = .05$, is to be found. It is desired that the probability of not rejecting the null hypothesis when $d = 1.0$ be 25 percent. Entering Exhibit IV.1–1 at $d = 1.0$, and proceeding vertically until reaching the $\beta = .25$ line, we find a value of slightly more than 5 on the n scale. This is rounded up to the next higher integer, 6, so that neither the α or β risks are greater than those specified.

Example B–2. A one-sided upper tail test on the mean of a normal population with unknown variance is conducted using a sample of 15 items and $\alpha = .05$. The probability of rejecting the null hypothesis when $d = 0.8$ is desired. Entering Exhibit IV.1–5, and finding the point of intersection of the $d = 0.8$ and $n = 15$ lines, we see that the point falls on the $\beta = .10$ line. Thus, the probability of a Type II error is 10 percent. In general, the intersection of the d and n lines may not fall so close to a line for a specified β. While it is possible to interpolate to roughly approximate the value of β, considerable caution should be used, as the interpolation is highly non-linear.

C. Using the Charts

Example C–1. A bag is labeled as containing 5 pounds of sugar. A consumer group is concerned that the full amount is not being included. Accepting the fact that some variation from bag to bag is unavoidable in volume processing, the consumer group decides to test the null hypothesis that the mean weight of sugar in the bags is 5 pounds or more. The assumption of a normal population seems reasonable, and producers of the equipment used to bag the sugar state that the standard deviation of fill weights is 0.025 pounds. The group decides that their investigation should have a high probability, say 90 percent, of detecting a problem in weights if the bags are underfilled by 0.02 pounds or more. To provide protection to the processor, the test is to have a 1-percent probability of concluding that there is a problem when none exists. How large a sample is required if the consumer group is to have a 90-percent probability of rejecting the null hypothesis when the true mean weight of sugar in the bags is $5.00 - 0.02 = 4.98$ pounds or less, and an α of .01 is used? As this is a one-sided test with $\alpha = .01$ and σ known, Exhibit IV.1–3 is used. The value of d is

$$|\mu_1 - \mu_0|/\sigma = |4.98 - 5.00|/0.025 = 0.80$$

Since the probability of rejecting the null hypothesis when it is false (required to be .90) plus β, the probability of accepting the null hypothesis when it is false is equal to one, $\beta = 1 - .90 = .10$. Locating the intersection of the $d = 0.80$ and $\beta = .10$ lines, we find that n is approximately 22.

Example C–2. Suppose that in Example C–1 no information concerning the true standard deviation was available. It is decided that if the true mean is as much as one standard deviation below 5 pounds, there should be a 90-percent probability of rejecting the null hypothesis (i.e., $\beta = .10$). Again, α is selected as .01. The value of d when $|\mu_1 - \mu_0| = \sigma$ is 1.0. Entering Exhibit IV.1–7 with $d = 1.0$ and $\beta = .10$ yields $n = 16$.

Example C–3. Suppose that only 15 observations were taken in Example C–1. What would the probability of a Type II error be (when the true mean was 4.98)? Again, entering Exhibit IV.1–3, we see that the intersection of the $n = 15$ and $d = 0.80$ lines is close to $\beta = .25$. Thus, there is a 25-percent probability of not detecting that bags are underfilled by as much as 0.02 pounds, on the average, when 15 samples are used in testing the hypothesis.

EXHIBIT IV.1–1

SAMPLE SIZES FOR TESTS ON MEANS

(σ Known, One-Sided $\alpha = .05$)

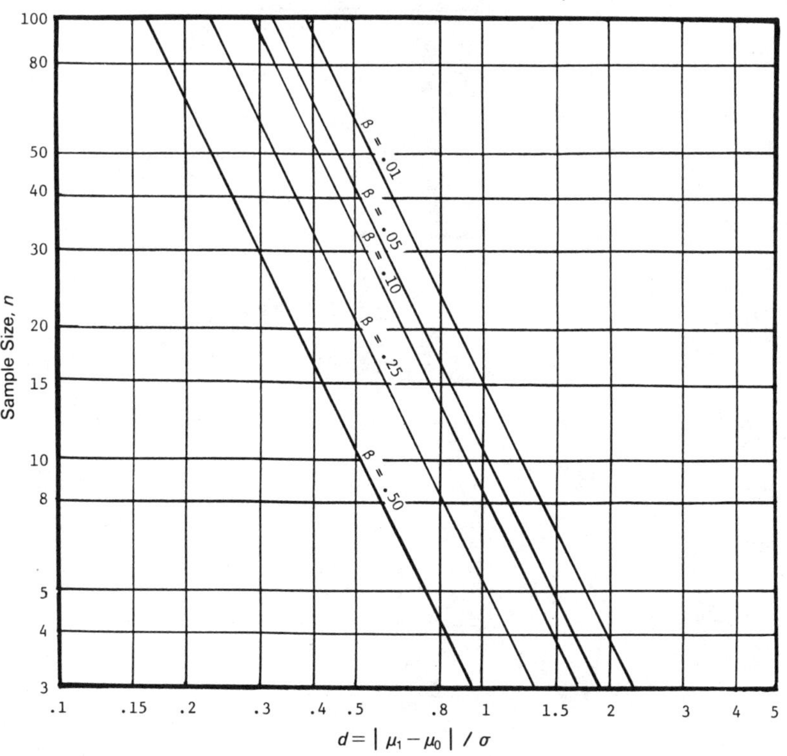

EXHIBIT IV.1–2

SAMPLE SIZES FOR TESTS ON MEANS

(σ Known, Two-Sided $\alpha = .05$)

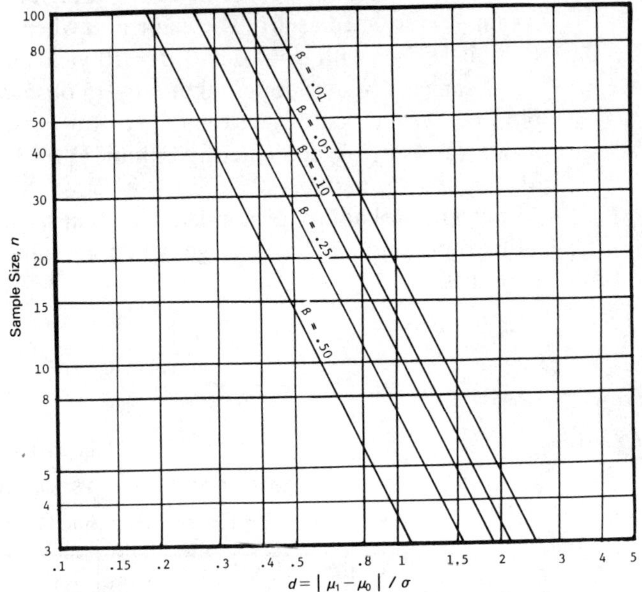

EXHIBIT IV.1–3

SAMPLE SIZES FOR TESTS ON MEANS

(σ Known, One-Sided $\alpha = .01$)

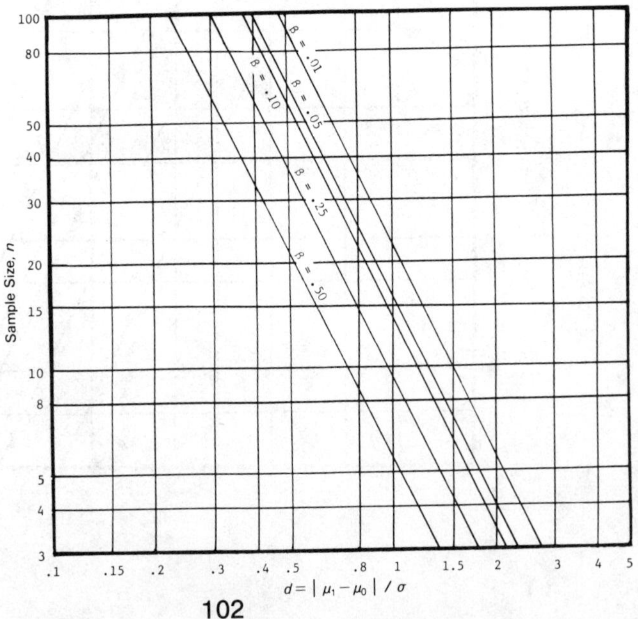

EXHIBIT IV.1–4

Sample Sizes for Tests on Means

(σ Known, Two-Sided $\alpha = .01$)

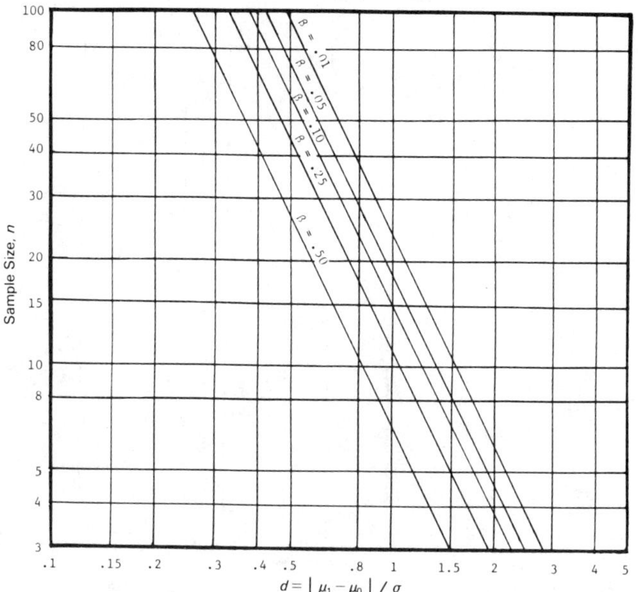

EXHIBIT IV.1–5

Sample Sizes for Tests on Means

(σ Unknown, One-Sided $\alpha = .05$)

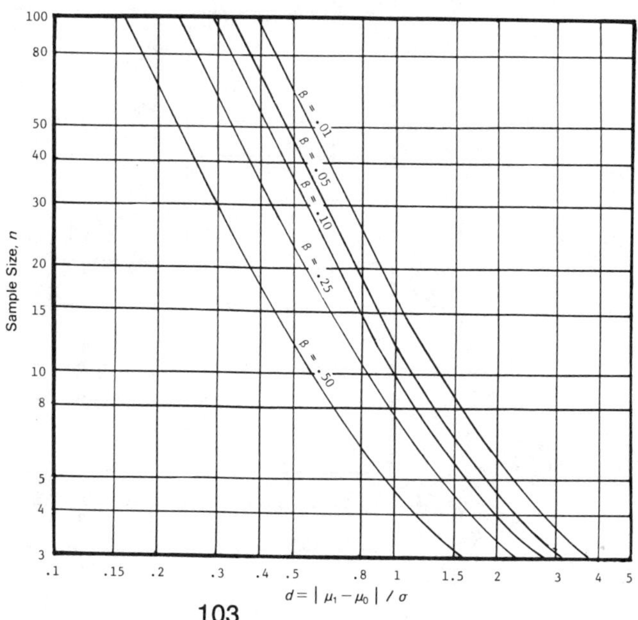

EXHIBIT IV.1–6

Sample Sizes for Tests on Means

(σ Unknown, Two-Sided $\alpha = .05$)

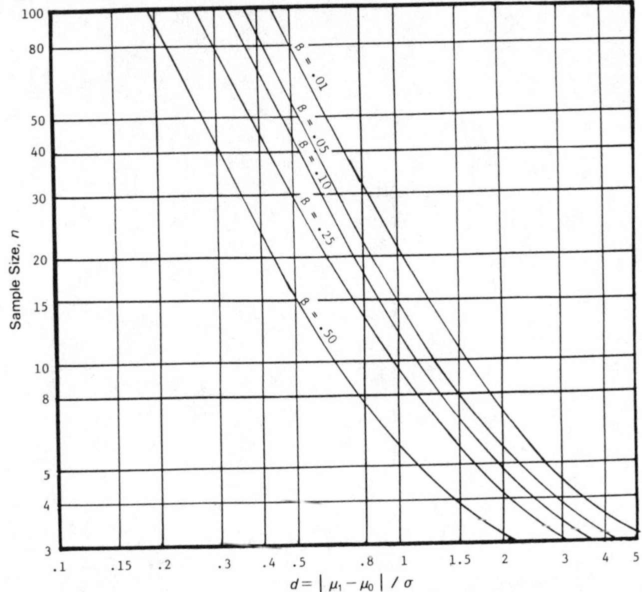

EXHIBIT IV.1–7

Sample Sizes for Tests on Means

(σ Unknown, One-Sided $\alpha = .01$)

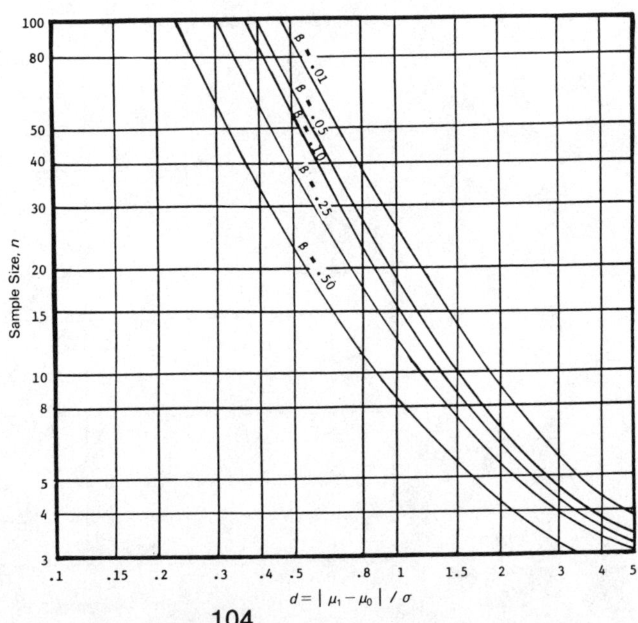

EXHIBIT IV.1–8

SAMPLE SIZES FOR TESTS ON MEANS

(σ Unknown, Two-Sided $\alpha = .01$)

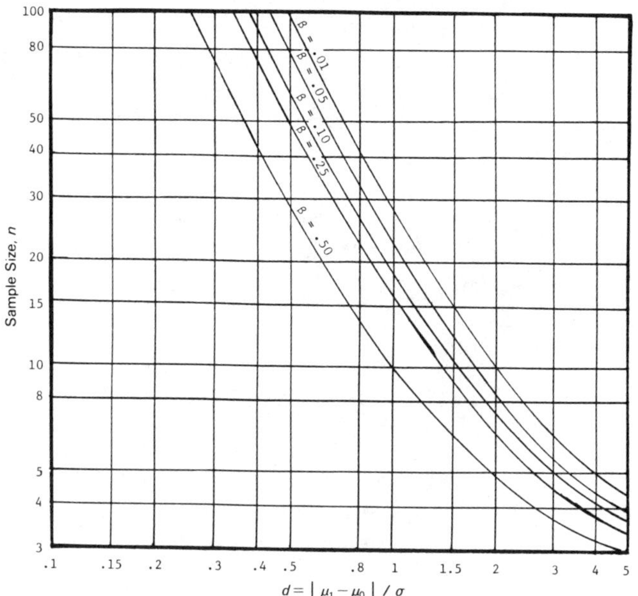

IV.2 Tests on the Means of Two Normal Populations

A. Description

The material considered in this section is closely related to that in Section IV.1. The reader should be familiar with the material in the earlier section prior to using Section IV.2.

The test considered here is the equality of the means of two normal populations. The probability of rejecting the null hypothesis that the means are equal is a function of the true difference between the means. This difference will be specified in standardized units using the parameter d. While this is similar to the procedure used in Section IV.1 concerning tests on the mean of a single population, the reader is cautioned that the definition of d used here is modified slightly. For one-sided tests, the case specifically considered is where the alternative hypothesis is $\mu_1 > \mu_2$, as switching the subscripts associated with the populations allows either comparison to be considered.

It is necessary to assume that the sample to be taken from each population will be the same size n and that the variances σ of the two populations (whether known or unknown) are equal. Exhibits IV.2–1 through IV.2–8 display the relationship between n and the probability of rejecting the null hypothesis, β. Exhibits IV.2–1 through IV.2–4 are provided for the case where σ is known, Exhibits IV.2–5 through IV.2–8 for the case where σ is unknown. In each case the $\alpha = .05$ one- and two-sided graphs are presented first, followed by the $\alpha = .01$ one- and two-sided graphs. The graphs for the two-sided tests can be used to approximate the one-sided cases by halving the stated α values. Similarly, the graphs for the one-sided tests can be used to approximate the two-sided cases by doubling the stated α values.

B. Using the Graphs

Example B–1. Prototypes of two competing pieces of equipment for producing a certain item are available for testing. One factor of interest is the efficiency of usage of raw material by each machine. The procedure proposed to investigate the efficiency is to process 100 pounds of raw material through each machine and observe the number of usable items produced. Assuming that the number produced is large, it may be reasonable to assume that the numbers of items produced follow a normal distribution. Further, previous testing has shown that the standard deviation σ of the numbers of pieces is about the same for each machine, with $\sigma = 15$. The hypothesis to be tested is that the mean number of items produced by each type is the same with $\alpha = .05$. This hypothesis implies a two-sided test. How many 100-pound batches must be run on each machine to have a 75-percent probability of rejecting the null hypothesis when the true difference in mean output per 100 pounds of raw material is as much as 30 items? Since the probability of rejecting correctly is $.75 = 1 - \beta$, then $\beta = .25$, and

$$d = |\mu_1 - \mu_2|/\sigma = 30/15 = 2.0$$

Entering Exhibit IV.2–2, we find the intersection of $d = 2.0$ and $\beta = .25$ lines at n between 3 and 4. Thus, four batches of 100 pounds would need to be run through each machine. Note that the value of β chosen here was quite high. If it were decreased, the required sample size would have to be increased considerably.

Example B–2. Suppose that in Example B–1 eight batches of raw material were available for each machine. What would the value of β be (at

EXHIBIT IV.2–1

SAMPLE SIZES FOR TESTS ON MEANS OF TWO POPULATIONS

(σ Known, One-Sided $\alpha = .05$)

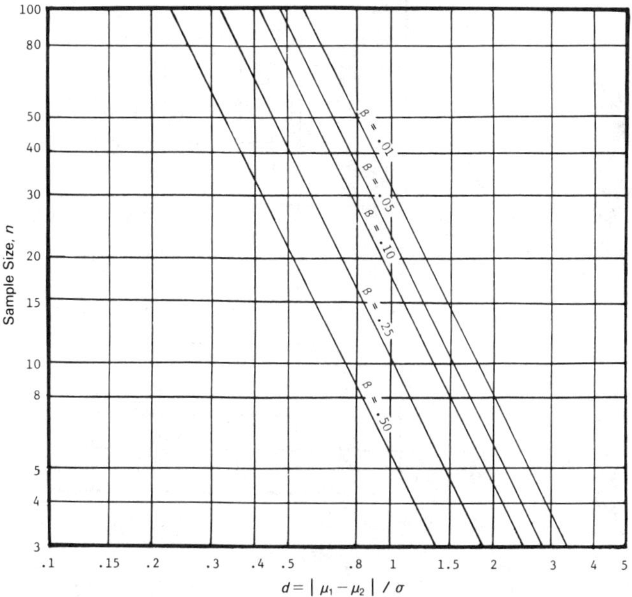

$d = 2.0$) if all of the raw material were used in the tests? Entering Exhibit IV.2–2, we see that the intersection of the $d = 2.0$ and $n = 8$ lines falls about halfway between the $\beta = .01$ and $\beta = .05$ lines. As the interpolation between the β lines is not linear, the value of β is visually estimated to be between .02 and .03.

Example B–3. If the equipment in Example B–1 were new innovations and no information was available about the values of the standard deviations, it would be necessary to use sample estimates of the standard deviations in conducting the hypothesis tests. Assuming that the standard deviations associated with each machine are equal (even though the true values are unknown), the value of β can be found from Exhibit IV.2–6, as this is a two-sided, $\alpha = .05$ test. The value of d is determined by the difference between the means in terms of multiples of σ. Suppose it is desired to construct a test that has a 75-percent probability of rejecting the null hypothesis when $|\mu_1 - \mu_2| = 2\sigma$. This gives $d = 2\sigma/\sigma = 2.0$, as before, but if the true value of σ is not 15, as assumed in Example B–1, the protection will not be valid for $|\mu_1 - \mu_2| = 30$. Entering Exhibit IV.2–6 with $d = 2.0$ and $\beta = .25$, we find, after rounding to the next higher integer, that $n = 7$.

EXHIBIT IV.2–2

Sample Sizes for Tests on Means of Two Populations

(σ Known, Two-Sided $\alpha = .05$)

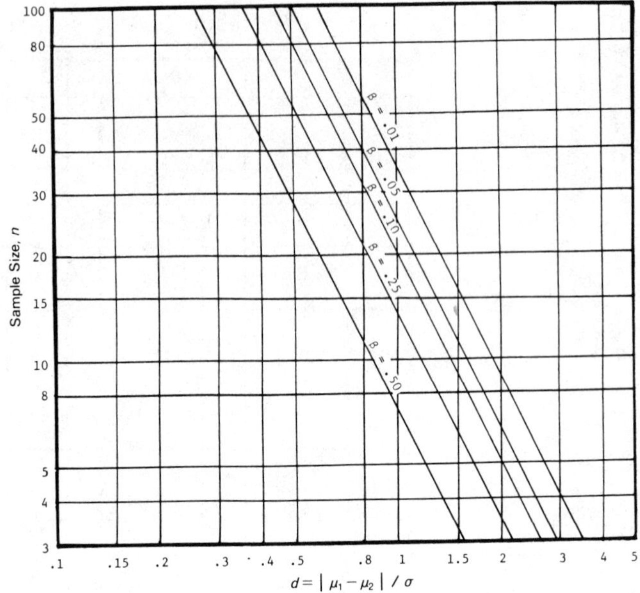

EXHIBIT IV.2–3

Sample Sizes for Tests on Means of Two Populations

(σ Known, One-Sided $\alpha = .01$)

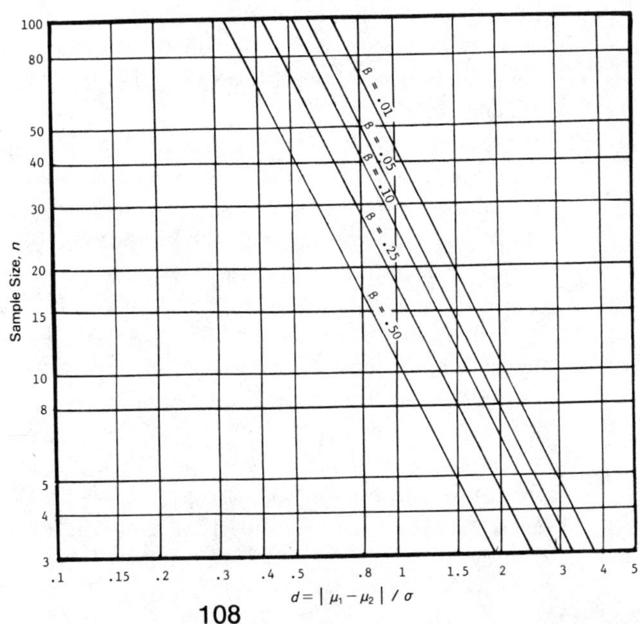

EXHIBIT IV.2–4

SAMPLE SIZES FOR TESTS ON MEANS OF TWO POPULATIONS
(σ Known, Two-Sided $\alpha = .01$)

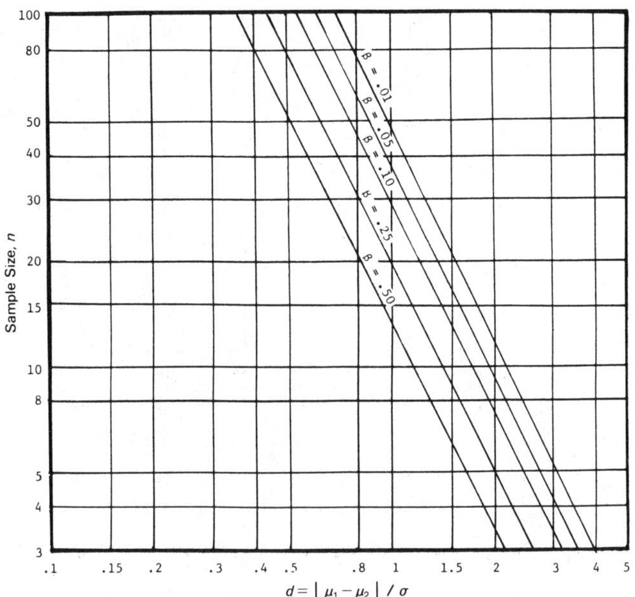

EXHIBIT IV.2–5

SAMPLE SIZES FOR TESTS ON MEANS OF TWO POPULATIONS
(σ Unknown, One-Sided $\alpha = .05$)

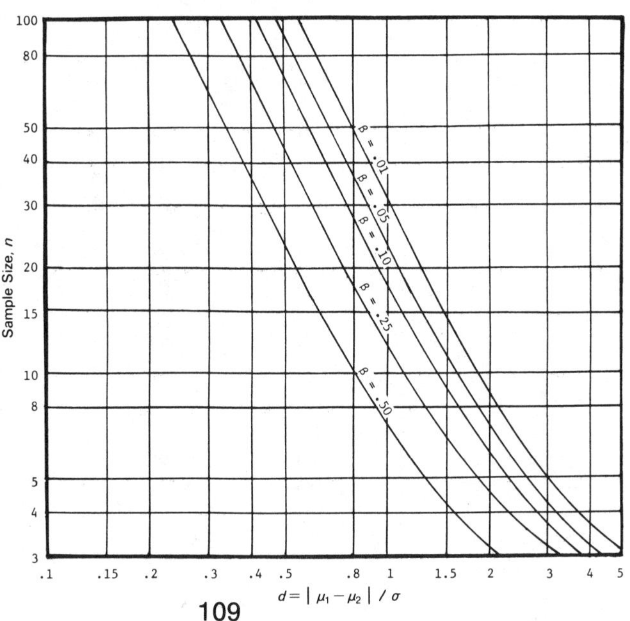

EXHIBIT IV.2–6

SAMPLE SIZES FOR TESTS ON MEANS OF TWO POPULATIONS

(σ Unknown, Two-Sided $\alpha = .05$)

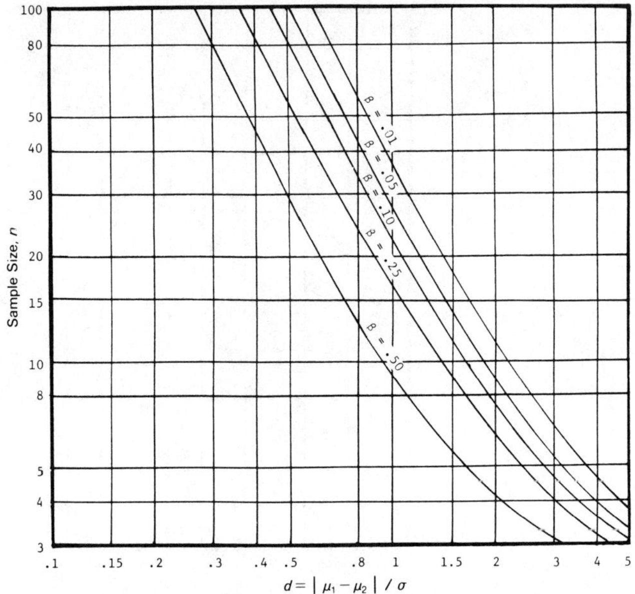

EXHIBIT IV.2–7

SAMPLE SIZES FOR TESTS ON MEANS OF TWO POPULATIONS

(σ Unknown, One-Sided $\alpha = .01$)

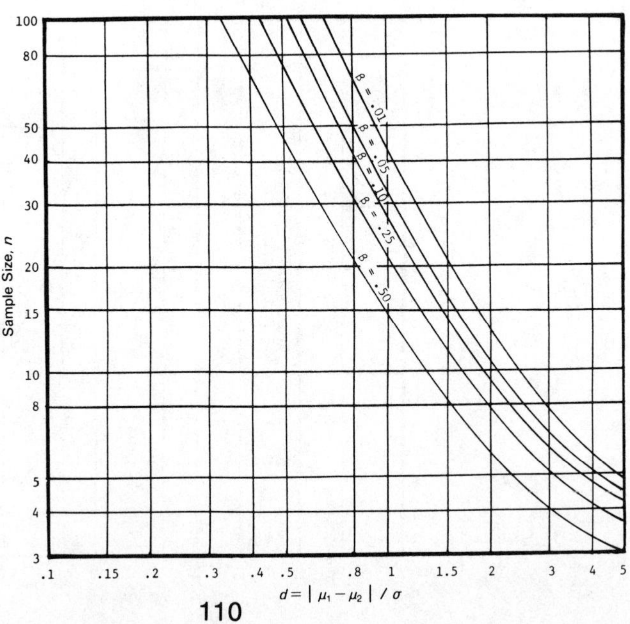

EXHIBIT IV.2–8

SAMPLE SIZES FOR TESTS ON MEANS OF TWO POPULATIONS

(σ Unknown, Two-Sided $\alpha = .01$)

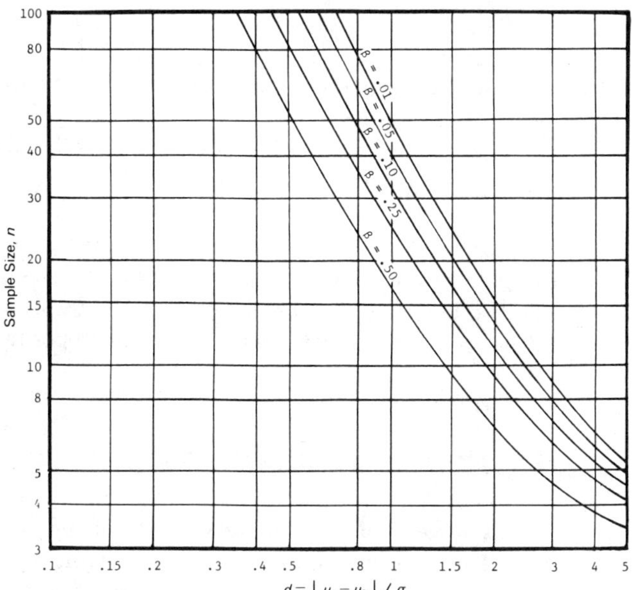

IV.3 Tests on the Variance of a Normal Population

A. Description

The hypothesis test considered in this section concerns the standard deviation of a normal population. As in the hypothesis tests concerning the means of a normal population (discussed in Sections IV.1 and IV.2), attention is focused on three quantities. They are the Type I error, α, the Type II error, β, both described in Section IV.1, and n, the sample size. Specifying any two of these quantities determines the third.

For the lower tail test, the hypotheses are

$$H_0: \sigma = \sigma_0$$

$$H_1: \sigma < \sigma_0$$

For the upper tail test, the hypotheses are

$H_0: \sigma = \sigma_0$

$H_1: \sigma > \sigma_0$

Here, σ is the standard deviation of the population, and σ_0 is the specific hypothesized value.

For a given value of n and α, the probability of a Type II error is dependent on the ratio of the true value of the standard deviation and the hypothesized value. We denote this ratio as $\lambda = \sigma/\sigma_0$.

Exhibits IV.3–1 and IV.3–2 provide tables of the sample sizes required to achieve a specified β as a function of λ when conducting a lower tail test. The two tables are for $\alpha = .05$ and $\alpha = .01$, respectively. Exhibits IV.3–3 and IV.3–4 provide comparable tables for the upper tail test.

B. Reading the Tables

Example B–1. When testing H_0: $\sigma = \sigma_0$ against H_1: $\sigma > \sigma_0$ using a Type I error probability of $\alpha = .05$, find the sample size required so that there is an 80-percent probability of rejecting H_0 when the true standard deviation is twice as large as the hypothesized value, i.e., $\lambda = 2.0$. Enter Exhibit IV.3–3 for H_1: $\sigma > \sigma_0$ and $\alpha = .05$, and follow the row for $\lambda = 2.0$ until reaching the column for $\beta = .10$, to find $n = 10$.

Example B–2. We plan to test H_0: $\sigma = 4.0$ against H_1: $\sigma < 4.0$ using $n = 20$ observations and $\alpha = .01$. Find the probability of rejecting H_0 when σ is as small as 3. Entering Exhibit IV.3–2 (since $\alpha = .01$ and H_1: $\sigma < \sigma_0$), we follow the row for $\lambda = 3.0/4.0 = 0.75$ until values that surround $n = 20$ are found. We find that for $\beta = .90$, $n = 12$ and for $\beta = .75$, $n = 24$. Interpolating to $n = 20$, we find the probability of accepting H_0 for $\lambda = 0.75$ to be .80.

C. Using the Tables

Example C–1. Consider a metal-rolling process. Concern is centered on the variability of the thickness of sheet stock that has passed through the process. The planned inspection procedure is to take measurements at random points along the length of the stock and use this data to test the hypotheses

$H_0: \sigma = \sigma_0$

EXHIBIT IV.3–1

Lower Tail Tests on the Variance of a Normal Population

($\alpha = .05$)

$\lambda = \sigma/\sigma_0$	β = Probability of a Type II Error						
	.90	.75	.50	.25	.10	.05	.01
.02	2	2	2	2	2	2	2
.05	2	2	2	2	2	2	2
.10	2	2	2	2	2	2	2
.15	2	2	2	2	3	3	3
.20	2	2	2	3	3	3	4
.25	2	2	2	3	4	4	5
.30	2	2	3	4	4	5	6
.35	2	2	3	4	5	6	8
.40	2	2	4	5	7	8	10
.45	2	3	4	6	8	10	13
.50	2	3	5	8	11	13	17
.55	2	4	6	10	14	16	22
.60	2	4	8	13	18	22	30
.65	2	5	11	17	25	31	42
.70	3	7	14	24	36	44	61
.75	3	9	21	36	54	67	94
.80	4	14	32	59	89	110	156
.85	6	24	58	108	166	206	295
.90	11	51	132	251	390	489	703
.95	33	195	533	1038	1636	2058	2981

EXHIBIT IV.3–2

Lower Tail Tests on the Variance of a Normal Population

($\alpha = .01$)

$\lambda = \sigma/\sigma_0$	β = Probability of a Type II Error						
	.90	.75	.50	.25	.10	.05	.01
.02	2	2	2	2	2	2	2
.05	2	2	2	2	2	2	3
.10	2	2	2	3	3	3	3
.15	2	2	3	3	4	4	5
.20	2	3	3	4	5	5	6
.25	2	3	4	5	6	6	7
.30	2	3	5	6	7	8	9
.35	3	4	5	7	8	9	11
.40	3	5	6	8	11	12	15
.45	4	5	8	10	13	15	19
.50	4	6	9	13	17	19	24
.55	5	8	12	17	22	25	32
.60	6	10	15	22	29	34	43
.65	7	12	20	30	39	46	60
.70	9	17	28	41	56	66	87
.75	12	24	40	62	85	100	133
.80	18	36	64	99	138	164	219
.85	30	63	115	182	256	306	412
.90	63	140	262	423	600	720	977
.95	234	552	1065	1745	2500	3016	4116

EXHIBIT IV.3–3

UPPER TAIL TESTS ON THE VARIANCE OF A NORMAL POPULATION

($\alpha = .05$)

	β = Probability of a Type II Error						
$\lambda = \sigma/\sigma_0$	.90	.75	.50	.25	.10	.05	.01
1.02	152	1164	3405	6822	10903	13800	20155
1.05	22	184	551	1116	1793	2274	3332
1.10	5	45	141	289	469	597	879
1.15	2	20	64	134	218	278	412
1.20	2	11	37	78	128	164	244
1.25	2	7	24	52	86	110	164
1.30	2	5	17	37	62	80	120
1.35	2	4	13	29	48	61	92
1.40	2	3	11	23	38	49	74
1.45	2	3	9	19	31	41	61
1.50	2	2	7	16	26	34	52
1.60	2	2	5	12	20	26	39
1.70	2	2	4	9	16	21	31
1.80	2	2	4	8	13	17	26
1.90	2	2	3	7	11	14	22
2.00	2	2	3	6	10	13	19
2.10	2	2	2	5	9	11	17
2.20	2	2	2	5	8	10	15
2.30	2	2	2	4	7	9	14
2.40	2	2	2	4	6	8	13
2.50	2	2	2	4	6	8	12
2.60	2	2	2	3	6	7	11
2.70	2	2	2	3	5	7	10
2.80	2	2	2	3	5	6	10
2.90	2	2	2	3	5	6	9
3.00	2	2	2	3	4	6	9
3.50	2	2	2	2	4	5	7
4.00	2	2	2	2	3	4	6
4.50	2	2	2	2	3	4	5
5.00	2	2	2	2	3	3	5

against

$$H_1: \sigma > \sigma_0.$$

where $\alpha = .01$.

Here the acceptable standard deviation σ_0 is set to 0.002, a value determined by customer requirements, past experience with the process, or a combination of the two. How many observations must be collected on a piece of stock to be 90-percent sure of rejecting H_0 if the true standard deviation has increased to 0.004? Since the probability of rejecting H_0

EXHIBIT IV.3–4

Upper Tail Tests on the Variance of a Normal Population

($\alpha = .01$)

$\lambda = \sigma/\sigma_0$	β = Probability of a Type II Error						
	.90	.75	.50	.25	.10	.05	.01
1.02	1330	3397	6811	11400	16535	20064	27603
1.05	205	541	1101	1859	2710	3296	4549
1.10	49	134	280	480	705	860	1193
1.15	21	60	127	220	326	399	556
1.20	11	33	73	128	190	234	327
1.25	7	21	48	84	127	156	219
1.30	5	15	34	61	91	113	159
1.35	3	11	25	46	70	86	122
1.40	3	9	20	36	55	69	97
1.45	2	7	16	30	45	56	80
1.50	2	6	13	25	38	47	68
1.60	2	4	10	18	28	35	51
1.70	2	3	8	14	22	28	40
1.80	2	3	6	12	18	23	33
1.90	2	2	5	10	15	19	28
2.00	2	2	4	8	13	17	24
2.10	2	2	4	7	12	15	21
2.20	2	2	3	7	10	13	19
2.30	2	2	3	6	9	12	17
2.40	2	2	3	5	8	11	16
2.50	2	2	3	5	8	10	15
2.60	2	2	2	5	7	9	13
2.70	2	2	2	4	7	9	13
2.80	2	2	2	4	6	8	12
2.90	2	2	2	4	6	8	11
3.00	2	2	2	4	6	7	11
3.50	2	2	2	3	5	6	8
4.00	2	2	2	3	4	5	7
4.50	2	2	2	2	3	4	6
5.00	2	2	2	2	3	4	6

correctly is 90-percent, $\beta = 1 - .90 = .10$ and $\lambda = \sigma/\sigma_0 = 0.004/0.002 = 2.0$. From Exhibit IV.3–4, the required sample size is 13.

Example C–2. Suppose that in Example C–1 a sample size of 10 had been used to save on inspection time. What would be the probability of rejecting H_0 for stock with $\sigma = 0.004$? Enter Exhibit IV.3–4, and look across the row for $\lambda = 2.0$ until values surrounding n are found. We find that for $\beta = .25$, $n = 8$ and for $\beta = .10$, $n = 13$. Interpolating to $n = 10$, we find the probability of accepting H_0 for $\lambda = 2.0$ to be .19. Since $\beta = .19$ is the probability of accepting H_0 when $\sigma = 0.004$, the probability of rejecting H_0 when $\sigma = 0.004$ is $1 - \beta = .81$. This is referred to as the *power of the test.*

IV.4 Tolerance Statements for Normal Populations

A. Description

We are interested in making a statement of the form "at least a fraction P of a normal population falls between $\overline{X} - kS$ and $\overline{X} + kS$," where k is a constant, $\overline{X}$ is the sample mean, and S is the sample standard deviation from a sample of n observations. For finite values of k, there is some risk of any interval stated not containing $100P$ percent of the distribution. We choose to state an interval that has this risk held at a specified level γ. This results in a two-sided γ-percent tolerance interval. Similarly, we can construct one-sided tolerance limits such that "at least a fraction P of a normal population is greater than $\overline{X} - kS$ with confidence γ" or "at least a fraction P of the normal population is less than $\overline{X} + kS$ with confidence γ."

The relationships between n and k for various values of P and γ are shown in Exhibits IV.4–1 and IV.4–2 for the two-sided case. Exhibits IV.4–3 and IV.4–4 provide comparable values for the one-sided case.

B. Reading the Charts

Example B–1. Find the sample size required so that a two-sided 95-percent tolerance interval constructed using $k = 3.0$ and using the sample to estimate the standard deviation, contains 99 percent of the population. Entering Exhibit IV.4–2, go vertically along the $k = 3.0$ line until reaching the $P = .99$ curve. Then proceed horizontally to the n scale to find an n of approximately 75.

Example B–2. Find the value of k required to construct a 90-percent upper tolerance bound on the 95th percentile of a normal population when $n = 20$ and the standard deviation is estimated from the sample. Entering Exhibit IV.4–3 with $\gamma = .90$, proceed horizontally along the $n = 20$ line until reaching the $P = .95$ curve. Then, drop vertically to read $k = 2.2$. The tolerance bound would be $\overline{X} + 2.2S$.

C. Using the Charts

Example C–1. The tensile strength of cord (assumed to follow a normal distribution) being used for manufacture of radiator hoses is of interest. A sample of $n = 15$ is used, and $\overline{X} = 140.0$ pounds and $S = 5.0$

EXHIBIT IV.4–1

TWO-SIDED NORMAL TOLERANCE LIMITS

($\gamma = .90$)

EXHIBIT IV.4–2

TWO-SIDED NORMAL TOLERANCE LIMITS

($\gamma = .95$)

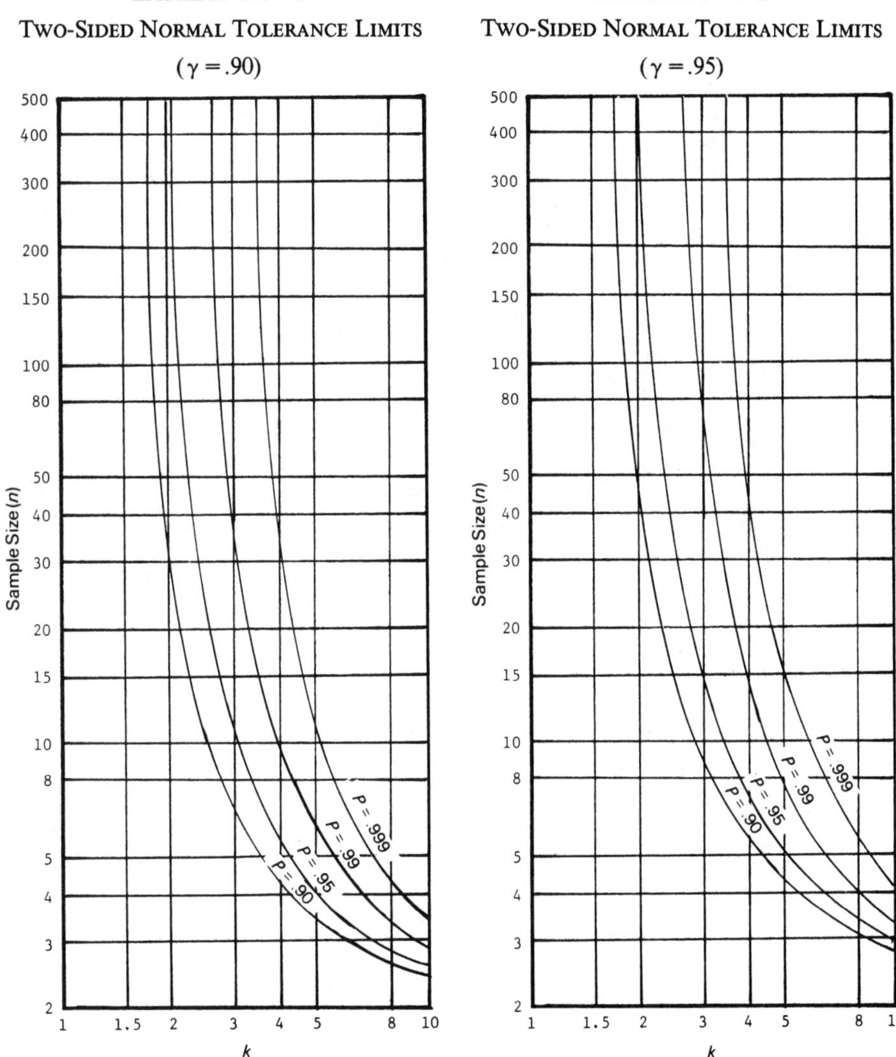

pounds are computed. We want to find the value of k to use when constructing a 90-percent lower tolerance bound, $\overline{X} - kS$, the point at which 99 percent of the population of cord strengths exceeds the bound. Using Exhibit IV.4–3 with $n = 15$ and $P = .99$, we find $k = 3.2$. We are 90-percent confident that 99 percent of the breaking strengths of cord are greater than $140.0 - (3.2)(5.0) = 124.0$ pounds.

Example C–2. Plastic parts are being manufactured, and the density of the parts is of interest. It is necessary to state limits within which we expect 90 percent of the densities of parts to fall with a confidence level of 95 percent. It is known that the densities follow a normal distribution with

EXHIBIT IV.4–3

ONE-SIDED NORMAL TOLERANCE LIMITS

($\gamma = .90$)

EXHIBIT IV.4–4

ONE-SIDED NORMAL TOLERANCE LIMITS

($\gamma = .95$)

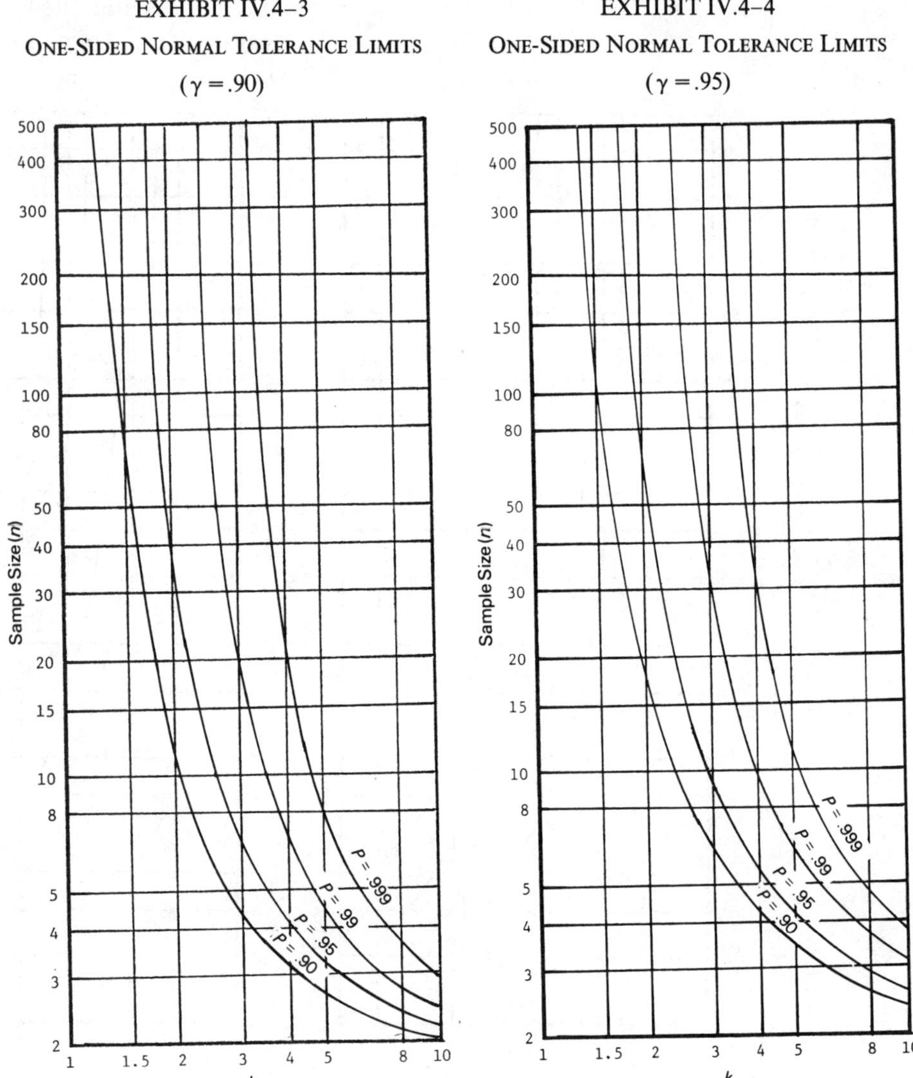

unknown standard deviation. What sample size is required if the distance between the limits is to be 0.12 or less? The distance between the limits is $(\bar{X}+kS)-(\bar{X}-kS)=2kS=0.12$. Since S will not be known until the data is collected, it is necessary to estimate a value of S using whatever information is available. Assume the estimate is $S=0.02$. This leads to $k=3.0$. Entering Exhibit IV.4-2, proceed vertically along the $k=3.0$ line until reaching the $P=.90$ curve. Reading the n scale at this point gives $n=9$, the tentative sample size. After the sample is taken, if the value of S is more than the estimate used, the value of n will have to be recomputed, and the additional units collected.

IV.5 Nonparametric Tolerance Statements

A. Description

We wish to determine the sample required to state with 100γ-percent confidence that at least $100P$-percent of a population (with a continuous distribution function) falls between the largest and smallest values in a random sample of n observations. When the underlying distribution is assumed to be unknown, this requires the construction of two-sided nonparametric tolerance limits. Two similar statements concerning the percent of a population falling below the largest observation or the percent falling above the smallest observation could also be made. One-sided tolerance limits are required in these two cases.

Exhibits IV.5–1 and IV.5–2 provide the values of n as a function of P for various values of γ for one- and two-sided cases, respectively.

B. Reading the Charts

Example B–1. The sample size required so that we can have 95-percent confidence that .90 of the population will fall between the largest and smallest values in the sample is desired. Enter Exhibit IV.5–2 with $P = .90$ and $\gamma = .95$ to find $n = 46$.

Example B–2. The sample size required so that we can be 95-percent confident that .90 of the population will fall below the largest value in the random sample is desired. Enter Exhibit IV.5–1 with $P = .90$ and $\gamma = .95$ to find $n = 29$.

Example B–3. How confident can we be that the interval between the largest and smallest values from a sample of $n = 100$ includes 95 percent of the population? Enter Exhibit IV.5–2 with $P = .90$. For $n = 96$, $\gamma = .9995$ and for $n = 113$, $\gamma = .9999$. Interpolation results in a γ value of approximately .9996.

C. Using the Charts

Example C–1. We are concerned with the chemical oxygen demand (COD) in the effluent discharged from a manufacturing plant. The COD is measured in parts per million. Daily measurements are taken, and past experience indicates that the distribution of these observations cannot be assumed to be any of the commonly known distributions. How many

EXHIBIT IV.5–1

Sample Sizes for One-Sided Tolerance Statements

Confidence Level γ	P = Fraction of Population						
	.500	.600	.700	.750	.800	.850	.900
.5000	1	2	2	3	4	5	7
.6000	2	2	3	4	5	6	9
.7000	2	3	4	5	6	8	12
.7500	3	3	4	5	7	9	14
.8000	3	4	5	6	8	10	16
.8500	3	4	6	7	9	12	19
.9000	4	5	7	9	11	15	22
.9500	5	6	9	11	14	19	29
.9750	6	8	11	13	17	23	36
.9800	6	8	11	14	18	25	38
.9900	7	10	13	17	21	29	44
.9950	8	11	15	19	24	33	51
.9990	10	14	20	25	31	43	66
.9995	11	15	22	27	35	47	73
.9999	14	19	26	33	42	57	88

Confidence Level γ	P = Fraction of Population						
	.950	.975	.980	.990	.995	.9990	.9995
.5000	14	28	35	69	139	693	1386
.6000	18	37	46	92	183	916	1833
.7000	24	48	60	120	241	1204	2408
.7500	28	55	69	138	277	1386	2772
.8000	32	64	80	161	322	1609	3219
.8500	37	75	94	189	379	1897	3794
.9000	45	91	114	230	460	2302	4605
.9500	59	119	149	299	598	2995	5990
.9750	72	146	183	368	736	3688	7376
.9800	77	155	194	390	781	3911	7823
.9900	90	182	228	459	919	4603	9209
.9950	104	210	263	528	1058	5296	10594
.9990	135	273	342	688	1379	6905	13813
.9995	149	301	377	757	1517	7598	15199
.9999	180	364	456	917	1838	9206	18417

observations must be taken before we can have 95-percent confidence that 99 percent of future COD readings will be less than the largest value observed in the sample? Using Exhibit IV.5–1 with $P = .99$ and $\gamma = .95$, we find n to be 299.

Example C–2. In the situation described in Example C–1, after 200 observations had been collected, the largest value was 225 ppm. How

EXHIBIT IV.5–2

SAMPLE SIZES FOR TWO-SIDED TOLERANCE STATEMENTS

Confidence Level γ	P = Fraction of Population						
	.500	.600	.700	.750	.800	.850	.900
.5000	3	4	6	7	9	11	17
.6000	4	5	7	8	10	13	20
.7000	5	6	8	10	12	16	24
.7500	5	6	9	10	13	18	27
.8000	5	7	9	11	14	19	29
.8500	6	8	10	13	16	22	33
.9000	7	9	12	15	18	25	38
.9500	8	10	14	18	22	30	46
.9750	9	12	17	20	26	35	54
.9800	9	12	17	21	27	37	56
.9900	11	14	20	24	31	42	64
.9950	12	16	22	27	34	47	72
.9990	14	19	27	33	42	58	89
.9995	15	21	29	36	46	63	96
.9999	18	24	34	42	54	73	113

Confidence Level γ	P = Fraction of Population						
	.950	.975	.980	.990	.995	.9990	.9995
.5000	34	67	84	168	336	1679	3357
.6000	40	81	101	202	404	2022	4045
.7000	49	97	122	244	488	2439	4878
.7500	53	107	134	269	538	2692	5385
.8000	59	119	149	299	598	2994	5988
.8500	67	134	168	337	674	3372	6744
.9000	77	155	194	388	777	3889	7778
.9500	93	188	236	473	947	4742	9486
.9750	110	221	277	555	1113	5570	11142
.9800	115	231	290	581	1165	5832	11666
.9900	130	263	330	662	1325	6636	13274
.9950	146	294	369	740	1483	7427	14858
.9990	181	366	458	920	1843	9230	18463
.9995	196	396	496	996	1996	9995	19993
.9999	230	465	583	1171	2346	11751	23508

confident could we be that 99 percent of future readings on COD would be less than 225 ppm? Using Exhibit IV.5–1 for one-sided limits, we find that $n = 200$ and $P = .99$ falls between $\gamma = .85$ and $\gamma = .90$. Interpolation indicates a confidence level of approximately 86 percent that 99 percent of future COD readings will be below 225 ppm based on the 200 data points available.

V

Design of Experiments: Differentiating Between Means

V.1 Duncan Multiple-Range Test

A. Description

In the Duncan multiple-range test there are k sample means available, all based on random samples from normal distributions that have the same variance σ^2. We wish to make statements about which pairs of means are different from which others. This problem typically arises when an experiment with several levels has been performed, the analysis of variance has shown that there are significant differences among the treatment levels, and we wish to know which levels are different.

Application of the procedure consists of the following steps:

1. Compute an estimate of the standard deviation, say $S_{\bar{Y}}$, of the sample *means*. For a fixed-effects model, $S_{\bar{Y}}^2$ will be found by dividing the mean square error MSE from the analysis of variance by the number of observations n in each sample mean $\bar{Y}$, or

   $$S_{\bar{Y}}^2 = \text{MSE}/n$$

   and

   $$S_{\bar{Y}} = \sqrt{S_{\bar{Y}}^2}$$

   Computation of MSE for a single factor fixed-effects model is described in Section C below.

2. Arrange the k means from lowest to highest.
3. Compute the range between each pair of means.
4. Compute $(k-1)$ least significant ranges

   $$R_p = S_{\bar{Y}} r_\alpha(p, f) \qquad p = 2, 3, \ldots, k$$

   where $r_\alpha(p, f)$ are the values from Exhibit V.1–1 or V.1–2, depending on the chosen level of α.

5. Compare each observed range with the least significant range R_p where the value of p is determined by adding two to the number of means that have values between those being used to compute the observed range.

If the observed range is greater than the least significant range, the means are significantly different, with the following exception: No pair of means can be significantly different if the means are contained within the range of a pair of means that are not significantly different.

Tables of $r_\alpha(p, f)$ are presented for $\alpha = .05$ and $\alpha = .01$ for various values of p and f in Exhibits V.1–1 and V.1–2, respectively.

Several alternative tests of the same general form exist for the above problem, and controversy as to which to use abounds. One of the elements of this controversy centers on the definition of α. This differs in the alternatives, and the choice of α affects the probability of a given true difference of a specified size between population means being declared significant. The Duncan test is less conservative in this aspect, as the least significant ranges are smaller than those generated by other alternatives for most values of p.

B. Reading the Tables

Exhibits V.1–1 and V.1–2 are indexed on p and f. The value of p is determined by the number of sample means in the ordered list in the range being tested. For example, if 5 means are being analyzed, and the comparison between the highest and lowest is being made, $p = 5$. When the smallest is tested against the next to largest, $p = 4$.

The value of f is the degrees of freedom associated with the estimate of the standard deviation of the $\overline{Y}$'s. Frequently, this will be the same as the degrees of freedom associated with the population error variance estimate in the analysis of variance.

Example B–1. The least significant range factors for $\alpha = .05, f = 8$, and $p = 2$, 3, and 4 are required. From Exhibit V.1–1, the values are

$$r_{.05}(2,8) = 3.26$$
$$r_{.05}(3,8) = 3.39$$
$$r_{.05}(4,8) = 3.47$$

C. Using the Tables

Example C–1. An experiment to measure the gas mileage of an automobile with four different modifications to the carburetor is performed. Three observations of miles per gallon are recorded for each modification as follows:

	Modification *A*	*B*	*C*	*D*
	31.2	32.0	28.1	26.2
	30.0	33.0	29.3	27.1
	28.6	29.7	29.8	27.6
Means	$\overline{Y}_A = 29.93$	$\overline{Y}_B = 31.57$	$\overline{Y}_C = 29.07$	$\overline{Y}_D = 26.97$

A fixed-effect analysis of variance indicates that the modifications do not have the same mean miles-per-gallon performance. The Duncan multiple-range test will be used to find which modifications differ from each other using $\alpha = .05$. The mean square error from the one-way analysis of variance is computed from

$$\text{MSE} = \sum_{i=1}^{k} \sum_{j=1}^{n} \left(Y_{ij} - \overline{Y}_i\right)^2 \Big/ [k(n-1)]$$

where Y_{ij} is the jth observation from the ith modification, and $\overline{Y}_i$ is the average of the observations for the ith modification. Using the data above with $k = 4$ and $n = 3$, MSE is determined as

$$\text{MSE} = \sum_{i=1}^{4} \sum_{j=1}^{3} \left(Y_{ij} - \overline{Y}_i\right)^2 \Big/ 8 = 1.46$$

As MSE is an estimate of the variance of the distribution of the original observations, the estimate of the standard deviation of the $\overline{Y}$'s is $S_{\overline{Y}} = \sqrt{1.46/3} = 0.698$. Since the mean-square-error term has eight degrees of freedom, $f = 8$. The ordered means are

$$\overline{Y}_D = 26.97$$
$$\overline{Y}_C = 29.07$$
$$\overline{Y}_A = 29.93$$
$$\overline{Y}_B = 31.57$$

The least significant ranges are

$$R_2 = S_{\overline{Y}} r_{.05}(p, f) = S_{\overline{Y}} r_{.05}(2,8) = (0.698)(3.26) = 2.27$$
$$R_3 = S_{\overline{Y}} r_{.05}(3,8) = (0.698)(3.39) = 2.36$$
$$R_4 = S_{\overline{Y}} r_{.05}(4,8) = (0.698)(3.47) = 2.42$$

The observed ranges and their associated least significant ranges are

$\overline{Y}_B - \overline{Y}_D = 4.60 > 2.42 = R_4$, significant

$\overline{Y}_B - \overline{Y}_C = 2.50 > 2.36 = R_3$, significant

$\overline{Y}_B - \overline{Y}_A = 1.64 < 2.27 = R_2$, not significant

$\overline{Y}_A - \overline{Y}_D = 2.96 < 2.36 = R_3$, not significant

$\overline{Y}_A - \overline{Y}_C = 0.86 < 2.27 = R_2$, not significant

$\overline{Y}_C - \overline{Y}_D = 2.10 < 2.27 = R_2$, not significant

EXHIBIT V.1–1

Least Significant Range Factors

($\alpha = .05$)

f \ p	2	3	4	5	6	7	8	9	10	12	14	16	18	20	50	100
1	18.0	18.0	18.0	18.0	18.0	18.0	18.0	18.0	18.0	18.0	18.0	18.0	18.0	18.0	18.0	18.0
2	6.09	6.09	6.09	6.09	6.09	6.09	6.09	6.09	6.09	6.09	6.09	6.09	6.09	6.09	6.09	6.09
3	4.50	4.50	4.50	4.50	4.50	4.50	4.50	4.50	4.50	4.50	4.50	4.50	4.50	4.50	4.50	4.50
4	3.93	4.01	4.02	4.02	4.02	4.02	4.02	4.02	4.02	4.02	4.02	4.02	4.02	4.02	4.02	4.02
5	3.64	3.74	3.79	3.83	3.83	3.83	3.83	3.83	3.83	3.83	3.83	3.83	3.83	3.83	3.83	3.83
6	3.46	3.58	3.64	3.68	3.68	3.68	3.68	3.68	3.68	3.68	3.68	3.68	3.68	3.68	3.68	3.68
7	3.35	3.47	3.54	3.58	3.60	3.61	3.61	3.61	3.61	3.61	3.61	3.61	3.61	3.61	3.61	3.61
8	3.26	3.39	3.47	3.52	3.55	3.56	3.56	3.56	3.56	3.56	3.56	3.56	3.56	3.56	3.56	3.56
9	3.20	3.34	3.41	3.47	3.50	3.52	3.52	3.52	3.52	3.52	3.52	3.52	3.52	3.52	3.52	3.52
10	3.15	3.30	3.37	3.43	3.46	3.47	3.47	3.47	3.47	3.47	3.47	3.47	3.47	3.48	3.48	3.48
11	3.11	3.27	3.35	3.39	3.43	3.44	3.45	3.46	3.46	3.46	3.46	3.46	3.47	3.48	3.48	3.48
12	3.08	3.23	3.33	3.36	3.40	3.42	3.44	3.44	3.46	3.46	3.46	3.46	3.47	3.48	3.48	3.48
13	3.06	3.21	3.30	3.35	3.38	3.41	3.42	3.44	3.45	3.45	3.46	3.46	3.47	3.47	3.47	3.47
14	3.03	3.18	3.27	3.33	3.37	3.39	3.41	3.42	3.44	3.45	3.46	3.46	3.47	3.47	3.47	3.47
15	3.01	3.16	3.25	3.31	3.36	3.38	3.40	3.42	3.43	3.44	3.45	3.46	3.47	3.47	3.47	3.47
16	3.00	3.15	3.23	3.30	3.34	3.37	3.39	3.41	3.43	3.44	3.45	3.46	3.47	3.47	3.47	3.47
17	2.98	3.13	3.22	3.28	3.33	3.36	3.38	3.40	3.42	3.44	3.45	3.46	3.47	3.47	3.47	3.47
18	2.97	3.12	3.21	3.27	3.32	3.35	3.37	3.39	3.41	3.43	3.45	3.46	3.47	3.47	3.47	3.47
19	2.96	3.11	3.19	3.26	3.31	3.35	3.37	3.39	3.41	3.43	3.44	3.46	3.47	3.47	3.47	3.47
20	2.95	3.10	3.18	3.25	3.30	3.34	3.36	3.38	3.40	3.43	3.44	3.46	3.46	3.47	3.47	3.47
22	2.93	3.08	3.17	3.24	3.29	3.32	3.35	3.37	3.39	3.42	3.44	3.45	3.46	3.47	3.47	3.47
24	2.92	3.07	3.15	3.22	3.28	3.31	3.34	3.37	3.38	3.41	3.44	3.45	3.46	3.47	3.47	3.47
26	2.91	3.06	3.14	3.21	3.27	3.30	3.34	3.36	3.38	3.41	3.43	3.45	3.46	3.47	3.47	3.47
28	2.90	3.04	3.13	3.20	3.26	3.30	3.33	3.35	3.37	3.40	3.43	3.45	3.46	3.47	3.47	3.47
30	2.89	3.04	3.12	3.20	3.25	3.29	3.32	3.35	3.37	3.40	3.43	3.44	3.46	3.47	3.47	3.47
40	2.86	3.01	3.10	3.17	3.22	3.27	3.30	3.33	3.35	3.39	3.42	3.44	3.46	3.47	3.47	3.47
60	2.83	2.98	3.08	3.14	3.20	3.24	3.28	3.31	3.33	3.37	3.40	3.43	3.45	3.47	3.48	3.48
100	2.80	2.95	3.05	3.12	3.18	3.22	3.26	3.29	3.32	3.36	3.40	3.42	3.45	3.47	3.53	3.53
∞	2.77	2.92	3.02	3.09	3.15	3.19	3.23	3.26	3.29	3.34	3.38	3.41	3.44	3.47	3.61	3.67

Source: D. B. Duncan, "Multiple Range and Multiple *F* Tests," *Biometrics* 11 (1955) 1–42. With permission from the Biometric Society.

EXHIBIT V.1–2

Least Significant Range Factors

$(\alpha = .01)$

f \ p	2	3	4	5	6	7	8	9	10	12	14	16	18	20	50	100
1	90.0	90.0	90.0	90.0	90.0	90.0	90.0	90.0	90.0	90.0	90.0	90.0	90.0	90.0	90.0	90.0
2	14.0	14.0	14.0	14.0	14.0	14.0	14.0	14.0	14.0	14.0	14.0	14.0	14.0	14.0	14.0	14.0
3	8.26	8.5	8.6	8.7	8.8	8.9	8.9	9.0	9.0	9.0	9.1	9.2	9.3	9.3	9.3	9.3
4	6.51	6.8	6.9	7.0	7.1	7.1	7.2	7.2	7.3	7.3	7.4	7.4	7.5	7.5	7.5	7.5
5	5.70	5.96	6.11	6.18	6.26	6.33	6.40	6.44	6.5	6.6	6.6	6.7	6.7	6.8	6.8	6.8
6	5.24	5.51	5.65	5.73	5.81	5.88	5.95	6.00	6.0	6.1	6.2	6.2	6.3	6.3	6.3	6.3
7	4.95	5.22	5.37	5.45	5.53	5.61	5.69	5.73	5.8	5.8	5.9	5.9	6.0	6.0	6.0	6.0
8	4.74	5.00	5.14	5.23	5.32	5.40	5.47	5.51	5.5	5.6	5.7	5.7	5.8	5.8	5.8	5.8
9	4.60	4.86	4.99	5.08	5.17	5.25	5.32	5.36	5.4	5.5	5.5	5.6	5.7	5.7	5.7	5.7
10	4.48	4.73	4.88	4.96	5.06	5.13	5.20	5.24	5.28	5.36	5.42	5.48	5.54	5.55	5.55	5.55
11	4.39	4.63	4.77	4.86	4.94	5.01	5.06	5.12	5.15	5.24	5.28	5.34	5.38	5.39	5.39	5.39
12	4.32	4.55	4.68	4.76	4.84	4.92	4.96	5.02	5.07	5.13	5.17	5.22	5.24	5.26	5.26	5.26
13	4.26	4.48	4.62	4.69	4.74	4.84	4.88	4.94	4.98	5.04	5.08	5.13	5.14	5.15	5.15	5.15
14	4.21	4.42	4.55	4.63	4.70	4.78	4.83	4.87	4.91	4.96	5.00	5.04	5.06	5.07	5.07	5.07
15	4.17	4.37	4.50	4.58	4.64	4.72	4.77	4.81	4.84	4.90	4.94	4.97	4.99	5.00	5.00	5.00
16	4.13	4.34	4.45	4.54	4.60	4.67	4.72	4.76	4.79	4.84	4.88	4.91	4.93	4.94	4.94	4.94
17	4.10	4.30	4.41	4.50	4.56	4.63	4.68	4.72	4.75	4.80	4.83	4.86	4.88	4.89	4.89	4.89
18	4.07	4.27	4.38	4.46	4.53	4.59	4.64	4.68	4.71	4.76	4.79	4.82	4.84	4.85	4.85	4.85
19	4.05	4.24	4.35	4.43	4.50	4.56	4.61	4.64	4.67	4.72	4.76	4.79	4.81	4.82	4.82	4.82
20	4.02	4.22	4.33	4.40	4.47	4.53	4.58	4.61	4.65	4.69	4.73	4.76	4.78	4.79	4.79	4.79
22	3.99	4.17	4.28	4.36	4.42	4.48	4.53	4.57	4.60	4.65	4.68	4.71	4.74	4.75	4.75	4.75
24	3.96	4.14	4.24	4.33	4.39	4.44	4.49	4.53	4.57	4.62	4.64	4.67	4.70	4.72	4.74	4.74
26	3.93	4.11	4.21	4.30	4.36	4.41	4.46	4.50	4.53	4.58	4.62	4.65	4.67	4.69	4.73	4.73
28	3.91	4.08	4.18	4.28	4.34	4.39	4.43	4.47	4.51	4.56	4.60	4.62	4.65	4.67	4.72	4.72
30	3.89	4.06	4.16	4.22	4.32	4.36	4.41	4.45	4.48	4.54	4.58	4.61	4.63	4.65	4.71	4.71
40	3.82	3.99	4.10	4.17	4.24	4.30	4.34	4.37	4.41	4.46	4.51	4.54	4.57	4.59	4.69	4.69
60	3.76	3.92	4.03	4.12	4.17	4.23	4.27	4.31	4.34	4.39	4.44	4.47	4.50	4.53	4.66	4.66
100	3.71	3.86	3.98	4.06	4.11	4.17	4.21	4.25	4.29	4.35	4.38	4.42	4.45	4.48	4.64	4.65
∞	3.64	3.80	3.90	3.98	4.04	4.09	4.14	4.17	4.20	4.26	4.31	4.34	4.38	4.41	4.60	4.68

Source: D. B. Duncan, "Multiple Range and Multiple *F* Tests," *Biometrics* 11 (1955) 1–42. With permission from the Biometric Society.

Thus, modification B performs significantly better than D or C, but is not significantly better than A, while A, C, and D do not differ significantly. This can be illustrated as follows:

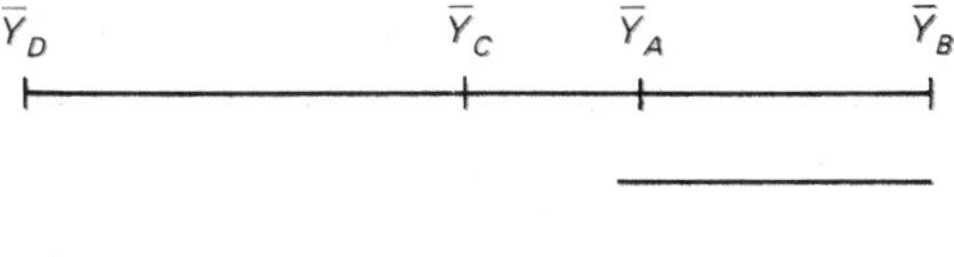

All means above a single line are not significantly different from each other.

V.2 Comparisons Between Treatment and Control Populations

A. Description

Suppose there are k sample means available, all based on n random samples from normal distributions that have the same standard deviation σ. One of the k means is considered to be a "control," and it is desired to identify which of the remaining $k-1$ means differ from the control mean when the *overall* level of significance is α. If $k=2$, this is equivalent to a t-test. If there is no control mean, a Duncan range test described in Section V.1 should be used. The following procedure developed by Dunnett (1955) is available for the specific case of interest.

Letting $\bar{Y}_i$ be the sample means, and $i=1$ be the control, it is necessary to compute

$$t_i = \frac{\bar{Y}_i - \bar{Y}_1}{S\sqrt{2/n}} \qquad i = 2,3,\ldots,k$$

where

$$S^2 = \sum_{i=1}^{k} \sum_{j=1}^{n} \left(Y_{ij} - \bar{Y}_i\right)^2 \Big/ [k(n-1)]$$

is the estimate of the within-population variance with f degrees of freedom, and n is the number of observations taken on each population. Note that S^2 is the same as the mean square error, MSE, if a single factor analysis of variance is performed. Each t_i is compared to $t_\alpha(k, f)$, the tabulated critical values. Separate tables are required for the one- and two-sided tests. For a two-sided test, if $|t_i| > t_\alpha(k, f)$, the ith population is significantly different than the control. The hypothesis H_0: $\mu_1 = \mu_i$ is rejected in favor of H_i: $\mu_1 < \mu_i$ if $t_i < -t_\alpha(k, f)$; and in favor of H_1: $\mu_1 > \mu_i$ if $t_i > t_\alpha(k, f)$ for one-sided tests.

Critical values for $\alpha = .05$ and $.01$ are presented for various values of k and f, for one-sided tests in Exhibits V.2–1 and V.2–2, and for two-sided tests in Exhibits V.2–3 and V.2–4.

B. Reading the Tables

Example B–1. For $k = 6$ populations, the critical value of the t_i's for a two-sided comparison with $\alpha = .05$ when the standard deviation estimate has $f = 18$ degrees of freedom is found in Exhibit V.2–3 to be $t_{.05}(6, 18) = 2.84$. For a one-sided comparison, the value obtained from Exhibit V.2–1 is $t_{.05}(6, 18) = 2.41$.

C. Using the Tables

Example C–1. An experiment to measure the gas mileage of an automobile with three modifications to the stock carburetor is performed. Three observations are made when each of the modifications is in place as well as for the original carburetor. The observed miles per gallon are:

		Modification		
	Original	*A*	*B*	*C*
	31.2	32.0	28.1	25.2
	30.0	33.0	29.3	26.1
	28.6	29.7	29.8	26.6
Means	$\overline{Y}_1 = 29.93$	$\overline{Y}_2 = 31.57$	$\overline{Y}_3 = 29.07$	$\overline{Y}_4 = 25.97$

The estimate of the within-population variance of the observations is calculated using

$$S^2 = \sum_{i=1}^{4} \sum_{j=1}^{3} \left(Y_{ij} - \bar{Y}_i\right)^2 / [k(n-1)]$$

where the Y_{ij}'s are the original observations. The computed value of $S^2 = 1.454$, so that $S = 1.206$. There are $k(n-1) = 4(2) = 8$ degrees of freedom associated with the estimate of S^2, so $f = 8$. Then

$$t_2 = \frac{33.56 - 29.93}{1.206\sqrt{2/3}} = 1.655$$

$$t_3 = \frac{29.07 - 29.93}{1.206\sqrt{2/3}} = -0.873$$

$$t_4 = \frac{25.97 - 29.93}{1.206\sqrt{2/3}} = -4.02$$

A two-sided test is to be performed, as increases or decreases in performance can be declared significant. Assume that $\alpha = .05$. With $k = 4$ and $f = 8$, the critical value from Exhibit V.2–3 for $t_{.05}(4,8)$ is 2.94. Since $|t_4| = 4.02 > 2.94 = t_{.05}(4,8)$, modification C has resulted in sufficient changes in performance while the other two modifications have not.

Example C–2. Suppose that the experiment in Example C–1 was performed, but concern was centered only on those modifications that could be shown to improve performance. Assume that α is to be .01. Thus, the hypotheses to be tested are

$$H_0\colon \mu_1 = \mu_i$$
$$H_1\colon \mu_1 < \mu_i$$

The values of t_2, t_3, and t_4 are unchanged. The critical value for the one-sided test from Exhibit V.2–2 for $t_{.01}(4,8)$ is 3.51. As none of the computed t_i's is greater than 3.51, no modifications are found to have significantly changed performance.

Reference

Dunnet, C. W., "A Multiple Comparison Procedure for Comparing Several Treatments," *Journal of the American Statistical Association*, Vol. 50 (1955).

EXHIBIT V.2–1

ONE-SIDED CRITICAL VALUES FOR DUNNETT'S TEST ($\alpha = .05$)

	k, NUMBER OF TREATMENT MEANS (INCLUDING THE CONTROL)								
f	2	3	4	5	6	7	8	9	10
5	2.02	2.44	2.68	2.85	2.98	3.08	3.16	3.24	3.30
6	1.94	2.34	2.56	2.71	2.83	2.92	3.00	3.07	3.12
7	1.89	2.27	2.48	2.62	2.73	2.82	2.89	2.95	3.01
8	1.86	2.22	2.42	2.55	2.66	2.74	2.81	2.87	2.92
9	1.83	2.18	2.37	2.50	2.60	2.68	2.75	2.81	2.86
10	1.81	2.15	2.34	2.47	2.56	2.64	2.70	2.76	2.81
11	1.80	2.13	2.31	2.44	2.53	2.60	2.67	2.72	2.77
12	1.78	2.11	2.29	2.41	2.50	2.58	2.64	2.69	2.74
13	1.77	2.09	2.27	2.39	2.48	2.55	2.61	2.66	2.71
14	1.76	2.08	2.25	2.37	2.46	2.53	2.59	2.64	2.69
15	1.75	2.07	2.24	2.36	2.44	2.51	2.57	2.62	2.67
16	1.75	2.06	2.23	2.34	2.43	2.50	2.56	2.61	2.65
17	1.74	2.05	2.22	2.33	2.42	2.49	2.54	2.59	2.64
18	1.73	2.04	2.21	2.32	2.41	2.48	2.53	2.58	2.62
19	1.73	2.03	2.20	2.31	2.40	2.47	2.52	2.57	2.61
20	1.72	2.03	2.19	2.30	2.39	2.46	2.51	2.56	2.60
24	1.71	2.01	2.17	2.28	2.36	2.43	2.48	2.53	2.57
30	1.70	1.99	2.15	2.25	2.33	2.40	2.45	2.50	2.54
40	1.68	1.97	2.13	2.23	2.31	2.37	2.42	2.47	2.51
60	1.67	1.95	2.10	2.21	2.28	2.35	2.39	2.44	2.48
120	1.66	1.93	2.08	2.18	2.26	2.32	2.37	2.41	2.45
∞	1.64	1.92	2.06	2.16	2.23	2.29	2.34	2.38	2.42

Source: Dunnett, C. W., "A Multiple Comparison Procedure for Comparing Several Treatments," *Journal of the American Statistical Association*, Vol. 50 (1955), p. 1117. Reproduced with permission.

EXHIBIT V.2–2

ONE-SIDED CRITICAL VALUES FOR DUNNETT'S TEST ($\alpha = .01$)

	k, NUMBER OF TREATMENT MEANS (INCLUDING THE CONTROL)								
f	2	3	4	5	6	7	8	9	10
5	3.37	3.90	4.21	4.43	4.60	4.73	4.85	4.94	5.03
6	3.14	3.61	3.88	4.07	4.21	4.33	4.43	4.51	4.59
7	3.00	3.42	3.66	3.83	3.96	4.07	4.15	4.23	4.30
8	2.90	3.29	3.51	3.67	3.79	3.88	3.96	4.03	4.09
9	2.82	3.19	3.40	3.55	3.66	3.75	3.82	3.89	3.94
10	2.76	3.11	3.31	3.45	3.56	3.64	3.71	3.78	3.83
11	2.72	3.06	3.25	3.38	3.48	3.56	3.63	3.69	3.74
12	2.68	3.01	3.19	3.32	3.42	3.50	3.56	3.62	3.67
13	2.65	2.97	3.15	3.27	3.37	3.44	3.51	3.56	3.61
14	2.62	2.94	3.11	3.23	3.32	3.40	3.46	3.51	3.56
15	2.60	2.91	3.08	3.20	3.29	3.36	3.42	3.47	3.52
16	2.58	2.88	3.05	3.17	3.26	3.33	3.39	3.44	3.48
17	2.57	2.86	3.03	3.14	3.23	3.30	3.36	3.41	3.45
18	2.55	2.84	3.01	3.12	3.21	3.27	3.33	3.38	3.42
19	2.54	2.83	2.99	3.10	3.18	3.25	3.31	3.36	3.40
20	2.53	2.81	2.97	3.08	3.17	3.23	3.29	3.34	3.38
24	2.49	2.77	2.92	3.03	3.11	3.17	3.22	3.27	3.31
30	2.46	2.72	2.87	2.97	3.05	3.11	3.16	3.21	3.24
40	2.42	2.68	2.82	2.92	2.99	3.05	3.10	3.14	3.18
60	2.39	2.64	2.78	2.87	2.94	3.00	3.04	3.08	3.12
120	2.36	2.60	2.73	2.82	2.89	2.94	2.99	3.03	3.06
∞	2.33	2.56	2.68	2.77	2.84	2.89	2.93	2.97	3.00

Source: Dunnett, C. W., "A Multiple Comparison Procedure for Comparing Several Treatments," *Journal of the American Statistical Association*, Vol. 50 (1955), p. 1118. Reproduced with permission.

EXHIBIT V.2–3

TWO-SIDED CRITICAL VALUES FOR DUNNETT'S TEST ($\alpha = .05$)

	k, NUMBER OF TREATMENT MEANS (INCLUDING THE CONTROL)								
f	2	3	4	5	6	7	8	9	10
5	2.57	3.03	3.39	3.66	3.88	4.06	4.22	4.36	4.49
6	2.45	2.86	3.18	3.41	3.60	3.75	3.88	4.00	4.11
7	2.36	2.75	3.04	3.24	3.41	3.54	3.66	3.76	3.86
8	2.31	2.67	2.94	3.13	3.28	3.40	3.51	3.60	3.68
9	2.26	2.61	2.86	3.04	3.18	3.29	3.39	3.48	3.55
10	2.23	2.57	2.81	2.97	3.11	3.21	3.31	3.39	3.46
11	2.20	2.53	2.76	2.92	3.05	3.15	3.24	3.31	3.38
12	2.18	2.50	2.72	2.88	3.00	3.10	3.18	3.25	3.32
13	2.16	2.48	2.69	2.84	2.96	3.06	3.14	3.21	3.27
14	2.14	2.46	2.67	2.81	2.93	3.02	3.10	3.17	3.23
15	2.13	2.44	2.64	2.79	2.90	2.99	3.07	3.13	3.19
16	2.12	2.42	2.63	2.77	2.88	2.96	3.04	3.10	3.16
17	2.11	2.41	2.61	2.75	2.85	2.94	3.01	3.08	3.13
18	2.10	2.40	2.59	2.73	2.84	2.92	2.99	3.05	3.11
19	2.09	2.39	2.58	2.72	2.82	2.90	2.97	3.04	3.09
20	2.09	2.38	2.57	2.70	2.81	2.89	2.96	3.02	3.07
24	2.06	2.35	2.53	2.66	2.76	2.84	2.91	2.96	3.01
30	2.04	2.32	2.50	2.62	2.72	2.79	2.86	2.91	2.96
40	2.02	2.29	2.47	2.58	2.67	2.75	2.81	2.86	2.90
60	2.00	2.27	2.43	2.55	2.63	2.70	2.76	2.81	2.85
120	1.98	2.24	2.40	2.51	2.59	2.66	2.71	2.76	2.80
∞	1.96	2.21	2.37	2.47	2.55	2.62	2.67	2.71	2.75

Source: Dunnett, C. W., "A Multiple Comparison Procedure for Comparing Several Treatments," *Journal of the American Statistical Association*, Vol. 50 (1955), p. 1119. Reproduced with permission.

EXHIBIT V.2–4

TWO-SIDED CRITICAL VALUES FOR DUNNETT'S TEST ($\alpha = .01$)

	k, NUMBER OF TREATMENT MEANS (INCLUDING THE CONTROL)								
f	2	3	4	5	6	7	8	9	10
5	4.03	4.63	5.09	5.44	5.73	5.97	6.18	6.36	6.53
6	3.71	4.22	4.60	4.88	5.11	5.30	5.47	5.61	5.74
7	3.50	3.95	4.28	4.52	4.71	4.87	5.01	5.13	5.24
8	3.36	3.77	4.06	4.27	4.44	4.58	4.70	4.81	4.90
9	3.25	3.63	3.90	4.09	4.24	4.37	4.48	4.57	4.65
10	3.17	3.53	3.78	3.95	4.10	4.21	4.31	4.40	4.47
11	3.11	3.45	3.68	3.85	3.98	4.09	4.18	4.26	4.33
12	3.05	3.39	3.61	3.76	3.89	3.99	4.08	4.15	4.22
13	3.01	3.33	3.54	3.69	3.81	3.91	3.99	4.06	4.13
14	2.98	3.29	3.49	3.64	3.75	3.84	3.92	3.99	4.05
15	2.95	3.25	3.45	3.59	3.70	3.79	3.86	3.93	3.99
16	2.92	3.22	3.41	3.55	3.65	3.74	3.82	3.88	3.93
17	2.90	3.19	3.38	3.51	3.62	3.70	3.77	3.83	3.89
18	2.88	3.17	3.35	3.48	3.58	3.67	3.74	3.80	3.85
19	2.86	3.15	3.33	3.46	3.55	3.64	3.70	3.76	3.81
20	2.85	3.13	3.31	3.43	3.53	3.61	3.67	3.73	3.78
24	2.80	3.07	3.24	3.36	3.45	3.52	3.58	3.64	3.69
30	2.75	3.01	3.17	3.28	3.37	3.44	3.50	3.55	3.59
40	2.70	2.95	3.10	3.21	3.29	3.36	3.41	3.46	3.50
60	2.66	2.90	3.04	3.14	3.22	3.28	3.33	3.38	3.42
120	2.62	2.84	2.98	3.08	3.15	3.21	3.25	3.30	3.33
∞	2.58	2.79	2.92	3.01	3.08	3.14	3.18	3.22	3.25

Source: Dunnett, C. W., "A Multiple Comparison Procedure for Comparing Several Treatments," *Journal of the American Statistical Association*, Vol. 50 (1955), p. 1120. Reproduced with permission.

VI Quality Control

Guide to Section VI

The quality control section includes nine subsections. What is commonly known as quality control can be divided into acceptance sampling and control charting, as shown in Exhibit VI.1. That the primary term is "quality control" is somewhat misleading, since much of what is found in textbooks (and in this Handbook) concerns acceptance sampling, which is after the fact. By "after the fact" is meant that control occurs at inspection downstream, not during production.

Acceptance sampling can be subdivided into attributes sampling and variables sampling. Five of the nine subsections in the quality control section are devoted to attributes sampling. However, prior to explaining the numerous types of attributes sampling procedures, the difference between attributes and variables sampling must be addressed.

In attributes sampling, a unit is classified as defective or nondefective on the basis of whether it meets established specifications. Each time a unit is inspected, it is placed in one of two categories. The unit either passes or fails the inspection, it's either go or no-go, it's either on or off, etc.

In variables sampling, only one characteristic is observed. The characteristic is generally a measurement along a continuum, such as the length or weight of the object. The variables sampling procedures described in this section pertain to a characteristic that is normally distributed. Variables sampling plans have an advantage over attributes sampling plans in that the sample size is (usually considerably) reduced.

There are five topics under attributes sampling in Exhibit VI.1. The first three of these, single, double, and multiple sampling, are closely related. The average number of samples for a double-sampling plan is smaller for the same desired consumer and producer risks than the average number sampled for a single-sampling plan. (In double sampling, there is an opportunity to make a decision by the end of the first sample.) If two decision points are better than one, then additional decision points, as used in multiple sampling, must have even lower average sample sizes for the same desired parameters. (This statement is true.) However, the reduction in the average number sampled is generally slight if more (than two or three) samples are taken. Also, administration of the plan becomes a problem as more samples are taken in an attempt to make a decision. Thus, single and double sampling continue to be quite popular with the practitioner.

Lastly, if production is continuous, such as on an assembly line, it may be feasible to form a lot or a batch of the product into one location for inspection. It may be possible to arbitrarily mark a lot for inspection, but the consequence could be the rejection of the product before it is even made.

This situation gives rise to continuous sampling which, in its simplest form, requires 100-percent inspection until a given point is reached without a defective, followed by a prescribed fractional random sampling, until a defective is found. At that point, 100-percent inspection begins anew.

Now that the subject of quality control has been briefly described, it will be noted in Exhibit VI.1 that there are often optional methods for accomplishing the same result. Whenever an option is shown, one of the alternatives is the abbreviation MIL-STD (for Military Standard), or ANSI (for American National Standards Institute), followed by some numbers, and perhaps a letter. The Standards are the products of a select group of quality control professionals. Through the combination of statistical expertise and practical experience, along with give and take by all parties, the plans evolved.

As a general rule, if a firm has agreed to produce under a Standard or if a buyer has agreed to receive goods under a Standard, then the plan must come from that source. For multiple sampling and continuous sampling we recommend the Standard in every instance. This Handbook does not include the entire Standard in any case, just the instructions on how to use the document, with examples. In no case should the brief description in the Handbook be used without reading the text of the Standard, even if the plan sought is obtainable from the example tables appearing herein.

In several instances, nomographs or tables are given for describing sampling plans. These nomographs or tables are convenient to use and save a great deal of time. The alternative in every instance is to revert to a discussion of the methodology such as found in Duncan [1974], and derive the plan directly. For example, in sequential sampling, there are three equations that must be solved to obtain the limit lines.

The last area of coverage in the area of quality control is control charting. Factors for variables control charts are given in summary form. Attribute control charts are not described since the tabled constants are of little value in their construction. The reader is referred to Duncan [1974] if these types of control charts are to be constructed.

The final section in the topic of quality control concerns cumulative (cusum) control charts. Cusum charts are used in maintaining current control of a process. They can be as effective as the previously described control charts, but at a lesser expense.

Reference

Duncan, Acheson J., *Quality Control and Industrial Statistics*, Irwin, Homewood, Illinois, 1974.

EXHIBIT VI–1

GUIDE TO QUALITY CONTROL SECTIONS

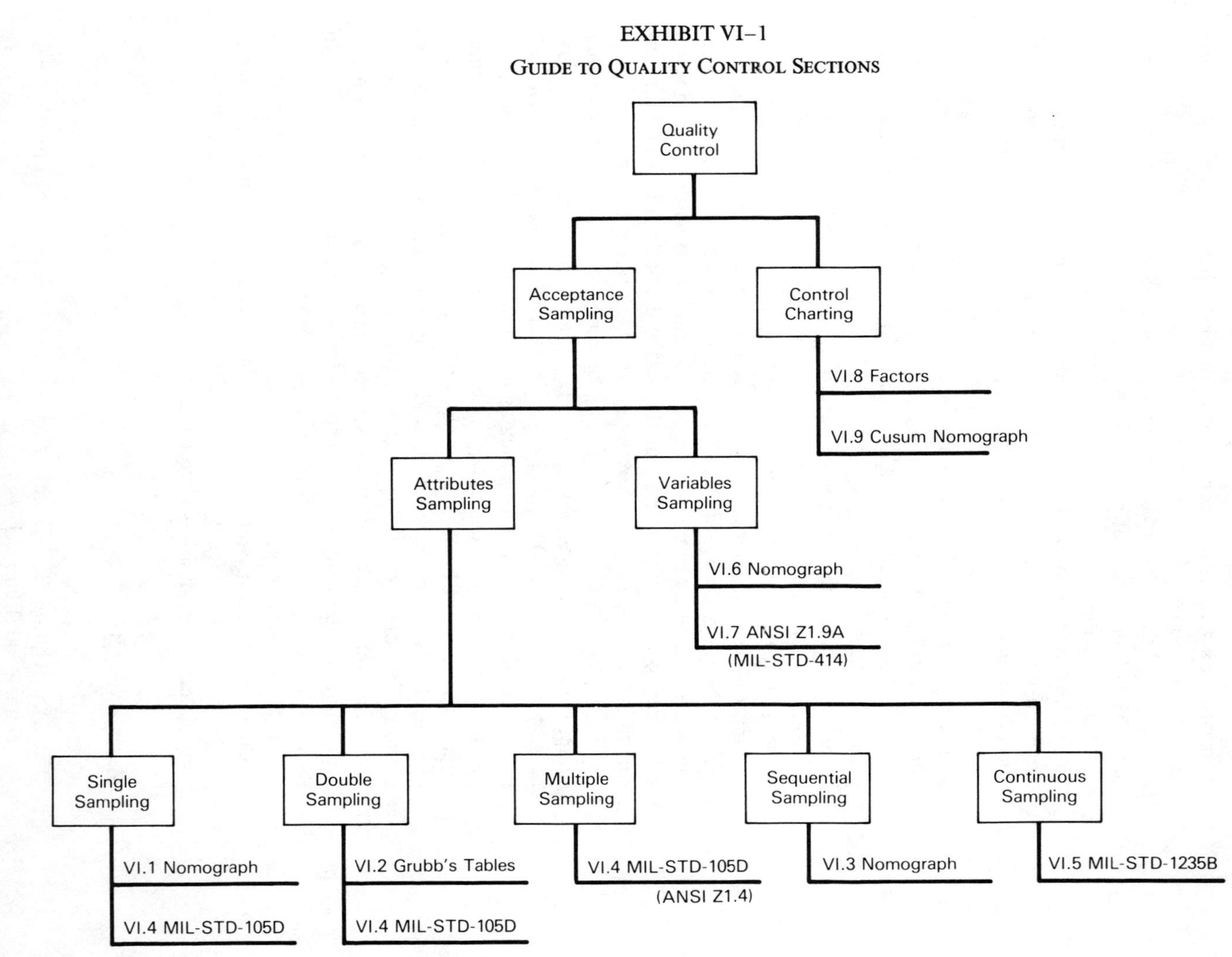

VI.1 Deriving Attribute Sampling Plans

A. Description*

Consider designing a sampling plan whose operating characteristic (OC) curve passes through two designated points. As an example, a purchaser may desire a single-sample attribute plan such that the probability of acceptance is $1-\alpha$ for material of p_1 quality and is β for material of p_2 quality. Such plans can be obtained using the nomogram shown as Exhibit VI.1–1 [Larson, 1965]. The plans obtained from using Exhibit VI.1–1 pertain to acceptance or rejection of lots from a randomly operating process whose output has average quality p. In addition, the plan may apply to the acceptance or rejection of a large isolated lot whose quality is p.

B. Reading the Nomogram

The general procedure is to form two lines, one connecting p_1 and $1-\alpha$, the other connecting p_2 and β. Their intersection gives the region of the desired plan. The plan is described by n, the sample size, and c, the acceptance number.

Note that c must be an integer value, but it is quite likely that the intersection of the two lines will not fall on an integer value of c. Two possibilities exist. Either α will be held constant and β will be adjusted, or β will be held constant and α adjusted. While the sample size must also be an integer, it is not feasible to select plans based on adjacent values of n. Rather, plans are selected between alternative values of c, and whatever n arises formulates the plan.

If α is to be held constant, the line connecting p_1 and $1-\alpha$ is followed either to the c-line just above the intersection point or to the c-line just below the intersection point, with the alternative n values being read from the nomograph. A similar maneuver is used to obtain the alternative c and n values when β is to remain fixed.

Thus, four alternative plans could be raised:

A. α held fixed, β decreased

B. α held fixed, β increased

C. α decreased, β held fixed

D. α increased, β held fixed

---

*Refer to the guide at the beginning of Section VI to determine the appropriate uses of the individual quality control procedures.

EXHIBIT VI.1-1

Nomograph for Deriving Attribute Sampling Plans

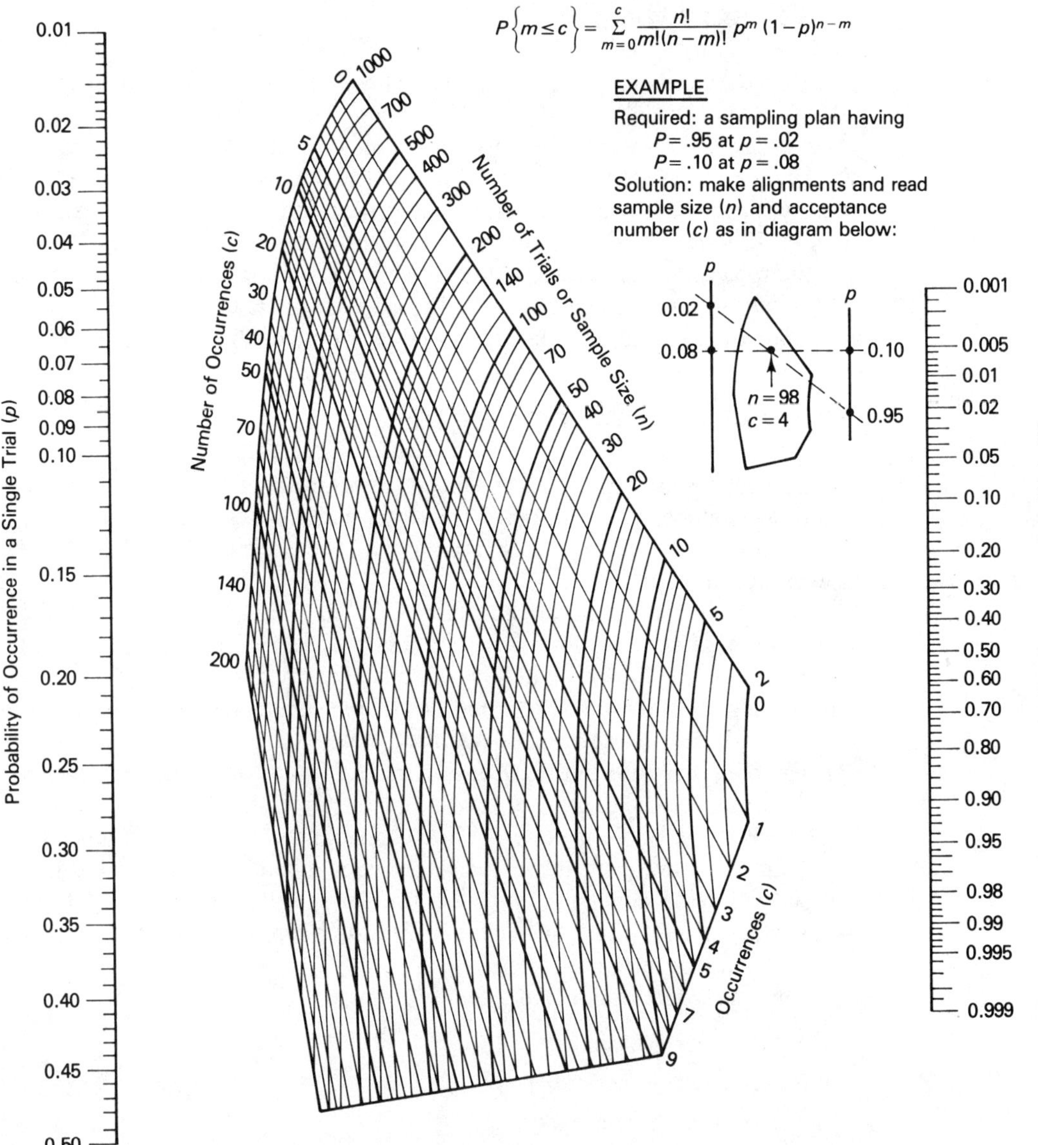

Note—If p is less than 0.01, set kp on the p-scale and n/k on the n-scale, where k = 0.01/p, rounded upward conveniently.

Source: Larson, Harry R., "A Nomograph of the Cumulative Binomial Distribution." Illustration reproduced with permission of *The Western Electric Engineer*,

Plan A treats the producer's risk, α, as desired, but gives extra protection to the consumer. Plan B again treats the producer's risk as desired, but decreases the protection of the consumer, i.e., increasing the consumer's risk, β. Plan C gives the consumer the desired protection, but reduces the requirements of the producer. Plan D also gives the consumer the desired protection, while also increasing the demands on the producer. To resolve the issue of which plan to choose requires policy input from management. Alternatively, a plan that comes close to the desired α, β, p_1 and p_2 requirements may be chosen.

C. Using the Nomogram

Example C–1. Finding *n* and *c*. Find a single-sample fraction-defective sampling plan that will come close to having $p_1 = .04$, $p_2 = .20$, $\alpha = .01$, and $\beta = .10$. From the nomograph, $n = 43$ and $c = 5$ comes close to satisfying the requirements.

Example C–2. Finding β. A plan consists of $n = 87$ and $c = 5$. If the product fraction defective (p) is .10, what is the resulting value of β? Project a line from $p = .10$ through the intersection of $n = 87$ and $c = 5$ to the scale on the right-hand side of the nomograph to read the value of $\beta = .11$. This procedure can be repeated for various values of p to construct an OC curve for the sampling plan.

Reference

Larson, Harry R., "A Nomograph of the Cumulative Binomial Distribution," *Western Electric Engineer*, 1965, p. 21.

VI.2 Deriving a Double-Sampling Plan

A. Description*

If a consumer wants a double-sampling plan such that the probability of acceptance is $1 - \alpha$ for material of p_1 quality and β for material of p_2 quality, "Grubb's Tables" may be used. Exhibits VI.2–1 and VI.2–2 are Grubb's Tables for $\alpha = .05$ and $\beta = .10$, two common values. It is useful to

*Refer to the guide at the beginning of Section VI to determine the appropriate uses of the individual quality control procedures.

have a fixed relationship between the first and second samples, whose sizes are given by n_1 and n_2. Exhibit VI.2–1 has the relationship $n_1 = n_2$, and Exhibit VI.2–2 has the relationship $n_2 = 2n_1$.

B. Reading the Tables

The tables are indexed on the ratio R, where

$$R = p_2/p_1$$

After computing R, the plan number coming closest to the result is selected.

Once the plan has been selected, the acceptance numbers for the first and combined samples, c_1 and c_2, are read. The value of n_1 is determined from the two columns headed pn_1. The two possibilities shown are associated with holding α constant, resulting in the probability of acceptance P, equal to .95, or holding β constant, resulting in the probability of acceptance P, equal to .10.

C. Using the Tables

C–1. Finding n_1 and n_2, c_1 and c_2 Holding α Constant.

When $\alpha = .05$ and $\beta = .10$, find the sampling plan for $p_1 = .02$ and $p_2 = .08$, where $n_2 = 2n_1$ and α is held constant. Compute

$$R = p_2/p_1 = .08/.02 = 4.0$$

A ratio of $R = 4.0$ leads to Plan 7 in Exhibit VI.2–2. This plan has an acceptance number of $c_1 = 1$ on the first sample and $c_2 = 5$ on the combined samples.

A pn_1 of .96 is obtained from the tables when holding α constant at .05. The sample size n_1 is then found from

$$n_1 = pn_1/p_1 = .96/.02 = 48$$

Then $n_2 = 2n_1 = 96$. In summary, the double-sampling plan is given by $n_1 = 48$, $n_2 = 96$, $c_1 = 1$, and $c_2 = 5$. Thus, we would take an initial sample size of 48, and if there were zero or one defectives in the sample, we would accept the lot. If there were two, three, four, or five defectives, a second sample of size 96 would be taken. If the combined defectives on these two samples exceeds five, we would reject the lot. Otherwise, we would accept the lot.

C–2. Finding n_1 and n_2, c_1 and c_2 Holding β Constant.

Consider the same problem as in Example C–1 above, except let β be held constant at .10. The appropriate value of pn_1 for Plan 7 in Exhibit VI.2–2 is 4.02. The sample size n_1 is then found from

$$n_1 = pn_1/p_2 = 4.02/.08 = 50.25$$

Rounding to the next higher integer gives $n_1 = 51$. Then $n_2 = 2n_1 = 102$. In summary, the double-sampling plan is given by $n_1 = 51$, $n_2 = 102$, $c_1 = 1$, and $c_2 = 5$.

EXHIBIT VI.2–1

GRUBB'S TABLES FOR $n_1 = n_2$

($\alpha = .05$, $\beta = .10$)

Plan Number	$R = p_2/p_1$	Acceptance Numbers		Approximate Values of pn_1 for	
		c_1	c_2	$P = .95$	$P = .10$
1	11.90	0	1	0.21	2.50
2	7.54	1	2	0.52	3.92
3	6.79	0	2	0.43	2.96
4	5.39	1	3	0.76	4.11
5	4.65	2	4	1.16	5.39
6	4.25	1	4	1.04	4.42
7	3.88	2	5	1.43	5.55
8	3.63	3	6	1.87	6.78
9	3.38	2	6	1.72	5.82
10	3.21	3	7	2.15	6.91
11	3.09	4	8	2.62	8.10
12	2.85	4	9	2.90	8.26
13	2.60	5	11	3.68	9.56
14	2.44	5	12	4.00	9.77
15	2.32	5	13	4.35	10.08
16	2.22	5	14	4.70	10.45
17	2.12	5	16	5.39	11.41

Source: Format adopted with permission from Duncan, A. J., *Quality Control and Industrial Statistics*, 4th Ed., Irwin, Homewood, Illinois, 1974. Values adopted from Chemical Corps Engineering Agency, Manual No. 2, *Master Sampling Plans for Single, Duplicate, Double and Multiple Sampling*, Army Chemical Center, Edgewood Arsenal, Maryland, 1953.

EXHIBIT VI.2–2

GRUBB'S TABLES FOR $n_2 = 2n_1$
($\alpha = .05$, $\beta = .10$)

Plan Number	$R = p_2/p_1$	Acceptance Numbers		Approximate Values of pn_1 for	
		c_1	c_2	$P = .95$	$P = .10$
1	14.50	0	1	0.16	2.32
2	8.07	0	2	0.30	2.42
3	6.48	1	3	0.60	3.89
4	5.39	0	3	0.49	2.64
5	5.09	1	4	0.77	3.92
6	4.31	0	4	0.68	2.93
7	4.19	1	5	0.96	4.02
8	3.60	1	6	1.16	4.17
9	3.26	2	8	1.68	5.47
10	2.96	3	10	2.27	6.72
11	2.77	3	11	2.46	6.82
12	2.62	4	13	3.07	8.05
13	2.46	4	14	3.29	8.11
14	2.21	3	15	3.41	7.55
15	1.97	4	20	4.75	9.35
16	1.74	6	30	7.45	12.96

Source: Format adopted with permission from Duncan, A. J., *Quality Control and Industrial Statistics*, 4th Ed., Irwin, Homewood, Illinois, 1974. Values are taken, in part, from Chemical Corps Engineering Agency, Manual No. 2, *Master Sampling Plans for Single, Duplicate, Double and Multiple Sampling*, Army Chemical Center, Edgewood Arsenal, Maryland, 1953 and adapted, in part, from Hamaker, H. C., "The Theory of Sampling Inspection Plans," *Philips Technical Review*, Vol. XI, (1950) p. 266.

VI.3 Sequential Attribute Sampling Plans

A. Description*

Sequential attribute sampling plans allow the number of samples to be determined entirely by the sampling process [Wald, 1947]. The procedure requires the setting of two "limit lines." If the cumulative sample results go above or below the limits, a decision to accept or reject a lot or batch is made. (Good quality leads to acceptance at the lower limit line, and poor quality leads to rejection at the upper limit line.) Otherwise, sampling is continued unless a truncation sample size, if stated, has been reached.

*Refer to the guide at the beginning of Section VI to determine the appropriate uses of the individual quality control procedures.

The equations for the limit lines for specified p_1, p_2, α, and β are given by

$$Y_1 = h_1 + sn$$

and

$$Y_2 = h_2 + sn$$

where Y_1 is the lower limit line, Y_2 is the upper limit line, h_1 and h_2 are the intercepts, s is the slope of the (parallel) limit lines, and n is the sequential unit drawn from the sample. (The probability of acceptance is α for material of p_1 quality and β for material of p_2 quality.)

The intercepts and slopes are obtained from the equations

$$h_1 = \frac{\ln[(1-\alpha)/\beta]}{k}$$

and

$$h_2 = \frac{\ln[(1-\beta)/\alpha]}{k}$$

where k is given by

$$k = \ln \frac{p_2(1-p_1)}{p_1(1-p_2)}$$

Finally, the slope is given by

$$s = \frac{\ln\left[\dfrac{1-p_1}{1-p_2}\right]}{k}$$

To facilitate the computation of h_1, h_2, and s, a nomogram has been prepared [Kroeber, 1980]. The nomogram is shown in Exhibit VI.3–1.

B. Using the Nomogram

To illustrate the use of the nomogram shown as Exhibit VI.3–1, consider a quality control problem that has $p_1 = .02$, $p_2 = .08$, $\alpha = .05$, and $\beta = .10$. The negative of the intercept of the acceptance line, h_1, can be determined from the nomogram by entering the left scale with the argument $(1-\alpha)/\beta = (1-.05)/.10 = 9.5$, and the center vertical scale with the argu-

EXHIBIT VI.3–1

Nomograph for Deriving Sequential Sampling Plans

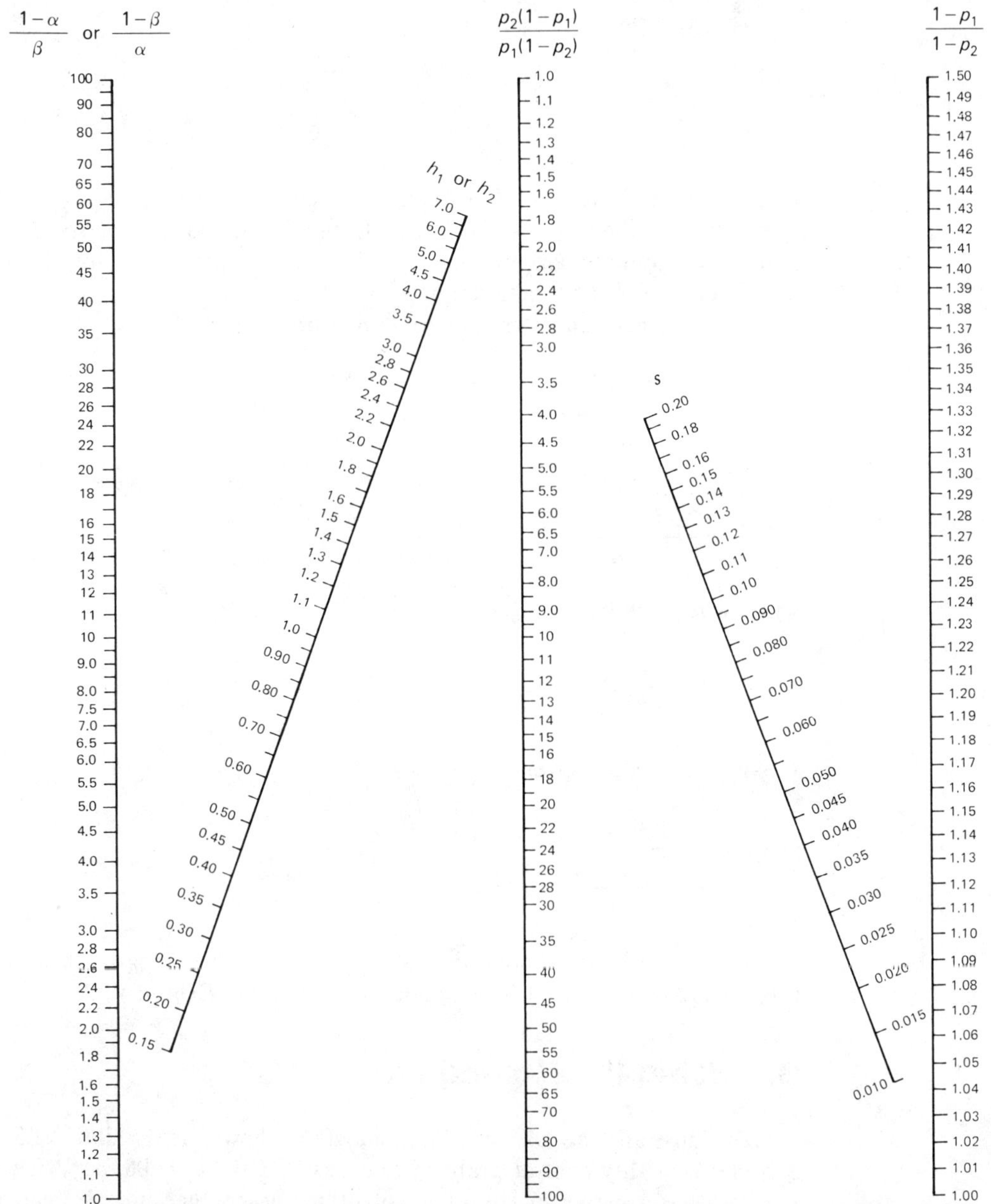

Source: Kroeber, D. W., "A Graphical Approach to the Design of Sequential Sampling Plans," *Journal of Quality Technology*, vol. 12, no. 1, p. 37, © 1980, American Society for Quality Control. Reprinted by permission.

ment $[p_2(1-p_1)]/[p_1(1-p_2)] = [(.08)(.98)]/[(.02)(.92)] = 4.26$. Connecting these two points gives an h_1 value of 1.55 on the scale labeled h_1 or h_2.

The value of h_2, the intercept for the rejection line, can be found by using the same scales, but the argument on the left scale is now $(1-\beta)/\alpha = (1-.10)/.05 = 18$. The argument for the center scale is still 4.26. Connecting these two points gives an h_2 value of 2.0.

The slope of the parallel lines uses the center vertical scale with the same argument as before, i.e., 4.26, and the right scale with the argument $(1-p_1)/(1-p_2) = (1-.02)/(1-.08) = 1.065$. Connecting these two points yields an $s = 0.044$.

Thus, the lower and upper limit lines are given by

$$Y_1 = -1.55 + 0.044n$$

and

$$Y_2 = 2.0 + 0.044n$$

References

Kroeber, Donald W., "A Graphical Approach to the Design of Sequential Attribute Sampling Plans," *Journal of Quality Technology*, Vol. 12, No. 1 (1980), pp. 36–39.

Wald, Abraham, *Sequential Analysis*, John-Wiley, New York, 1947, pp. 104–5.

MIL-STD-105D (ANSI Z1.4)

A. Description*

Standard plans for attribute sampling are provided by MIL-STD-105D. These internationally developed plans include schemes for single, double, and multiple sampling. Sampling plans for normal, tightened, and reduced

*Refer to the guide at the beginning of Section VI to determine the appropriate uses of the individual quality control procedures.

inspection are included. The key to the appropriate sampling plan is the table of sample size code letters shown in Exhibit VI.4–1. Also provided herein is the master table for normal inspection under single sampling shown in Exhibit VI.4–2.

Additional tables and the full text of the standard are available from other sources. Our intent here is to show the reader how the tables are used. It is highly advisable that the reader study the complete text, even if the desired plan is obtainable from Exhibit VI.4–2.

The text of MIL-STD-105D describes when switching from one to another level of inspection occurs. Normal inspection is initially used and continues on successive lots or batches. Briefly stated, switching occurs in the following instances:

1. *Normal to Tightened.* When normal inspection is in effect, tightened inspection is instituted when 2 out of 5 consecutive lots or batches have been rejected on original inspection.
2. *Tightened to Normal.* When tightened inspection is in effect, normal inspection is instituted when 5 consecutive lots or batches are accepted on original inspection.
3. *Normal to Reduced.* When normal inspection is in effect, reduced inspection is instituted when all of the following conditions are met:
    a. The preceding 10 lots or batches have been accepted.
    b. The total number of defectives (or defects) in the samples from the preceding 10 lots or batches is less than the "limit number" (given in Table VIII of the full text of MIL-STD-105D).
    c. The production is at a steady rate.
    d. Reduced inspection is considered desirable by the responsible authorities.
4. *Reduced to Normal.* When reduced inspection is in effect, normal inspection is instituted if any of the following occur on original inspection.
    a. A lot or batch is rejected.
    b. Production becomes irregular or delayed.
    c. Other conditions warrant that normal inspection be instituted.

The civilian version of MIL-STD-105D is ANSI Z1.4 updated as of 1980. The tables in ANSI Z1.4 are completely compatible with those in MIL-STD-105D. The major differences in ANSI Z1.4 include

1. Substitution of the word "nonconformity" for "defect" throughout.
2. Inclusion of an optional procedure, without limit numbers, for switching from normal to reduced inspection.
3. Introduction of new tables and operating characteristic curves for quality control "schemes" rather than quality control "plans."

B. Using the Tables

The first table used contains sample size code letters. The table, shown as Exhibit VI.4–1, is indexed on lot or batch sizes and then on the inspection level. There are four special inspection levels and three general inspection levels. Unless stated otherwise, general inspection level II is used. Thus, the code letter for a lot of 2000 would be K.

Exhibit VI.4–2 applies to normal inspection, single sampling. This table is indexed by the sample size code letter and the AQL. For fraction-defective plans, the AQL values are in percents from .010 through 10 percent. For defects-per-unit plans there are an additional 10 AQL's through 1000 defects per 100 units.

Example B–1. For code letter K and an AQL = 4 percent, the plan is given by $n = 125$ and $c = 10$. (A sample of 125 is taken and the lot is accepted if 10 or fewer defectives are found.) The value of n is obtained from the column of sample sizes. The value of c is the acceptance number denoted "Ac" for the appropriate AQL.

EXHIBIT VI.4–1

SAMPLE SIZE CODE LETTERS

Lot or batch size	Special Inspection Levels				General Inspection Levels		
	S-1	S-2	S-3	S-4	I	II	III
2 to 8	A	A	A	A	A	A	B
9 to 15	A	A	A	A	A	B	C
16 to 25	A	A	B	B	B	C	D
26 to 50	A	B	B	C	C	D	E
51 to 90	B	B	C	C	C	E	F
91 to 150	B	B	C	D	D	F	G
151 to 280	B	C	D	E	E	G	H
281 to 500	B	C	D	E	F	H	J
501 to 1200	C	C	E	F	G	J	K
1201 to 3200	C	D	E	G	H	K	L
3201 to 10,000	C	D	F	G	J	L	M
10,001 to 35,000	C	D	F	H	K	M	N
35,001 to 150,000	D	E	G	J	L	N	P
150,001 to 500,000	D	E	G	J	M	P	Q
500,001 and over	D	E	H	K	N	Q	R

EXHIBIT VI.4–2

Single Sampling Plans for Normal Inspection

Sample size code letter	Sample size	Acceptable Quality Levels (normal inspection): 0.010	0.015	0.025	0.040	0.065	0.10	0.15	0.25	0.40	0.65	1.0	1.5	2.5	4.0	6.5	10	15	25	40	65	100	150	250	400	650	1000
		Ac Re	Ac Re	Ac Re	Ac Re	Ac Re	Ac Re	Ac Re	Ac Re	Ac Re	Ac Re	Ac Re	Ac Re	Ac Re	Ac Re	Ac Re	Ac Re	Ac Re	Ac Re	Ac Re	Ac Re	Ac Re	Ac Re	Ac Re	Ac Re	Ac Re	Ac Re
A	2	↓	↓	↓	↓	↓	↓	↓	↓	↓	↓	↓	↓	↓	↓	0 1	↓	↓	1 2	2 3	3 4	5 6	7 8	10 11	14 15	21 22	30 31
B	3	↓	↓	↓	↓	↓	↓	↓	↓	↓	↓	↓	↓	↓	0 1	↑	↓	1 2	2 3	3 4	5 6	7 8	10 11	14 15	21 22	30 31	44 45
C	5	↓	↓	↓	↓	↓	↓	↓	↓	↓	↓	↓	↓	0 1	↑	↓	1 2	2 3	3 4	5 6	7 8	10 11	14 15	21 22	30 31	44 45	↑
D	8	↓	↓	↓	↓	↓	↓	↓	↓	↓	↓	↓	0 1	↑	↓	1 2	2 3	3 4	5 6	7 8	10 11	14 15	21 22	30 31	44 45	↑	↑
E	13	↓	↓	↓	↓	↓	↓	↓	↓	↓	↓	0 1	↑	↓	1 2	2 3	3 4	5 6	7 8	10 11	14 15	21 22	30 31	44 45	↑	↑	↑
F	20	↓	↓	↓	↓	↓	↓	↓	↓	↓	0 1	↑	↓	1 2	2 3	3 4	5 6	7 8	10 11	14 15	21 22	↑	↑	↑	↑	↑	↑
G	32	↓	↓	↓	↓	↓	↓	↓	↓	0 1	↑	↓	1 2	2 3	3 4	5 6	7 8	10 11	14 15	21 22	↑	↑	↑	↑	↑	↑	↑
H	50	↓	↓	↓	↓	↓	↓	↓	0 1	↑	↓	1 2	2 3	3 4	5 6	7 8	10 11	14 15	21 22	↑	↑	↑	↑	↑	↑	↑	↑
J	80	↓	↓	↓	↓	↓	↓	0 1	↑	↓	1 2	2 3	3 4	5 6	7 8	10 11	14 15	21 22	↑	↑	↑	↑	↑	↑	↑	↑	↑
K	125	↓	↓	↓	↓	↓	0 1	↑	↓	1 2	2 3	3 4	5 6	7 8	10 11	14 15	21 22	↑	↑	↑	↑	↑	↑	↑	↑	↑	↑
L	200	↓	↓	↓	↓	0 1	↑	↓	1 2	2 3	3 4	5 6	7 8	10 11	14 15	21 22	↑	↑	↑	↑	↑	↑	↑	↑	↑	↑	↑
M	315	↓	↓	↓	0 1	↑	↓	1 2	2 3	3 4	5 6	7 8	10 11	14 15	21 22	↑	↑	↑	↑	↑	↑	↑	↑	↑	↑	↑	↑
N	500	↓	↓	0 1	↑	↓	1 2	2 3	3 4	5 6	7 8	10 11	14 15	21 22	↑	↑	↑	↑	↑	↑	↑	↑	↑	↑	↑	↑	↑
P	800	↓	0 1	↑	↓	1 2	2 3	3 4	5 6	7 8	10 11	14 15	21 22	↑	↑	↑	↑	↑	↑	↑	↑	↑	↑	↑	↑	↑	↑
Q	1250	0 1	↑	↓	1 2	2 3	3 4	5 6	7 8	10 11	14 15	21 22	↑	↑	↑	↑	↑	↑	↑	↑	↑	↑	↑	↑	↑	↑	↑
R	2000	↑	↑	1 2	2 3	3 4	5 6	7 8	10 11	14 15	21 22	↑	↑	↑	↑	↑	↑	↑	↑	↑	↑	↑	↑	↑	↑	↑	↑

↓ = Use first sampling plan below arrow. If sample size equals, or exceeds, lot or batch size, do 100 percent inspection.

↑ = Use first sampling plan above arrow.

Ac = Acceptance number.

Re = Rejection number.

VI.5 MIL-STD-1235B

A. Description*

MIL-STD-1235B provides for five different types of continuous sampling plans (CSP) for inspection by attributes. Tables for each of the five plans are presented in the MIL-STD. However, only three of the tables are briefly discussed here: CSP-1, CSP-2, and CSP-T. The reader is advised to study the full text of MIL-STD-1235B when applying these continuous sampling plans.

A–1. CSP-1

This single-level continuous sampling procedure requires alternating between sequences of 100-percent inspection and sampling inspection, with no limit on the number of such sequences. The procedure is diagrammed in Exhibit VI.5–1. Two values are obtained from Exhibit VI.5–2: i, the clearance number, and f, the sampling fraction. These two values define a sampling plan.

A–2. CSP-2

This continuous sampling plan is a modification of CSP-1 in that 100-percent inspection resumes only after a prescribed number of defect-free units separate any two defective sample units. The procedure is diagrammed in Exhibit VI.5–3. Exhibit VI.5–4 provides i, the clearance number, and f, the sampling fraction, to define a plan just as in CSP-1.

A–3. CSP-T

This is a multilevel continuous sampling procedure that provides for reducing the sampling frequency upon demonstration of superior product quality. The procedure is diagrammed in Exhibit VI.5–5. Exhibit VI.5–6 provides i and f to define a plan as in CSP-1 and CSP-2.

B. Reading the Tables

MIL-STD-1235B tables are indexed on sampling frequency code letters and average outgoing quality level (AOQL) values in percentage notation.

*Refer to the guide at the beginning of Section VI to determine the appropriate uses of the individual quality control procedures.

The permissible code letters for varying production intervals are as follows:

Number of Units in Production Interval	Permissible Code Letters
2–8	A–B
9–25	A–C
26–90	A–D
91–500	A–E
501–1200	A–F
1201–3200	A–G
3201–10,000	A–H
10,001–35,000	A–I
35,001–150,000	A–J
> 150,000	A–K

The code letters relate directly to the sampling fraction. For example, the code letter F is associated with a sampling fraction of 1/10th, i.e., 1/10th of the items are randomly selected and sampled. For the larger production intervals (number of units in production at an instant of time), there are several permissible code letters, viz., sampling fractions. The selection of a code letter is based on the amount of fractional inspection deemed desirable and economical.

The second index, the AOQL in percent, raises a controversial issue with respect to MIL-STD-1235B. The index across the top of each plan is acceptable quality level (AQL) in percent, with a footnote. However, leaders in the field of quality control objected strongly to such an index during the development of MIL-STD-1235B. Hence, the footnote that AQL's "have no...meaning relative to the plans."

The intersection of the code letter and the AOQL in percent is a value of i. The value of i is the clearance number. Now, f and i define a plan.

C. Using the Tables

Example C–1. CSP-1. CSP-1 is to be used for an AOQL of 0.79 percent. There are 2500 units in the production interval, so the permissible code letters are A through G. The sampling fraction $f = 1/5$ associated with code letter D is selected. From Exhibit VI.5–2, the clearance number i is 91.

Example C–2. CSP-2. CSP-2 is being used for a continuous manufacturing process which has 200 items in the production interval. The AOQL is 1.90 percent. Code letter C is selected from those permissible. Under 100-percent initial inspection, the 31st unit was defective. The next defective unit was the 63rd. What action should be taken? From Exhibit VI.5–4, the clearance number is $i = 45$. In order to begin sampling at fraction $f = 1/4$, 45 units would have to be cleared. Thus, continue inspecting 100 percent of the items.

Example C–3. CSP-2. Reconsider Example C–2. If there are no further defectives up to the 108th sample unit, the proper action would then be to sample 1/4th of the units selected in a random manner. If the 23rd consecutive sampling unit, beginning at the point where the fractional sampling commenced, is defective, the proper action is to continue sampling. However, if there is another defective before 45 further consecutively sampled units have passed, the correct action is to revert to 100-percent inspection.

Example C–4. CSP-T. CSP-T is being used with $f = 1/10$th for an AOQL of 2.90 percent. No defectives have been found during 100-percent inspection of the initial 41 units. From Exhibit VI.5–6, the clearance number is $i = 41$. Thus, the proper action is to sample 1/10th of the units selected in a random manner.

Example C–5. CSP-T. Reconsider Example C–4. If an additional 41 units are cleared, the sampling fraction can be reduced to 1/20th. If a defective is found at any time during fractional sampling, 100-percent inspection is reinstituted.

EXHIBIT VI.5–1

PROCEDURE FOR CSP-1 PLANS

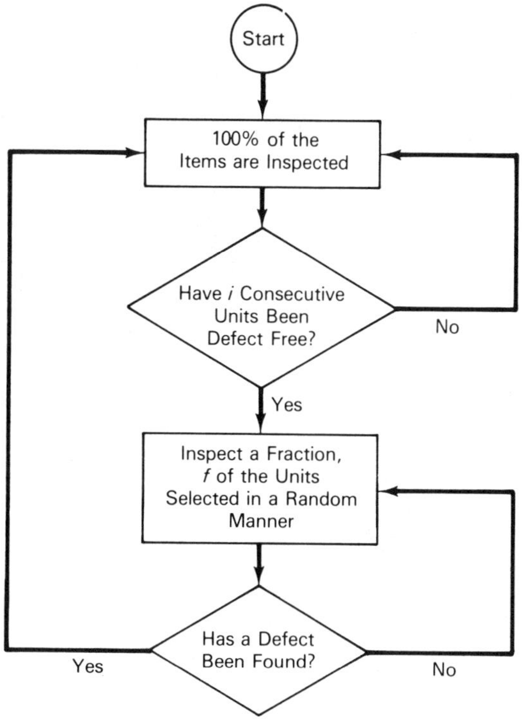

EXHIBIT VI.5–2

VALUES OF i FOR CSP-1 PLANS

Sample Frequency Code Letter	f	AQL* in %															
		.010	.015	.025	.040	.065	0.10	0.15	0.25	0.40	0.65	1.0	1.5	2.5	4.0	6.5	10.0
A	1/2	1540	840	600	375	245	194	140	84	53	36	23	15	10	6	5	3
B	1/3	2550	1390	1000	620	405	321	232	140	87	59	38	25	16	10	7	5
C	1/4	3340	1820	1310	810	530	420	303	182	113	76	49	32	21	13	9	6
D	1/5	3960	2160	1550	965	630	498	360	217	135	91	58	38	25	15	11	7
E	1/7	4950	2700	1940	1205	790	623	450	270	168	113	73	47	31	18	13	8
F	1/10	6050	3300	2370	1470	965	762	550	335	207	138	89	57	38	22	16	10
G	1/15	7390	4030	2890	1800	1180	930	672	410	255	170	108	70	46	27	19	12
H	1/25	9110	4970	3570	2215	1450	1147	828	500	315	210	134	86	57	33	23	14
I	1/50	11,730	6400	4590	2855	1870	1477	1067	640	400	270	175	110	72	42	29	18
J	1/100	14,320	7810	5600	3485	2305	1820	1302	790	500	330	215	135	89	52	36	22
K	1/200	17,420	9500	6810	4235	2760	2178	1583	950	590	400	255	165	106	62	43	26
		.018	.033	.046	.074	.113	.143	.198	0.33	.053	0.79	1.22	1.90	2.90	4.94	7.12	11.46
		AOQL in %															

*AQL's are provided as indices to simplify use of this table, but have no other meaning relative to the plans.

EXHIBIT VI.5–3

PROCEDURE FOR CSP-2 PLANS

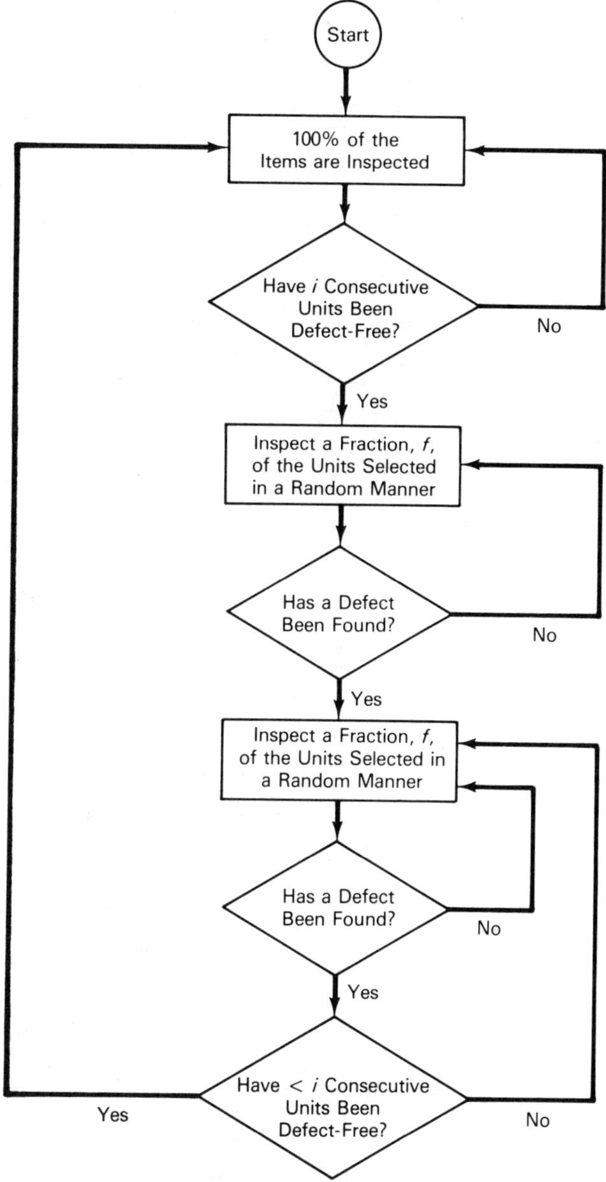

EXHIBIT VI.5–4

VALUES OF i FOR CSP-2 PLANS

Sample Frequency Code Letter	f	AQL* in %							
		0.40	0.65	1.0	1.5	2.5	4.0	6.5	10.0
A	1/2	80	54	35	23	15	9	7	4
B	1/3	128	86	55	36	24	14	10	7
C	1/4	162	109	70	45	30	18	12	8
D	1/5	190	127	81	52	35	20	14	9
E	1/7	230	155	99	64	42	25	17	11
F	1/10	275	185	118	76	50	29	20	13
G	1/15	330	220	140	90	59	35	24	15
H	1/25	395	265	170	109	71	42	29	18
I, J, K	1/50	490	330	210	134	88	52	36	22
		0.53	0.79	1.22	1.90	2.90	4.94	7.12	11.46
		AOQL in %							

*AQL's are provided as indices to simplify use of this table, but have no other meaning relative to the plans.

EXHIBIT VI.5–6

VALUES OF i FOR CSP-T PLANS

Sample Frequency Code Letter	f	AQL* in %							
		0.40	0.65	1.0	1.5	2.5	4.0	6.5	10.0
A	1/2	87	58	38	25	16	10	7	5
B	1/3	116	78	51	33	22	13	9	6
C	1/4	139	93	61	39	26	15	11	7
D	1/5	158	106	69	44	29	17	12	8
E	1/7	189	127	82	53	35	21	14	9
F	1/10	224	150	97	63	41	24	17	11
G	1/15	266	179	116	74	49	29	20	13
H	1/25	324	217	141	90	59	35	24	15
I	1/50	409	274	177	114	75	44	30	19
J, K	1/100	499	335	217	139	91	53	37	23
		0.53	0.79	1.22	1.90	2.90	4.94	7.12	11.46
		AOQL in %							

*AQL's are provided as indices to simplify use of this table, but have no other meaning relative to the plans.

EXHIBIT VI.5–5

Procedure for CSP-T Plans

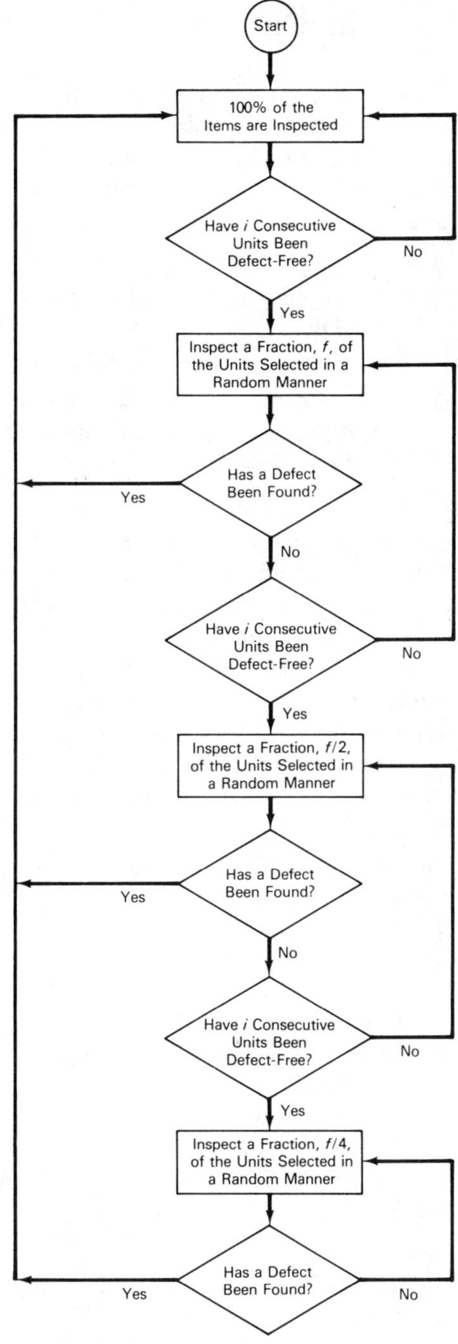

VI.6 Variables Sampling Plans

A. Description*

Variables sampling plans specify the number of items to be sampled and the critical value of the criterion to be used for deciding whether lot quality is acceptable when measurements data is collected on a quality characteristic of interest. When the probability distribution of these measurements is known, it is possible to specify the sampling plan parameters so that the following two conditions are met:

1. When a population (not the sample) has a specified fraction, say p_1, of individuals which have values beyond prescribed specification limits, the probability of deciding that the lot quality is acceptable is $(1-\alpha)$.
2. When the fraction of the population that is defective is p_2, where $p_2 > p_1$, the probability of concluding that the lot quality is acceptable is β.

Three conditions may exist with respect to specification limits. It may be that only items with values less than some specified value, say L, are undesirable. Alternatively, only items with values greater than an upper limit, say U, are undesirable. The third case is when both large and small values are undesirable. This will be called the double-specification limit case. Under the assumption that the values of the quality characteristic follow a normal distribution with mean μ and standard deviation σ, the decision to accept the lot will be based on the distance, in multiples of σ, from the limit to the sample mean of the data. That is, the quantity $(\bar{X}-L)/\sigma$ is computed if items with values less than L are undesirable, or $(U-\bar{X})/\sigma$ if values greater than U are undesirable. If the computed value is less than some critical value, say k, the lot is unacceptable. For the double-specification limit case, L and U must be far enough apart so that when the fraction of the population below L is p, the fraction above U is negligible. Also, both $(\bar{X}-L)/\sigma$ and $(U-\bar{X})/\sigma$ must be greater than the critical value if the lot is to be accepted.

When the variance of the distribution, σ, is not known, it is replaced in the above with the sample standard deviation, S, where

$$S = \sqrt{\left(\sum_{i=1}^{n} X_i^2 - n\bar{X}^2\right) \Big/ (n-1)}$$

and $X_1, X_2, \ldots, X_n$ is the random sample of n observations.

---

*Refer to the guide at the beginning of Section VI to determine the appropriate uses of the individual quality control procedures.

The nomograph shown in Exhibit VI.6–1 enables the user to find the required sample size n and the critical value k to meet a prescribed set of conditions p_1, p_2, α, and β for both the σ-known and the σ-unknown cases. The nomograph contains separate scales for n for these two cases. The greater uncertainty in the case where σ is unknown requires a larger sample size for a given set of conditions, but the same value of k is used.

In addition, for a given plan, the probability of acceptance for any value of fraction defective can be found. By plotting several of these points, the user can construct an operating characteristic (OC) curve of the plan.

B. Reading the Nomograph

B–1. Finding n and k given p_1, p_2, $(1-\alpha)$, and β

On the nomograph in Exhibit VI.6–1 a line is drawn connecting the points p_1 on the fraction defective scale and $(1-\alpha)$ on the probability of acceptance scale. A second line is drawn connecting the p_2 point on the fraction defective scale to the β point on the probability of acceptance scale. The point where these two lines intersect establishes the values of n and k. If the process variability is unknown, the sample size is found by following the curved lines to the scale labeled "Sample Size n" near the top of the nomograph. If the process variability is known, it is necessary to drop *vertically* from the intersection of the two lines to the scale "Sample Size n for σ-Known Plan."

Example B–1. Let $p_1 = .01$, $p_2 = .06$, $(1-\alpha) = .95$, $\beta = .10$. Connecting the .01 point on the fraction defective scale to the .95 point on the probability of acceptance scale, and then connecting the .06 point on the fraction defective scale to the .10 point on the probability of acceptance scale provides the two lines necessary. At the intersection of these two lines, $k = 1.9$. If this is to be a plan for σ unknown, the scale near the top of the nomograph is used to find $n = 40$. If σ is known, $n = 15$ is found by dropping vertically to the lower sample size scale.

B–2. Finding Points on the OC Curve of a Given Plan

Any line from the fraction defective scale to the probability of acceptance scale that passes through the (n, k) point gives a point, say (p, β), on the OC curve. Here p is the end point of the line on the fraction defective scale, and β is the end point on the probability of acceptance scale.

Example B–2. For the σ-unknown plan in Example B–1, where $n = 40$ and $k = 1.9$, find the probability of accepting lots with $p = .04$ fraction defective. Passing a line from $p = .04$ through the $(n, k) = (40, 1.9)$ point to the probability of acceptance scale, we find $\beta = .28$.

In order to construct an OC curve, this procedure is repeated for several values of p, giving the following results:

p	β
.02	.72
.03	.48
.05	.18
.08	.035

These values, along with the points used to generate the plan, can be plotted to produce an OC curve for the $n = 40$, $k = 1.9$ variables sampling plan.

C. Designing Variables Sampling Plans

Example C–1. σ Unknown. The density of a plastic part is required to be at least 0.80 grams per cubic centimeter. The parts are supplied in large lots, and a variables sampling plan is to be used to determine the acceptance of the lots. It is desired to have $p_1 = .02$, $p_2 = .10$, $(1 - \alpha) = .90$, and $\beta = .05$. No information is available concerning density variability. Constructing the two lines as in Example B–1, we find $n = 37$ and $k = 1.62$. Measurements on a sample of 37 were taken, and $\overline{X} = 0.83$ and $S^2 = (\Sigma_{i=1}^{37} X_i^2 - 37\overline{X}^2)/36 = 1.96 \times 10^{-4}$ were computed. Since $(\overline{X} - L)/S = (0.83 - 0.80)/0.014 = 2.1$ is greater than $k = 1.62$, the lot is rejected.

The probability of accepting lots that are 5-percent defective can be found by drawing a line from $p = .05$ through the $(n, k) = (37, 1.62)$ point, yielding $\beta \doteq .40$.

Example C–2. σ Known. Cord used in the manufacture of V-belts is required to have a minimum tensile breaking strength of $L = 150$ pounds. It is known that $\sigma = 5$ pounds for this particular cord. Find a variables sampling plan so that $p_1 = .005$, $p_2 = .02$, $(1 - \alpha) = .95$, and $\beta = .10$. Drawing the lines on the nomograph in Exhibit VI–6.1 as described in Example B–2, we find $k = 2.29$ and $n = 30$ (from the scale at the bottom of the nomograph). The plan calls for samples of 30 items to be tested and the average breaking strength $\overline{X}$ computed. If $(\overline{X} - 150)/5 \leq 2.29$, the lot of cord from which the samples were taken is accepted.

EXHIBIT VI.6–1

NOMOGRAPH FOR DERIVING VARIABLES SAMPLING PLANS

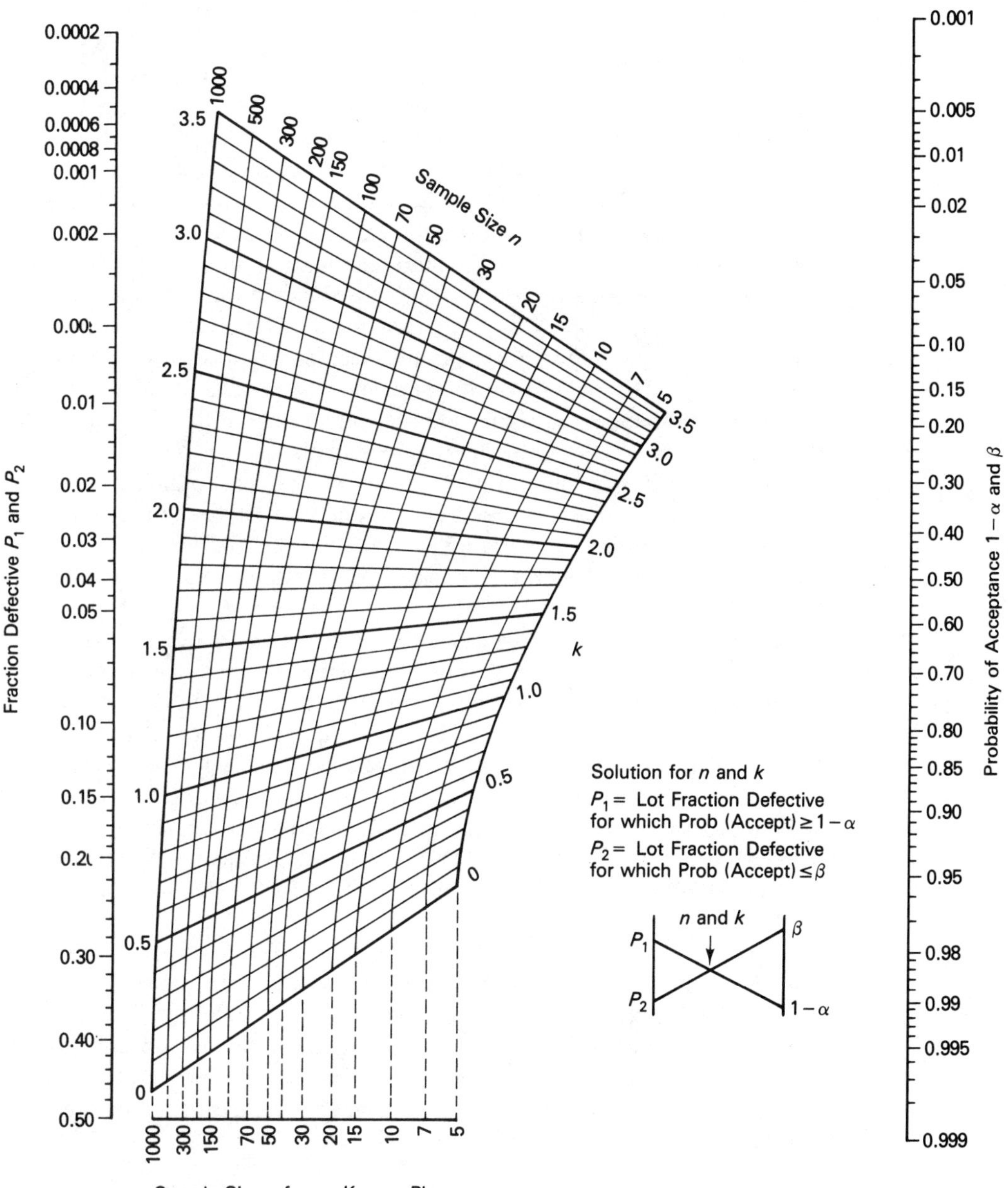

Source: Nelson, L. S., "Nomograph for Variable Sampling Plans," *Journal of Quality Technology*, vol. 13, no. 4, © 1981, American Society for Quality Control. Reprinted by permission.

VI.7 ANSI Z-1.9 (MIL-STD-414)

A. Description*

ANSI Z-1.9 and MIL-STD-414 both provide tables of variables sampling plans and rules for selection of plans. ANSI Z-1.9 is an updated civilian version of MIL-STD-414. The modifications made to MIL-STD-414 include some changes in terminology, modifications in lot size groupings to match those in MIL-STD-105D, and elimination of specific plans for extreme acceptable quality levels. While, as of this writing, ANSI Z-1.9 has not been officially adopted by the Department of Defense, it is felt that it will be widely used in the future, and the discussion will refer to ANSI Z-1.9 rather than to MIL-STD-414. However, since the general form and content of the two standards is so similar, the reader can obtain an introduction to the nature of MIL-STD-414 from this section also.

ANSI Z-1.9 provides an alternative method of obtaining variables sampling plans to that discussed in Section VI.6. It is required that the quality characteristic of interest follow a normal distribution. The sampling plan is selected as a function of lot size and acceptable quality level (AQL). Five "inspection levels" are available to reflect the overall level of quality assurance required. Three of these are referred to as "general" and two as "special" levels. General level II is considered usual, but general level I might be adopted if the consequences of lessened quality in an item are not as critical. General level III might be used if quality assurance is of greater than normal importance. The special levels are used when relatively small sample sizes are necessary or if large sampling risks can be tolerated. The standard also provides for switching to alternative plans when recent measurements indicate either higher or lower levels of quality than expected. These alternative plans are referred to as plans for "tightened" and "loosened" inspection, respectively.

The developers of the standard based their selection of plans on several statistical as well as nonstatistical criteria. Hence, the plans are recommended for use only if the entire procedure is to be followed. The reader is encouraged to study the entire text of the standard, even if a specific plan of interest is available from the exhibits in this section. The intent here is to inform the reader of the types of tables available in ANSI Z-1.9 and how to use them.

---

*Refer to the guide at the beginning of Section VI to determine the appropriate uses of the individual quality control procedures.

The standard provides plans for single- and double-specification limits, for process standard deviation σ both known and unknown. In addition, two different forms of the decision criterion are given: *Form 1*, in which the distance from the sample mean to the specification limits, in terms of standard deviations of the process, is compared to a critical value k, and *Form 2*, in which the fraction of production exceeding the specification limit(s) is estimated and compared to a critical value M. Only Form 2 is presented for the double-specification limits case in the standard.

Selection of a plan from ANSI Z-1.9 consists of the following steps:

1. Choose an inspection level. This, combined with the lot size anticipated, allows selection of the sample size code letter from a table provided. This table is shown in Exhibit VI.7–1.
2. Select an AQL. Since individual plans cannot be given for all AQL's, the table given in Exhibit VI.7–2 is provided for selection of a nominal AQL value when using the standard.
3. For the selected AQL and sample size code letter, find the plans for tightened and loosened inspection levels in the tables in the standard. Exhibits VI.7–3 and VI.7–4 are examples of these tables for the Form 1 and Form 2 decision criterion, respectively.

Estimation of the fraction defective is required to make decisions on the acceptability of lots when using Form 2. In the standard, three tables are provided for estimating the fraction defective. The choice of tables depends on whether the standard deviation is a) assumed to be known, b) to be estimated from the sample standard deviation, or c) to be estimated from ranges of the sample data. Exhibit VI.7–5 provides the tables for b). These are sometimes referred to as the Lieberman-Resnikoff tables, after their developers [1955]. These tables are useful not only for variables sampling, but also for any situation where estimation of percentiles of a normal distribution with unknown mean and standard deviation are required.

B. Using the Tables

Example B–1. Assume general inspection level II is desired, and lots of 1000 are expected. Using Exhibit VI.7–1, we find that the sample size code letter is J. A single-specification limit, σ-unknown plan with AQL = 0.8 percent is desired using Form 2. For a required AQL of 0.8 percent, we find in Exhibit VI.7–2 that the AQL to use in the tables is 1.0 percent. From Exhibit VI.7–4, we find, for code letter J, that $n = 35$, and under the AQL = 1.00 column, we find $M = 2.68$ percent. Thus, samples of 35 are to be taken, and if the estimated fraction defective exceeds 2.68 percent, the lot is rejected.

EXHIBIT VI.7–1

SAMPLE SIZE CODE LETTERS

Lot Size	Inspection Levels				
	Special		General		
	S3	S4	I	II	III
2 to 8	B	B	B	B	C
9 to 15	B	B	B	B	D
16 to 25	B	B	B	C	E
26 to 50	B	B	C	D	F
51 to 90	B	B	D	E	G
91 to 150	B	C	E	F	H
151 to 280	B	D	F	G	I
281 to 400	C	E	G	H	J
401 to 500	C	E	G	I	J
501 to 1200	D	F	H	J	K
1201 to 3200	E	G	I	K	L
3201 to 10,000	F	H	J	L	M
10,001 to 35,000	G	I	K	M	N
35,001 to 150,000	H	J	L	N	P
150,001 to 500,000	H	K	M	P	P
500,001 and over	H	K	N	P	P

EXHIBIT VI.7–2

AQL CONVERSION TABLE

For Specified AQL Values Falling Within These Ranges (in Percent)	Use This AQL Value
— to 0.109	0.10
0.110 to 0.164	0.15
0.165 to 0.279	0.25
0.280 to 0.439	0.40
0.440 to 0.699	0.65
0.700 to 1.09	1.0
1.10 to 1.64	1.5
1.65 to 2.79	2.5
2.80 to 4.39	4.0
4.40 to 6.99	6.5
7.00 to 10.9	10.0

Example B–2. Continuing Example B–1, we assume that the (lower) specification limit is $L = 58.2$, and that a sample of 35 results in an $\overline{X} = 65.4$ and $S = 3.15$. Then $Q_L = (\overline{X} - L)/S = 2.28$. Entering Exhibit VI.7–5 for $Q_L = 2.28$ and sample size of 35 gives the estimated fraction defective $\hat{p} = .00915$, or 0.915 percent. Since $\hat{p} < M = 2.68$, the lot quality is acceptable.

EXHIBIT VI.7–3

INSPECTION PLANS BASED ON VARIANCE UNKNOWN

(Single Specification Limit-Form 1)

Sample size code letter	Sample size	Acceptable Quality Levels (normal inspection)											
		T	.10	.15	.25	.40	.65	1.00	1.50	2.50	4.00	6.50	10.00
		k	k	k	k	k	k	k	k	k	k	k	k
B	3	↓	↓	↓	↓	↓	↓	▼	▼	1.12	.958	.765	.566
C	4	↓	↓	↓	↓	↓	↓	1.45	1.34	1.17	1.01	.814	.617
D	5	↓	↓	↓	↓	↓	1.65	1.53	1.40	1.24	1.07	.874	.675
E	7	↓	↓	↓	2.00	1.88	1.75	1.62	1.50	1.33	1.15	.955	.755
F	10	↓	↓	2.24	2.11	1.98	1.84	1.72	1.58	1.41	1.23	1.03	.828
G	15	2.53	2.42	2.32	2.20	2.06	1.91	1.79	1.65	1.47	1.30	1.09	.886
H	20	2.58	2.47	2.36	2.24	2.11	1.96	1.82	1.69	1.51	1.33	1.12	.917
I	25	2.61	2.50	2.40	2.26	2.14	1.98	1.85	1.72	1.53	1.35	1.14	.936
J	35	2.65	2.54	2.45	2.31	2.18	2.03	1.89	1.76	1.57	1.39	1.18	.969
K	50	2.71	2.60	2.50	2.35	2.22	2.08	1.93	1.80	1.61	1.42	1.21	1.00
L	75	2.77	2.66	2.55	2.41	2.27	2.12	1.98	1.84	1.65	1.46	1.24	1.03
M	100	2.80	2.69	2.58	2.43	2.29	2.14	2.00	1.86	1.67	1.48	1.26	1.05
N	150	2.84	2.73	2.61	2.47	2.33	2.18	2.03	1.89	1.70	1.51	1.29	1.07
P	200	2.85	2.73	2.62	2.47	2.33	2.18	2.04	1.89	1.70	1.51	1.29	1.07
		.10	.15	.25	.40	.65	1.00	1.50	2.50	4.00	6.50	10.00	
		Acceptable Quality Levels (tightened inspection)											

Note: All *AQL* values are in percent nonconforming. *T* denotes plan used exclusively on tightened inspection and provides symbol for identification of appropriate *OC* curve.

Note: ↓ Use first sampling plan below arrow; that is, both sample size as well as *k* value. When sample size equals or exceeds lot size, every item in the lot must be inspected.

EXHIBIT VI.7–4

INSPECTION PLANS BASED ON VARIANCE UNKNOWN

(Form 2-Single and Double Specification Limits)

Sample size code letter	Sample size	Acceptable Quality Levels (normal inspection)											
		T	.10	.15	.25	.40	.65	1.00	1.50	2.50	4.00	6.50	10.00
		M	M	M	M	M	M	M	M	M	M	M	M
B	3	↓	↓	↓	↓	↓	↓	▼	▼	7.59	18.86	26.94	33.69
C	4							1.53	5.50	10.92	16.45	22.86	29.45
D	5						1.33	3.32	5.83	9.80	14.39	20.19	26.56
E	7				0.422	1.06	2.14	3.55	5.35	8.40	12.20	17.35	23.29
F	10			0.349	0.716	1.30	2.17	3.26	4.77	7.29	10.54	15.17	20.74
G	15	0.186	0.312	0.503	0.818	1.31	2.11	3.05	4.31	6.56	9.46	13.71	18.94
H	20	0.228	0.365	0.544	0.846	1.29	2.05	2.95	4.09	6.17	8.92	12.99	18.03
I	25	0.250	0.380	0.551	0.877	1.29	2.00	2.86	3.97	5.97	8.63	12.57	17.51
J	35	0.264	0.388	0.535	0.847	1.23	1.87	2.68	3.70	5.57	8.10	11.87	16.65
K	50	0.250	0.363	0.503	0.789	1.17	1.71	2.49	3.45	5.20	7.61	11.23	15.87
L	75	0.228	0.330	0.467	0.720	1.07	1.60	2.29	3.20	4.87	7.15	10.63	15.13
M	100	0.220	0.317	0.447	0.689	1.02	1.53	2.20	3.07	4.69	6.91	10.32	14.75
N	150	0.203	0.293	0.413	0.638	0.949	1.43	2.05	2.89	4.43	6.57	9.88	14.20
P	200	0.204	0.294	0.414	0.637	0.945	1.42	2.04	2.87	4.40	6.53	9.81	14.12
		.10	.15	.25	.40	.65	1.00	1.50	2.50	4.00	6.50	10.00	
		Acceptability Quality Levels (tightened inspection)											

Note: All *AQL* values are in percent nonconforming. *T* denotes plan used exclusively on tightened inspection and provides symbol for identification of appropriate *OC* curve.

Note: ↓ Use first sampling plan below arrow; that is, both sample size as well as *M* value. When sample size equals or exceeds lot size, every item in the lot must be inspected.

EXHIBIT VI.7–5

LIEBERMAN-RESNIKOFF TABLES FOR ESTIMATING FRACTION DEFECTIVE[1]

Q_U or Q_L	Sample Size															
	3	4	5	7	10	15	20	25	30	35	40	50	75	100	150	200
0	50.00	50.00	50.00	50.00	50.00	50.00	50.00	50.00	50.00	50.00	50.00	50.00	50.00	50.00	50.00	50.00
.1	47.24	46.67	46.44	46.26	46.16	46.10	46.08	46.06	46.05	46.05	46.04	46.04	46.03	46.03	46.02	46.02
.2	44.46	43.33	42.90	42.54	42.35	42.24	42.19	42.16	42.15	42.13	42.13	42.11	42.10	42.09	42.06	42.06
.3	41.63	40.00	39.37	38.87	38.60	38.44	38.37	38.33	38.31	38.29	38.28	38.27	38.25	38.24	38.22	38.22
.31	41.35	39.67	39.02	38.50	38.23	38.06	37.99	37.95	37.93	37.91	37.90	37.89	37.87	37.86	37.84	37.84
.32	41.06	39.33	38.67	38.14	37.86	37.69	37.62	37.58	37.55	37.54	37.52	37.51	37.49	37.48	37.46	37.46
.33	40.77	39.00	38.32	37.78	37.49	37.31	37.24	37.20	37.18	37.16	37.15	37.13	37.11	37.10	37.09	37.06
.34	40.49	38.67	37.97	37.42	37.12	36.94	36.87	36.83	36.80	36.78	36.77	36.75	36.73	36.72	36.71	36.71
.35	40.20	38.33	37.62	37.06	36.75	36.57	36.49	36.45	36.43	36.41	36.40	36.38	36.36	36.35	36.33	36.33
.36	39.91	38.00	37.28	36.69	36.38	36.20	36.12	36.06	36.05	36.04	36.02	36.01	35.98	35.97	35.96	35.96
.37	39.62	37.67	36.93	36.33	36.02	35.83	35.75	35.71	35.68	35.66	35.65	35.63	35.61	35.60	35.59	35.58
.38	39.33	37.33	36.58	35.98	35.65	35.46	35.38	35.34	35.31	35.29	35.28	35.26	35.24	35.23	35.22	35.21
.39	39.03	37.00	36.23	35.62	35.29	35.10	35.01	34.97	34.94	34.93	34.91	34.89	34.87	34.86	34.85	34.84
.40	38.74	36.67	35.88	35.26	34.93	34.73	34.65	34.60	34.58	34.56	34.54	34.53	34.50	34.49	34.48	34.47
.41	38.45	36.33	35.54	34.90	34.57	34.37	34.28	34.24	34.21	34.19	34.18	34.16	34.13	34.12	34.11	34.10
.42	38.15	36.00	35.19	34.55	34.21	34.00	33.92	33.87	33.85	33.83	33.81	33.79	33.77	33.76	33.74	33.74
.43	37.85	35.67	34.85	34.19	33.85	33.64	33.56	33.51	33.48	33.46	33.45	33.43	33.40	33.39	33.38	33.37
.44	37.56	35.33	34.50	33.84	33.49	33.28	33.20	33.15	33.12	33.10	33.09	33.07	33.04	33.03	33.02	33.01
.45	37.26	35.00	34.16	33.49	33.13	32.92	32.84	32.79	32.76	32.74	32.73	32.71	32.68	32.67	32.66	32.65
.46	36.96	34.67	33.81	33.13	32.78	32.57	32.48	32.43	32.40	32.38	32.37	32.35	32.32	32.31	32.30	32.29
.47	36.66	34.33	33.47	32.78	32.42	32.21	32.12	32.07	32.04	32.02	32.01	31.99	31.96	31.95	31.94	31.93
.48	36.35	34.00	33.12	32.43	32.07	31.85	31.77	31.72	31.69	31.67	31.65	31.63	31.61	31.60	31.58	31.58
.49	36.05	33.67	32.78	32.08	31.72	31.50	31.41	31.36	31.33	31.31	31.30	31.28	31.25	31.24	31.23	31.22
.50	35.75	33.33	32.44	31.74	31.37	31.15	31.06	31.01	30.98	30.96	30.95	30.93	30.90	30.89	30.87	30.87
.51	35.44	33.00	32.10	31.39	31.02	30.80	30.71	30.66	30.63	30.61	30.60	30.57	30.55	30.54	30.52	30.52
.52	35.13	32.67	31.76	31.04	30.67	30.45	30.36	30.31	30.28	30.26	30.25	30.23	30.20	30.19	30.17	30.17
.53	34.82	32.33	31.42	30.70	30.32	30.10	30.01	29.96	29.93	29.91	29.90	29.88	29.85	29.84	29.83	29.82
.54	34.51	32.00	31.08	30.36	29.98	29.76	29.67	29.62	29.59	29.57	29.55	29.53	29.51	29.49	29.48	29.48
.55	34.20	31.67	30.74	30.01	29.64	29.41	29.32	29.27	29.24	29.22	29.21	29.19	29.16	29.15	29.14	29.13
.56	33.88	31.33	30.40	29.67	29.29	29.07	28.96	28.93	28.90	28.88	28.87	28.85	28.82	28.81	28.79	28.79
.57	33.57	31.00	30.06	29.33	28.95	28.73	28.64	28.59	28.56	28.54	28.53	28.51	28.48	28.47	28.45	28.45
.58	33.25	30.67	29.73	28.99	28.61	28.39	28.30	28.25	28.22	28.20	28.19	28.17	28.14	28.13	28.12	28.11
.59	32.93	30.33	29.39	28.66	28.28	28.05	27.96	27.92	27.89	27.87	27.85	27.83	27.81	27.79	27.78	27.77
.60	32.61	30.00	29.05	28.32	27.94	27.72	27.63	27.58	27.55	27.53	27.52	27.50	27.47	27.46	27.45	27.44
.61	32.28	29.67	28.72	27.98	27.60	27.39	27.30	27.25	27.22	27.20	27.18	27.16	27.14	27.13	27.11	27.11
.62	31.96	29.33	28.39	27.65	27.27	27.05	26.96	26.92	26.89	26.87	26.85	26.83	26.81	26.80	26.78	26.78
.63	31.63	29.00	28.05	27.32	26.94	26.72	26.63	26.59	26.56	26.54	26.52	26.50	26.48	26.47	26.45	26.45
.64	31.30	28.67	27.72	26.99	26.61	26.39	26.31	26.26	26.23	26.21	26.20	26.18	26.15	26.14	26.13	26.12
.65	30.97	28.33	27.39	26.66	26.28	26.07	25.98	25.93	25.90	25.88	25.87	25.85	25.83	25.82	25.80	25.80
.66	30.63	28.00	27.06	26.33	25.96	25.74	25.66	25.61	25.58	25.56	25.55	25.53	25.51	25.49	25.48	25.48
.67	30.30	27.67	26.73	26.00	25.63	25.42	25.33	25.29	25.26	25.24	25.23	25.21	25.19	25.17	25.16	25.16
.68	29.96	27.33	26.40	25.68	25.31	25.10	25.01	24.97	24.94	24.92	24.91	24.89	24.87	24.86	24.84	24.84
.69	29.61	27.00	26.07	25.35	24.99	24.78	24.70	24.65	24.62	24.60	24.59	24.57	24.55	24.54	24.53	24.52

[1] Values tabulated are read in percent.

EXHIBIT VI.7–5—CONTINUED

Q_U or Q_L	Sample Size															
	3	4	5	7	10	15	20	25	30	35	40	50	75	100	150	200
.70	29.27	26.67	25.74	25.03	24.67	24.46	24.38	24.33	24.31	24.29	24.28	24.26	24.24	24.23	24.21	24.21
.71	28.92	26.33	25.41	24.71	24.35	24.15	24.06	24.02	23.99	23.98	23.96	23.95	23.92	23.91	23.90	23.90
.72	28.57	26.00	25.09	24.39	24.03	23.83	23.75	23.71	23.68	23.67	23.65	23.64	23.61	23.60	23.59	23.59
.73	28.22	25.67	24.76	24.07	23.72	23.52	23.44	23.40	23.37	23.36	23.34	23.33	23.31	23.30	23.29	23.28
.74	27.86	25.33	24.44	23.75	23.41	23.21	23.13	23.09	23.07	23.05	23.04	23.02	23.00	22.99	22.98	22.98
.75	27.50	25.00	24.11	23.44	23.10	22.90	22.83	22.79	22.76	22.75	22.73	22.72	22.70	22.69	22.68	22.67
.76	27.13	24.67	23.79	23.12	22.79	22.60	22.52	22.48	22.46	22.44	22.43	22.42	22.40	22.39	22.38	22.37
.77	26.77	24.33	23.47	22.81	22.48	22.30	22.22	22.18	22.16	22.14	22.13	22.12	22.10	22.09	22.08	22.08
.78	26.39	24.00	23.15	22.50	22.18	21.99	21.92	21.89	21.86	21.85	21.84	21.82	21.80	21.79	21.78	21.78
.79	26.02	23.67	22.83	22.19	21.87	21.70	21.63	21.59	21.57	21.55	21.54	21.53	21.51	21.50	21.49	21.49
.80	25.64	23.33	22.51	21.88	21.57	21.40	21.33	21.29	21.27	21.26	21.25	21.23	21.22	21.21	21.20	21.20
.81	25.25	23.00	22.19	21.58	21.27	21.10	21.04	21.00	20.98	20.97	20.96	2.094	20.93	20.92	20.91	20.91
.82	24.86	22.67	21.87	21.27	20.98	20.81	20.75	20.71	20.69	20.68	20.67	20.65	20.64	20.63	20.62	20.62
.83	24.47	22.33	21.56	20.97	20.68	20.52	20.46	20.42	20.40	20.39	20.38	20.37	20.35	20.35	20.34	20.34
.84	24.07	22.00	21.24	20.67	20.39	20.23	20.17	20.14	20.12	20.11	20.10	20.09	20.07	20.06	20.06	20.05
.85	23.67	21.67	20.93	20.37	20.10	19.94	19.89	19.86	19.84	19.82	19.82	19.80	19.79	19.78	19.78	19.77
.86	23.26	21.33	20.62	20.07	19.81	19.66	19.60	19.57	19.56	19.54	19.54	19.53	19.51	19.51	19.50	19.50
.87	22.84	21.00	20.31	19.78	19.52	19.38	19.32	19.30	19.28	19.27	19.26	19.25	19.24	19.23	19.22	19.22
.88	22.42	20.67	20.00	19.48	19.23	19.10	19.04	19.02	19.00	18.99	18.98	18.98	18.96	18.96	18.95	18.95
.89	21.99	20.33	19.69	19.19	18.95	18.82	18.77	18.74	18.73	18.72	18.71	18.70	18.69	18.69	18.68	18.68
.90	21.55	20.00	19.38	18.90	18.67	18.54	18.50	18.47	18.46	18.45	18.44	18.43	18.42	18.42	18.41	18.41
.91	21.11	19.67	19.07	18.61	18.39	18.27	18.22	18.20	18.19	18.18	18.17	18.17	18.16	18.15	18.15	18.15
.92	20.66	19.33	18.77	18.33	18.11	18.00	17.96	17.94	17.92	17.92	17.91	17.90	17.89	17.89	17.88	17.88
.93	20.20	19.00	18.46	18.04	17.84	17.73	17.69	17.67	17.66	17.65	17.65	17.64	17.63	17.63	17.62	17.62
.94	19.74	18.67	18.16	17.76	17.57	17.46	17.43	17.41	17.40	17.39	17.39	17.38	17.37	17.37	17.36	17.36
.95	19.25	18.33	17.86	17.48	17.29	17.20	17.17	17.15	17.14	17.13	17.13	17.12	17.12	17.11	17.11	17.11
.96	18.76	18.00	17.56	17.20	17.03	16.94	16.91	16.89	16.88	16.88	16.87	16.87	16.86	16.86	16.86	16.85
.97	18.25	17.67	17.25	16.92	16.76	16.68	16.65	16.63	16.63	16.62	16.62	16.61	16.61	16.61	16.60	16.60
.98	17.74	17.33	16.96	16.65	16.49	16.42	16.39	16.38	16.37	16.37	16.37	16.36	16.36	16.36	16.36	16.36
.99	17.21	17.00	16.66	16.37	16.23	16.16	16.14	16.13	16.12	16.12	16.12	16.12	16.11	16.11	16.11	16.11
1.00	16.67	16.67	16.36	16.10	15.97	15.91	15.89	15.88	15.88	15.87	15.87	15.87	15.87	15.87	15.87	15.87
1.01	16.11	16.33	16.07	15.83	15.72	15.66	15.64	15.63	15.63	15.63	15.63	15.63	15.62	15.62	15.62	15.62
1.02	15.53	16.00	15.78	15.56	15.46	15.41	15.40	15.39	15.39	15.39	15.39	15.38	15.38	15.38	15.38	15.38
1.03	14.93	15.67	15.48	15.30	15.21	15.17	15.15	15.15	15.15	15.15	15.15	15.15	15.15	15.15	15.15	15.15
1.04	14.31	15.33	15.19	15.03	14.96	14.92	14.91	14.91	14.91	14.91	14.91	14.91	14.91	14.91	14.91	14.91
1.05	13.66	15.00	14.91	14.77	14.71	14.68	14.67	14.67	14.67	14.67	14.68	14.68	14.68	14.68	14.68	14.68
1.06	12.98	14.67	14.62	14.51	14.46	14.44	14.44	14.44	14.44	14.44	14.44	14.45	14.45	14.45	14.45	14.45
1.07	12.27	14.33	14.33	14.26	14.22	14.20	14.20	14.21	14.21	14.21	14.21	14.22	14.22	14.22	14.22	14.23
1.08	11.51	14.00	14.05	14.00	13.97	13.97	13.97	13.98	13.98	13.98	13.99	13.99	13.99	14.00	14.00	14.00
1.09	10.71	13.67	13.76	13.75	13.73	13.74	13.74	13.75	13.75	13.67	13.76	13.77	13.77	13.77	13.78	13.78

EXHIBIT VI.7–5—CONTINUED

Q_U or Q_L	Sample Size															
	3	4	5	7	10	15	20	25	30	35	40	50	75	100	150	200
1.10	9.84	13.33	13.48	13.49	13.50	13.51	13.52	13.52	13.53	13.54	13.54	13.54	13.55	13.55	13.56	13.56
1.11	8.89	13.00	13.20	13.25	13.26	13.28	13.29	13.30	13.31	13.31	13.32	13.32	13.33	13.34	13.34	13.34
1.12	7.82	12.67	12.93	13.00	13.03	13.05	13.07	13.08	13.09	13.10	13.10	13.11	13.12	13.12	13.12	13.13
1.13	6.60	12.33	12.65	12.75	12.80	12.83	12.85	12.86	12.87	12.88	12.89	12.89	12.90	12.91	12.91	12.92
1.14	5.08	12.00	12.37	12.51	12.57	12.61	12.63	12.65	12.66	12.67	12.67	12.68	12.69	12.70	12.70	12.70
1.15	0.29	11.67	12.10	12.27	12.34	12.39	12.42	12.44	12.45	12.46	12.46	12.47	12.48	12.49	12.49	12.50
1.16	0.00	11.33	11.83	12.03	12.12	12.18	12.21	12.22	12.24	12.25	12.25	12.26	12.28	12.28	12.29	12.29
1.17	0.00	11.00	11.56	11.79	11.90	11.96	12.00	12.02	12.03	12.04	12.05	12.06	12.07	12.08	12.08	12.09
1.18	0.00	10.67	11.29	11.56	11.68	11.75	11.79	11.81	11.82	11.84	11.84	11.85	11.87	11.88	11.88	11.89
1.19	0.00	10.33	11.02	11.33	11.46	11.54	11.58	11.61	11.62	11.63	11.64	11.65	11.67	11.68	11.69	11.69
1.20	0.00	10.00	10.76	11.10	11.24	11.34	11.38	11.41	11.42	11.43	11.44	11.46	11.47	11.48	11.49	11.49
1.21	0.00	9.67	10.50	10.87	11.03	11.13	11.18	11.21	11.22	11.24	11.25	11.26	11.28	11.29	11.30	11.30
1.22	0.00	9.33	10.23	10.65	10.82	10.93	10.98	11.01	11.03	11.04	11.05	11.07	11.09	11.09	11.10	11.11
1.23	0.00	9.00	9.97	10.42	10.61	10.73	10.78	10.81	10.84	10.85	10.86	10.88	10.90	10.91	10.91	10.92
1.24	0.00	8.67	9.72	10.20	10.41	10.53	10.59	10.62	10.64	10.66	10.67	10.69	10.71	10.72	10.73	10.73
1.25	0.00	8.33	9.46	9.98	10.21	10.34	10.40	10.43	10.46	10.47	10.48	10.50	10.52	10.53	10.54	10.55
1.26	0.00	8.00	9.21	9.77	10.00	10.15	10.21	10.25	10.27	10.29	10.30	10.32	10.34	10.35	10.36	10.37
1.27	0.00	7.67	8.96	9.55	9.81	9.96	10.02	10.06	10.09	10.10	10.12	10.13	10.16	10.17	10.18	10.19
1.28	0.00	7.33	8.71	9.34	9.61	9.77	9.84	9.88	9.90	9.92	9.94	9.95	9.98	9.99	10.00	10.01
1.29	0.00	7.00	8.46	9.13	9.42	9.58	9.65	9.70	9.72	9.74	9.76	9.78	9.80	9.82	9.83	8.83
1.30	0.00	6.67	8.21	8.93	9.22	9.40	9.48	9.52	9.55	9.57	9.58	9.60	9.63	9.64	9.65	9.66
1.31	0.00	6.33	7.97	8.72	9.03	9.22	9.30	9.34	9.37	9.39	9.41	9.43	9.46	9.47	9.48	9.49
1.32	0.00	6.00	7.73	8.52	8.85	9.04	9.12	9.17	9.20	9.22	9.24	9.26	9.29	9.30	9.31	9.32
1.33	0.00	5.67	7.49	8.32	8.66	8.86	8.95	9.00	9.03	9.05	9.07	9.09	9.12	9.13	9.15	9.15
1.34	0.00	5.33	7.25	8.12	8.48	8.69	8.78	8.83	8.86	8.88	8.90	8.92	8.95	8.97	8.98	8.99
1.35	0.00	5.00	7.02	7.92	8.30	8.52	8.61	8.66	8.69	8.72	8.74	8.76	8.79	8.81	8.82	8.83
1.36	0.00	4.67	6.79	7.73	8.12	8.35	8.44	8.50	8.53	8.55	8.57	8.60	8.63	8.65	8.66	8.67
1.37	0.00	4.33	6.56	7.54	7.95	8.18	8.28	8.33	8.37	8.39	8.41	8.44	8.47	8.49	8.50	8.51
1.38	0.00	4.00	6.33	7.35	7.77	8.01	8.12	8.17	8.21	8.24	8.25	8.28	8.31	8.33	8.35	8.35
1.39	0.00	3.67	6.10	7.17	7.60	7.85	7.96	8.01	8.05	8.08	8.10	8.12	8.16	8.18	8.19	8.20
1.40	0.00	3.33	5.88	6.98	7.44	7.69	7.80	7.86	7.90	7.92	7.94	7.97	8.01	8.02	8.04	8.05
1.41	0.00	3.00	5.66	6.80	7.27	7.53	7.64	7.70	7.74	7.77	7.79	7.82	7.86	7.87	7.89	7.90
1.42	0.00	2.67	5.44	6.62	7.10	7.37	7.49	7.55	7.59	7.62	7.64	7.67	7.71	7.73	7.74	7.75
1.43	0.00	2.33	5.23	6.45	6.94	7.22	7.34	7.40	7.44	7.47	7.50	7.52	7.56	7.58	7.60	7.61
1.44	0.00	2.00	5.01	6.27	6.78	7.07	7.19	7.26	7.30	7.33	7.35	7.38	7.42	7.44	7.46	7.47
1.45	0.00	1.67	4.81	6.10	6.63	6.92	7.04	7.11	7.15	7.18	7.21	7.24	7.28	7.30	7.31	7.33
1.46	0.00	1.33	4.60	5.93	6.47	6.77	6.90	6.97	7.01	7.04	7.07	7.10	7.14	7.16	7.18	7.19
1.47	0.00	1.00	4.39	5.77	6.32	6.63	6.75	6.83	6.87	6.90	6.93	6.96	7.00	7.02	7.04	7.05
1.48	0.00	.67	4.19	5.60	6.17	6.48	6.61	6.69	6.73	6.77	6.79	6.82	6.86	6.88	6.90	6.91
1.49	0.00	.33	3.99	5.44	6.02	6.34	6.48	6.55	6.60	6.63	6.65	6.69	6.73	6.75	6.77	6.78

EXHIBIT VI.7-5—Continued

Q_U or Q_L	Sample Size														
	3	4	5	7	10	15	20	25	30	35	40	50	75	100	150	200
1.50	0.00	0.00	3.80	5.28	5.87	6.20	6.34	6.41	6.46	6.50	6.52	6.55	6.60	6.62	6.64	6.65
1.51	0.00	0.00	3.61	5.13	5.73	6.06	6.20	6.28	6.33	6.36	6.39	6.42	6.47	6.49	6.51	6.52
1.52	0.00	0.00	3.42	4.97	5.59	5.93	6.07	6.15	6.20	6.23	6.26	6.29	6.34	6.36	6.38	6.39
1.53	0.00	0.00	3.23	4.82	5.45	5.80	5.94	6.02	6.07	6.11	6.13	6.17	6.21	6.24	6.26	6.27
1.54	0.00	0.00	3.05	4.67	5.31	5.67	5.81	5.89	5.95	5.98	6.01	6.04	6.09	6.11	6.13	6.15
1.55	0.00	0.00	2.87	4.52	5.18	5.54	5.69	5.77	5.82	5.86	5.88	5.92	5.97	5.99	6.01	6.02
1.56	0.00	0.00	2.69	4.38	5.05	5.41	5.56	5.65	5.70	5.74	5.76	5.80	5.85	5.87	5.89	5.90
1.57	0.00	0.00	2.52	4.24	4.92	5.29	5.44	5.53	5.58	5.62	5.64	5.68	5.73	5.75	5.78	5.79
1.58	0.00	0.00	2.35	4.10	4.79	5.16	5.32	5.41	5.46	5.50	5.53	5.56	5.61	5.64	5.66	5.67
1.59	0.00	0.00	2.19	3.96	4.66	5.04	5.20	5.29	5.34	5.38	5.41	5.45	5.50	5.52	5.54	5.56
1.60	0.00	0.00	2.03	3.83	4.54	4.92	5.09	5.17	5.23	5.27	5.30	5.33	5.38	5.41	5.43	5.44
1.61	0.00	0.00	1.87	3.69	4.41	4.81	4.97	5.06	5.12	5.16	5.18	5.22	5.27	5.30	5.32	5.33
1.62	0.00	0.00	1.72	3.57	4.30	4.69	4.86	4.95	5.01	5.04	5.07	5.11	5.16	5.19	5.21	5.23
1.63	0.00	0.00	1.57	3.44	4.18	4.58	4.75	4.84	4.90	4.94	4.97	5.01	5.06	5.08	5.11	5.12
1.64	0.00	0.00	1.42	3.31	4.06	4.47	4.64	4.73	4.79	4.83	4.86	4.90	4.95	4.98	5.00	5.01
1.65	0.00	0.00	1.28	3.19	3.95	4.36	4.53	4.62	4.68	4.72	4.75	4.79	4.85	4.87	4.90	4.91
1.66	0.00	0.00	1.15	3.07	3.84	4.25	4.43	4.52	4.58	4.62	4.65	4.69	4.74	4.77	4.80	4.81
1.67	0.00	0.00	1.02	2.95	3.73	4.15	4.32	4.42	4.48	4.52	4.55	4.59	4.64	4.67	4.70	4.71
1.68	0.00	0.00	0.89	2.84	3.62	4.05	4.22	4.32	4.38	4.42	4.45	4.49	4.55	4.57	4.60	4.61
1.69	0.00	0.00	0.77	2.73	3.52	3.94	4.12	4.22	4.28	4.32	4.35	4.39	4.45	4.47	4.50	4.51
1.70	0.00	0.00	0.66	2.62	3.41	3.84	4.02	4.12	4.18	4.22	4.25	4.30	4.35	4.38	4.41	4.42
1.71	0.00	0.00	0.55	2.51	3.31	3.75	3.93	4.02	4.09	4.13	4.16	4.20	4.26	4.29	4.31	4.32
1.72	0.00	0.00	0.45	2.41	3.21	3.65	3.83	3.93	3.99	4.04	4.07	4.11	4.17	4.19	4.22	4.23
1.73	0.00	0.00	0.36	2.30	3.11	3.56	3.74	3.84	3.90	3.94	3.98	4.02	4.08	4.10	4.13	4.14
1.74	0.00	0.00	0.27	2.20	3.02	3.46	3.65	3.75	3.81	3.85	3.89	3.93	3.99	4.01	4.04	4.05
1.75	0.00	0.00	0.19	2.11	2.93	3.37	3.56	3.66	3.72	3.77	3.80	3.84	3.90	3.93	3.95	3.97
1.76	0.00	0.00	0.12	2.01	2.83	3.28	3.47	3.57	3.63	3.68	3.71	3.76	3.81	3.84	3.87	3.88
1.77	0.00	0.00	0.06	1.92	2.74	3.20	3.38	3.48	3.55	3.59	3.63	3.67	3.73	3.76	3.78	3.80
1.78	0.00	0.00	0.02	1.83	2.66	3.11	3.30	3.40	3.47	3.51	3.54	3.59	3.64	3.67	3.70	3.71
1.79	0.00	0.00	0.00	1.74	2.57	3.03	3.21	3.32	3.38	3.43	3.46	3.51	3.56	3.59	3.63	3.63
1.80	0.00	0.00	0.00	1.65	2.49	2.94	3.13	3.24	3.30	3.35	3.38	3.43	3.48	3.51	3.54	3.55
1.81	0.00	0.00	0.00	1.57	2.40	2.86	3.05	3.16	3.22	3.27	3.30	3.35	3.40	3.43	3.46	3.47
1.82	0.00	00.0	0.00	1.49	2.32	2.79	2.98	3.08	3.15	3.19	3.22	3.27	3.33	3.36	3.38	3.40
1.83	0.00	0.00	0.00	1.41	2.25	2.71	2.90	3.00	3.07	3.11	3.15	3.19	3.25	3.28	3.31	3.32
1.84	0.00	0.00	0.00	1.34	2.17	2.63	2.82	2.93	2.99	3.04	3.07	3.12	3.18	3.21	3.23	3.25
1.85	0.00	0.00	0.00	1.26	2.09	2.56	2.75	2.85	2.92	2.97	3.00	3.05	3.10	3.13	3.16	3.17
1.86	0.00	0.00	0.00	1.19	2.02	2.48	2.68	2.78	2.85	2.89	2.93	2.97	3.03	3.06	3.09	3.10
1.87	0.00	0.00	0.00	1.12	1.95	2.41	2.61	2.71	2.78	2.82	2.86	2.90	2.96	2.99	3.02	3.03
1.88	0.00	0.00	0.00	1.06	1.88	2.34	2.54	2.64	2.71	2.75	2.79	2.83	2.89	2.92	2.95	2.96
1.89	0.00	0.00	0.00	0.99	1.81	2.28	2.47	2.57	2.64	2.69	2.72	2.77	2.83	2.85	2.88	2.90

EXHIBIT VI.7–5—CONTINUED

Q_U or Q_L	Sample Size															
	3	4	5	7	10	15	20	25	30	35	40	50	75	100	150	200
1.90	0.00	0.00	0.00	0.93	1.75	2.21	2.40	2.51	2.57	2.62	2.65	2.70	2.76	2.79	2.82	2.83
1.91	0.00	0.00	0.00	0.87	1.68	2.14	2.34	2.44	2.51	2.56	2.59	2.63	2.69	2.72	2.75	2.77
1.92	0.00	0.00	0.00	0.81	1.62	2.08	2.27	2.38	2.45	2.49	2.52	2.57	2.63	2.66	2.69	2.70
1.93	0.00	0.00	0.00	0.76	1.56	2.02	2.21	2.32	2.38	2.43	2.46	2.51	2.57	2.60	2.62	2.64
1.94	0.00	0.00	0.00	0.70	1.50	1.96	2.15	2.25	2.32	2.37	2.40	2.45	2.51	2.54	2.56	2.58
1.95	0.00	0.00	0.00	0.65	1.44	1.90	2.09	2.19	2.26	2.31	2.34	2.39	2.45	2.48	2.50	2.52
1.96	0.00	0.00	0.00	0.60	1.38	1.84	2.03	2.14	2.20	2.25	2.28	2.33	2.39	2.42	2.44	2.46
1.97	0.00	0.00	0.00	0.56	1.33	1.78	1.97	2.08	2.14	2.19	2.22	2.27	2.33	2.36	2.39	2.40
1.98	0.00	0.00	0.00	0.51	1.27	1.73	1.92	2.02	2.09	2.13	2.17	2.21	2.27	2.30	2.33	2.34
1.99	0.00	0.00	0.00	0.47	1.22	1.67	1.86	1.97	2.03	2.08	2.11	2.16	2.22	2.25	2.27	2.29
2.00	0.00	0.00	0.00	0.43	1.17	1.62	1.81	1.91	1.98	2.03	2.06	2.10	2.16	2.19	2.22	2.23
2.01	0.00	0.00	0.00	0.39	1.12	1.57	1.76	1.86	1.93	1.97	2.01	2.05	2.11	2.14	2.17	2.18
2.02	0.00	0.00	0.00	0.36	1.07	1.52	1.71	1.81	1.87	1.92	1.95	2.00	2.06	2.09	2.11	2.13
2.03	0.00	0.00	0.00	0.32	1.03	1.47	1.66	1.76	1.82	1.87	1.90	1.95	2.01	2.04	2.06	2.08
2.04	0.00	0.00	0.00	0.29	0.98	1.42	1.61	1.71	1.77	1.82	1.85	1.90	1.96	1.99	2.01	2.03
2.05	0.00	0.00	0.00	0.26	0.94	1.37	1.56	1.66	1.73	1.77	1.80	1.85	1.91	1.94	1.96	1.98
2.06	0.00	0.00	0.00	0.23	0.90	1.33	1.51	1.61	1.68	1.72	1.76	1.80	1.86	1.89	1.92	1.93
2.07	0.00	0.00	0.00	0.21	0.86	1.28	1.47	1.57	1.63	1.68	1.71	1.76	1.81	1.84	1.87	1.88
2.08	0.00	0.00	0.00	0.18	0.82	1.24	1.42	1.52	1.59	1.63	1.66	1.71	1.77	1.79	1.82	1.84
2.09	0.00	0.00	0.00	0.16	0.78	1.20	1.38	1.48	1.54	1.59	1.62	1.66	1.72	1.75	1.78	1.79
2.10	0.00	0.00	0.00	0.14	0.74	1.16	1.34	1.44	1.50	1.54	1.58	1.62	1.68	1.71	1.73	1.75
2.11	0.00	0.00	0.00	0.12	0.71	1.12	1.30	1.39	1.46	1.50	1.53	1.58	1.63	1.66	1.69	1.70
2.12	0.00	0.00	0.00	0.10	0.67	1.08	1.26	1.35	1.42	1.46	1.49	1.54	1.59	1.62	1.65	1.66
2.13	0.00	0.00	0.00	0.08	0.64	1.04	1.22	1.31	1.38	1.42	1.45	1.50	1.55	1.58	1.61	1.62
2.14	0.00	0.00	0.00	0.07	0.61	1.00	1.18	1.28	1.34	1.38	1.41	1.46	1.51	1.54	1.57	1.58
2.15	0.00	0.00	0.00	0.06	0.58	0.97	1.14	1.24	1.30	1.34	1.37	1.42	1.47	1.50	1.53	1.54
2.16	0.00	0.00	0.00	0.05	0.55	0.93	1.10	1.20	1.26	1.30	1.34	1.38	1.43	1.46	1.49	1.50
2.17	0.00	0.00	0.00	0.04	0.52	0.90	1.07	1.16	1.22	1.27	1.30	1.34	1.40	1.42	1.45	1.46
2.18	0.00	0.00	0.00	0.03	0.49	0.87	1.03	1.13	1.19	1.23	1.26	1.30	1.36	1.39	1.41	1.42
2.19	0.00	0.00	0.00	0.02	0.46	0.83	1.00	1.09	1.15	1.20	1.23	1.27	1.32	1.35	1.38	1.39
2.20	0.000	0.000	0.000	0.015	0.437	0.803	0.968	1.061	1.120	1.161	1.192	1.233	1.287	1.314	1.340	1.352
2.21	0.000	0.000	0.000	0.010	0.413	0.772	0.936	1.028	1.067	1.128	1.158	1.199	1.253	1.279	1.305	1.318
2.22	0.000	0.000	0.000	0.006	0.389	0.743	0.905	0.996	1.054	1.095	1.125	1.166	1.219	1.245	1.271	1.283
2.23	0.000	0.000	0.000	0.003	0.366	0.715	0.875	0.965	1.023	1.063	1.093	1.134	1.186	1.212	1.238	1.250
2.24	0.000	0.000	0.000	0.002	0.345	0.687	0.845	0.935	0.992	1.032	1.061	1.102	1.154	1.180	1.205	1.218
2.25	0.000	0.000	0.000	0.001	0.324	0.660	0.816	0.905	0.962	1.002	1.031	1.071	1.123	1.148	1.173	1.186
2.26	0.000	0.000	0.000	0.000	0.304	0.634	0.789	0.876	0.933	0.972	1.001	1.041	1.092	1.117	1.142	1.155
2.27	0.000	0.000	0.000	0.000	0.285	0.609	0.762	0.848	0.904	0.943	0.972	1.011	1.062	1.087	1.112	1.124
2.28	0.000	0.000	0.000	0.000	0.267	0.585	0.735	0.821	0.876	0.915	0.943	0.982	1.033	1.058	1.082	1.094
2.29	0.000	0.000	0.000	0.000	0.250	0.561	0.710	0.794	0.849	0.887	0.915	0.954	1.004	1.029	1.053	1.065

EXHIBIT VI.7–5—CONTINUED

Q_U or Q_L	Sample Size															
	3	4	5	7	10	15	20	25	30	35	40	50	75	100	150	200
2.30	0.000	0.000	0.000	0.000	0.233	0.538	0.685	0.769	0.823	0.861	0.888	0.927	0.977	1.001	1.025	1.037
2.31	0.000	0.000	0.000	0.000	0.218	0.516	0.661	0.743	0.797	0.834	0.862	0.900	0.949	0.974	0.997	1.009
2.32	0.000	0.000	0.000	0.000	0.203	0.495	0.637	0.719	0.772	0.809	0.836	0.874	0.923	0.947	0.971	0.982
2.33	0.000	0.000	0.000	0.000	0.189	0.474	0.614	0.695	0.748	0.784	0.811	0.848	0.897	0.921	0.944	0.956
2.34	0.000	0.000	0.000	0.000	0.175	0.454	0.592	0.672	0.724	0.760	0.787	0.824	0.872	0.895	0.915	0.930
2.35	0.000	0.000	0.000	0.000	0.163	0.435	0.571	0.650	0.701	0.736	0.763	0.799	0.847	0.870	0.893	0.905
2.36	0.000	0.000	0.000	0.000	0.151	0.416	0.550	0.628	0.678	0.714	0.740	0.776	0.823	0.846	0.869	0.880
2.37	0.000	0.000	0.000	0.000	0.139	0.398	0.530	0.606	0.656	0.691	0.717	0.753	0.799	0.822	0.845	0.856
2.38	0.000	0.000	0.000	0.000	0.128	0.381	0.510	0.586	0.635	0.670	0.695	0.730	0.777	0.799	0.822	0.833
2.39	0.000	0.000	0.000	0.000	0.118	0.364	0.491	0.566	0.614	0.648	0.674	0.709	0.754	0.777	0.799	0.810
2.40	0.000	0.000	0.000	0.000	0.109	0.348	0.473	0.546	0.594	0.628	0.653	0.687	0.732	0.755	0.777	0.787
2.41	0.000	0.000	0.000	0.000	0.100	0.332	0.455	0.527	0.575	0.608	0.633	0.667	0.711	0.733	0.755	0.766
2.42	0.000	0.000	0.000	0.000	0.091	0.317	0.437	0.509	0.555	0.588	0.613	0.646	0.691	0.712	0.734	0.744
2.43	0.000	0.000	0.000	0.000	0.083	0.302	0.421	0.491	0.537	0.569	0.593	0.627	0.670	0.692	0.713	0.724
2.44	0.000	0.000	0.000	0.000	0.076	0.288	0.404	0.474	0.519	0.551	0.575	0.608	0.651	0.672	0.693	0.703
2.45	0.000	0.000	0.000	0.000	0.069	0.275	0.389	0.457	0.501	0.533	0.556	0.589	0.632	0.653	0.673	0.684
2.46	0.000	0.000	0.000	0.000	0.063	0.262	0.373	0.440	0.484	0.516	0.539	0.571	0.613	0.634	0.654	0.664
2.47	0.000	0.000	0.000	0.000	0.057	0.249	0.359	0.425	0.468	0.499	0.521	0.553	0.595	0.615	0.635	0.646
2.48	0.000	0.000	0.000	0.000	0.051	0.237	0.344	0.409	0.452	0.482	0.505	0.536	0.577	0.597	0.617	0.627
2.49	0.000	0.000	0.000	0.000	0.046	0.226	0.331	0.394	0.436	0.466	0.488	0.519	0.560	0.580	0.600	0.609
2.50	0.000	0.000	0.000	0.000	0.041	0.214	0.317	0.380	0.421	0.451	0.473	0.503	0.543	0.563	0.582	0.592
2.51	0.000	0.000	0.000	0.000	0.037	0.204	0.304	0.366	0.407	0.436	0.457	0.487	0.527	0.546	0.565	0.575
2.52	0.000	0.000	0.000	0.000	0.033	0.193	0.292	0.352	0.392	0.421	0.442	0.472	0.511	0.530	0.549	0.558
2.53	0.000	0.000	0.000	0.000	0.029	0.184	0.280	0.339	0.379	0.407	0.428	0.457	0.495	0.514	0.533	0.542
2.54	0.000	0.000	0.000	0.000	0.026	0.174	0.268	0.326	0.365	0.393	0.413	0.442	0.480	0.499	0.517	0.527
2.55	0.000	0.000	0.000	0.000	0.023	0.165	0.257	0.314	0.352	0.379	0.400	0.428	0.465	0.484	0.502	0.511
2.56	0.000	0.000	0.000	0.000	0.020	0.156	0.246	0.302	0.340	0.366	0.386	0.414	0.451	0.469	0.487	0.496
2.57	0.000	0.000	0.000	0.000	0.017	0.148	0.236	0.291	0.327	0.354	0.373	0.401	0.437	0.455	0.473	0.482
2.58	0.000	0.000	0.000	0.000	0.015	0.140	0.226	0.279	0.316	0.341	0.361	0.388	0.424	0.441	0.459	0.468
2.59	0.000	0.000	0.000	0.000	0.013	0.133	0.216	0.269	0.304	0.330	0.349	0.375	0.410	0.428	0.445	0.454
2.60	0.000	0.000	0.000	0.000	0.011	0.125	0.207	0.258	0.293	0.318	0.337	0.363	0.398	0.415	0.432	0.441
2.61	0.000	0.000	0.000	0.000	0.009	0.118	0.198	0.248	0.282	0.307	0.325	0.351	0.385	0.402	0.419	0.428
2.62	0.000	0.000	0.000	0.000	0.008	0.112	0.189	0.238	0.272	0.296	0.314	0.339	0.373	0.390	0.406	0.415
2.63	0.000	0.000	0.000	0.000	0.007	0.105	0.181	0.229	0.262	0.285	0.303	0.328	0.361	0.378	0.394	0.402
2.64	0.000	0.000	0.000	0.000	0.005	0.099	0.172	0.220	0.252	0.275	0.293	0.317	0.350	0.366	0.382	0.390
2.65	0.000	0.000	0.000	0.000	0.005	0.094	0.165	0.211	0.243	0.265	0.282	0.307	0.339	0.355	0.371	0.379
2.66	0.000	0.000	0.000	0.000	0.004	0.088	0.157	0.202	0.233	0.256	0.273	0.296	0.328	0.344	0.359	0.367
2.67	0.000	0.000	0.000	0.000	0.003	0.083	0.150	0.194	0.224	0.246	0.263	0.286	0.317	0.333	0.348	0.356
2.68	0.000	0.000	0.000	0.000	0.002	0.078	0.143	0.186	0.216	0.237	0.254	0.277	0.307	0.322	0.338	0.345
2.69	0.000	0.000	0.000	0.000	0.002	0.073	0.136	0.179	0.208	0.229	0.245	0.267	0.297	0.312	0.327	0.335

EXHIBIT VI.7-5—CONTINUED

Q_U or Q_L	Sample Size															
	3	4	5	7	10	15	20	25	30	35	40	50	75	100	150	200
2.70	0.000	0.000	0.000	0.000	0.001	0.069	0.130	0.171	0.200	0.220	0.236	0.258	0.288	0.302	0.317	0.325
2.71	0.000	0.000	0.000	0.000	0.001	0.064	0.124	0.164	0.192	0.212	0.227	0.249	0.278	0.293	0.307	0.315
2.72	0.000	0.000	0.000	0.000	0.000	0.060	0.118	0.157	0.184	0.204	0.219	0.241	0.269	0.283	0.298	0.305
2.73	0.000	0.000	0.000	0.000	0.000	0.057	0.112	0.151	0.177	0.197	0.211	0.232	0.260	0.274	0.288	0.296
2.74	0.000	0.000	0.000	0.000	0.000	0.053	0.107	0.144	0.170	0.189	0.204	0.224	0.252	0.266	0.279	0.286
2.75	0.000	0.000	0.000	0.000	0.000	0.049	0.102	0.138	0.163	0.182	0.196	0.216	0.243	0.257	0.271	0.277
2.76	0.000	0.000	0.000	0.000	0.000	0.046	0.097	0.132	0.157	0.175	0.189	0.209	0.235	0.249	0.262	0.269
2.77	0.000	0.000	0.000	0.000	0.000	0.043	0.092	0.126	0.151	0.168	0.182	0.201	0.227	0.241	0.254	0.260
2.78	0.000	0.000	0.000	0.000	0.000	0.040	0.087	0.121	0.145	0.162	0.175	0.194	0.220	0.233	0.246	0.252
2.79	0.000	0.000	0.000	0.000	0.000	0.037	0.083	0.115	0.139	0.156	0.169	0.187	0.212	0.225	0.238	0.244
2.80	0.000	0.000	0.000	0.000	0.000	0.035	0.079	0.110	0.133	0.150	0.162	0.181	0.205	0.218	0.230	0.237
2.81	0.000	0.000	0.000	0.000	0.000	0.032	0.075	0.105	0.128	0.144	0.156	0.174	0.198	0.211	0.223	0.229
2.82	0.000	0.000	0.000	0.000	0.000	0.030	0.071	0.101	0.122	0.138	0.150	0.168	0.192	0.204	0.216	0.222
2.83	0.000	0.000	0.000	0.000	0.000	0.028	0.067	0.096	0.117	0.133	0.145	0.162	0.185	0.197	0.209	0.215
2.84	0.000	0.000	0.000	0.000	0.000	0.026	0.064	0.092	0.112	0.128	0.139	0.156	0.179	0.190	0.202	0.208
2.85	0.000	0.000	0.000	0.000	0.000	0.024	0.060	0.088	0.108	0.122	0.134	0.150	0.173	0.184	0.195	0.201
2.86	0.000	0.000	0.000	0.000	0.000	0.022	0.057	0.084	0.103	0.118	0.129	0.145	0.167	0.178	0.189	0.195
2.87	0.000	0.000	0.000	0.000	0.000	0.020	0.054	0.080	0.099	0.113	0.124	0.139	0.161	0.172	0.183	0.188
2.88	0.000	0.000	0.000	0.000	0.000	0.019	0.051	0.076	0.094	0.108	0.119	0.134	0.155	0.166	0.177	0.182
2.89	0.000	0.000	0.000	0.000	0.000	0.017	0.048	0.073	0.090	0.104	0.114	0.129	0.150	0.160	0.171	0.176
2.90	0.000	0.000	0.000	0.000	0.000	0.016	0.046	0.069	0.087	0.100	0.110	0.125	0.145	0.155	0.165	0.171
2.91	0.000	0.000	0.000	0.000	0.000	0.015	0.043	0.066	0.083	0.096	0.106	0.120	0.140	0.150	0.160	0.165
2.92	0.000	0.000	0.000	0.000	0.000	0.013	0.041	0.063	0.079	0.092	0.101	0.115	0.135	0.145	0.155	0.160
2.93	0.000	0.000	0.000	0.000	0.000	0.012	0.038	0.060	0.076	0.088	0.097	0.111	0.130	0.140	0.149	0.154
2.94	0.000	0.000	0.000	0.000	0.000	0.011	0.036	0.057	0.072	0.084	0.093	0.107	0.125	0.135	0.144	0.149
2.95	0.000	0.000	0.000	0.000	0.000	0.010	0.034	0.054	0.069	0.081	0.090	0.103	0.121	0.130	0.140	0.144
2.96	0.000	0.000	0.000	0.000	0.000	0.009	0.032	0.051	0.066	0.077	0.086	0.099	0.117	0.126	0.135	0.140
2.97	0.000	0.000	0.000	0.000	0.000	0.009	0.030	0.049	0.063	0.074	0.083	0.095	0.112	0.121	0.130	0.135
2.98	0.000	0.000	0.000	0.000	0.000	0.008	0.028	0.046	0.060	0.071	0.079	0.091	0.108	0.117	0.126	0.130
2.99	0.000	0.000	0.000	0.000	0.000	0.007	0.027	0.044	0.057	0.068	0.076	0.088	0.104	0.113	0.122	0.126
3.00	0.000	0.000	0.000	0.000	0.000	0.006	0.025	0.042	0.055	0.065	0.073	0.084	0.101	0.109	0.118	0.122
3.01	0.000	0.000	0.000	0.000	0.000	0.006	0.024	0.040	0.052	0.062	0.070	0.081	0.097	0.105	0.114	0.118
3.02	0.000	0.000	0.000	0.000	0.000	0.005	0.022	0.038	0.050	0.059	0.067	0.078	0.093	0.101	0.110	0.114
3.03	0.000	0.000	0.000	0.000	0.000	0.005	0.021	0.036	0.048	0.057	0.064	0.075	0.090	0.098	0.106	0.110
3.04	0.000	0.000	0.000	0.000	0.000	0.004	0.019	0.034	0.045	0.054	0.061	0.072	0.087	0.094	0.102	0.106
3.05	0.000	0.000	0.000	0.000	0.000	0.004	0.018	0.032	0.043	0.052	0.059	0.069	0.083	0.091	0.099	0.103
3.06	0.000	0.000	0.000	0.000	0.000	0.003	0.017	0.030	0.041	0.050	0.056	0.066	0.080	0.088	0.095	0.099
3.07	0.000	0.000	0.000	0.000	0.000	0.003	0.016	0.029	0.039	0.047	0.054	0.064	0.077	0.085	0.092	0.096
3.08	0.000	0.000	0.000	0.000	0.000	0.003	0.015	0.027	0.037	0.045	0.052	0.061	0.074	0.081	0.089	0.092
3.09	0.000	0.000	0.000	0.000	0.000	0.002	0.014	0.026	0.036	0.043	0.049	0.059	0.072	0.079	0.086	0.089

EXHIBIT VI.7-5—Continued

Q_U or Q_L	Sample Size															
	3	4	5	7	10	15	20	25	30	35	40	50	75	100	150	200
3.10	0.000	0.000	0.000	0.000	0.000	0.002	0.013	0.024	0.034	0.041	0.047	0.056	0.069	0.076	0.083	0.086
3.11	0.000	0.000	0.000	0.000	0.000	0.002	0.012	0.023	0.032	0.039	0.045	0.054	0.066	0.073	0.080	0.083
3.12	0.000	0.000	0.000	0.000	0.000	0.002	0.011	0.022	0.031	0.038	0.043	0.052	0.064	0.070	0.077	0.080
3.13	0.000	0.000	0.000	0.000	0.000	0.002	0.011	0.021	0.029	0.036	0.041	0.050	0.061	0.068	0.074	0.077
3.14	0.000	0.000	0.000	0.000	0.000	0.001	0.010	0.019	0.028	0.034	0.040	0.048	0.059	0.065	0.071	0.075
3.15	0.000	0.000	0.000	0.000	0.000	0.001	0.009	0.018	0.026	0.033	0.038	0.046	0.057	0.063	0.069	0.072
3.16	0.000	0.000	0.000	0.000	0.000	0.001	0.009	0.017	0.025	0.031	0.036	0.044	0.055	0.060	0.066	0.069
3.17	0.000	0.000	0.000	0.000	0.000	0.001	0.008	0.016	0.024	0.030	0.035	0.042	0.053	0.058	0.064	0.067
3.18	0.000	0.000	0.000	0.000	0.000	0.001	0.007	0.015	0.022	0.028	0.033	0.040	0.050	0.056	0.062	0.065
3.19	0.000	0.000	0.000	0.000	0.000	0.001	0.007	0.015	0.021	0.027	0.032	0.038	0.049	0.054	0.059	0.062
3.20	0.000	0.000	0.000	0.000	0.000	0.001	0.006	0.014	0.020	0.026	0.030	0.037	0.047	0.052	0.057	0.060
3.21	0.000	0.000	0.000	0.000	0.000	0.000	0.006	0.013	0.019	0.024	0.029	0.035	0.045	0.050	0.055	0.058
3.22	0.000	0.000	0.000	0.000	0.000	0.000	0.005	0.012	0.018	0.023	0.027	0.034	0.043	0.048	0.053	0.056
3.23	0.000	0.000	0.000	0.000	0.000	0.000	0.005	0.011	0.017	0.022	0.026	0.032	0.041	0.046	0.051	0.054
3.24	0.000	0.000	0.000	0.000	0.000	0.000	0.005	0.011	0.016	0.021	0.025	0.031	0.040	0.044	0.049	0.052
3.25	0.000	0.000	0.000	0.000	0.000	0.000	0.004	0.010	0.015	0.020	0.024	0.030	0.038	0.043	0.048	0.050
3.26	0.000	0.000	0.000	0.000	0.000	0.000	0.004	0.009	0.015	0.019	0.023	0.028	0.037	0.041	0.046	0.048
3.27	0.000	0.000	0.000	0.000	0.000	0.000	0.004	0.009	0.014	0.019	0.022	0.027	0.035	0.040	0.044	0.046
3.28	0.000	0.000	0.000	0.000	0.000	0.000	0.003	0.008	0.013	0.017	0.021	0.026	0.034	0.038	0.042	0.045
3.29	0.000	0.000	0.000	0.000	0.000	0.000	0.003	0.008	0.012	0.016	0.020	0.025	0.032	0.037	0.041	0.043
3.30	0.000	0.000	0.000	0.000	0.000	0.000	0.003	0.007	0.012	0.015	0.019	0.024	0.031	0.035	0.039	0.042
3.31	0.000	0.000	0.000	0.000	0.000	0.000	0.003	0.007	0.011	0.015	0.018	0.023	0.030	0.034	0.038	0.040
3.32	0.000	0.000	0.000	0.000	0.000	0.000	0.002	0.006	0.010	0.014	0.017	0.022	0.029	0.032	0.036	0.039
3.33	0.000	0.000	0.000	0.000	0.000	0.000	0.002	0.006	0.010	0.013	0.016	0.021	0.027	0.031	0.035	0.037
3.34	0.000	0.000	0.000	0.000	0.000	0.000	0.002	0.006	0.009	0.013	0.015	0.020	0.026	0.030	0.034	0.036
3.35	0.000	0.000	0.000	0.000	0.000	0.000	0.002	0.005	0.009	0.012	0.015	0.019	0.025	0.029	0.032	0.034
3.36	0.000	0.000	0.000	0.000	0.000	0.000	0.002	0.005	0.008	0.011	0.014	0.018	0.024	0.028	0.031	0.033
3.37	0.000	0.000	0.000	0.000	0.000	0.000	0.002	0.005	0.008	0.011	0.013	0.017	0.023	0.026	0.030	0.032
3.38	0.000	0.000	0.000	0.000	0.000	0.000	0.001	0.004	0.007	0.010	0.013	0.016	0.022	0.025	0.029	0.031
3.39	0.000	0.000	0.000	0.000	0.000	0.000	0.001	0.004	0.007	0.010	0.012	0.016	0.021	0.024	0.028	0.029
3.40	0.000	0.000	0.000	0.000	0.000	0.000	0.001	0.004	0.007	0.009	0.011	0.015	0.020	0.023	0.027	0.028
3.41	0.000	0.000	0.000	0.000	0.000	0.000	0.001	0.003	0.006	0.009	0.011	0.014	0.020	0.022	0.026	0.027
3.42	0.000	0.000	0.000	0.000	0.000	0.000	0.001	0.003	0.006	0.008	0.010	0.014	0.019	0.022	0.025	0.026
3.43	0.000	0.000	0.000	0.000	0.000	0.000	0.001	0.003	0.005	0.008	0.010	0.013	0.018	0.021	0.024	0.025
3.44	0.000	0.000	0.000	0.000	0.000	0.000	0.001	0.003	0.005	0.007	0.009	0.012	0.017	0.020	0.023	0.024
3.45	0.000	0.000	0.000	0.000	0.000	0.000	0.001	0.003	0.005	0.007	0.009	0.012	0.016	0.019	0.022	0.023
3.46	0.000	0.000	0.000	0.000	0.000	0.000	0.001	0.002	0.005	0.007	0.008	0.011	0.016	0.018	0.021	0.022
3.47	0.000	0.000	0.000	0.000	0.000	0.000	0.001	0.002	0.004	0.006	0.008	0.011	0.015	0.017	0.020	0.022
3.48	0.000	0.000	0.000	0.000	0.000	0.000	0.001	0.002	0.004	0.006	0.007	0.010	0.014	0.017	0.019	0.021
3.49	0.000	0.000	0.000	0.000	0.000	0.000	0.000	0.002	0.004	0.005	0.007	0.010	0.014	0.016	0.019	0.020

EXHIBIT VI.7-5—CONTINUED

Q_U or Q_L	Sample Size															
	3	4	5	7	10	15	20	25	30	35	40	50	75	100	150	200
3.50	0.000	0.000	0.000	0.000	0.000	0.000	0.000	0.002	0.003	0.005	0.007	0.009	0.013	0.015	0.018	0.019
3.51	0.000	0.000	0.000	0.000	0.000	0.000	0.000	0.002	0.003	0.005	0.006	0.009	0.013	0.015	0.017	0.018
3.52	0.000	0.000	0.000	0.000	0.000	0.000	0.000	0.002	0.003	0.005	0.006	0.008	0.012	0.014	0.017	0.018
3.53	0.000	0.000	0.000	0.000	0.000	0.000	0.000	0.001	0.003	0.004	0.006	0.008	0.012	0.014	0.016	0.017
3.54	0.000	0.000	0.000	0.000	0.000	0.000	0.000	0.001	0.003	0.004	0.005	0.008	0.011	0.013	0.015	0.016
3.55	0.000	0.000	0.000	0.000	0.000	0.000	0.000	0.001	0.003	0.004	0.005	0.007	0.011	0.012	0.015	0.016
3.56	0.000	0.000	0.000	0.000	0.000	0.000	0.000	0.001	0.002	0.004	0.005	0.007	0.010	0.012	0.014	0.015
3.57	0.000	0.000	0.000	0.000	0.000	0.000	0.000	0.001	0.002	0.003	0.005	0.006	0.010	0.011	0.013	0.014
3.58	0.000	0.000	0.000	0.000	0.000	0.000	0.000	0.001	0.002	0.003	0.004	0.006	0.009	0.011	0.013	0.014
3.59	0.000	0.000	0.000	0.000	0.000	0.000	0.000	0.001	0.002	0.003	0.004	0.006	0.009	0.010	0.012	0.013
3.60	0.000	0.000	0.000	0.000	0.000	0.000	0.000	0.001	0.002	0.003	0.004	0.006	0.008	0.010	0.012	0.013
3.61	0.000	0.000	0.000	0.000	0.000	0.000	0.000	0.001	0.002	0.003	0.004	0.005	0.008	0.010	0.011	0.012
3.62	0.000	0.000	0.000	0.000	0.000	0.000	0.000	0.001	0.002	0.003	0.003	0.005	0.008	0.009	0.011	0.012
3.63	0.000	0.000	0.000	0.000	0.000	0.000	0.000	0.001	0.001	0.002	0.003	0.005	0.007	0.009	0.010	0.011
3.64	0.000	0.000	0.000	0.000	0.000	0.000	0.000	0.001	0.001	0.002	0.003	0.004	0.007	0.008	0.010	0.011
3.65	0.000	0.000	0.000	0.000	0.000	0.000	0.000	0.001	0.001	0.002	0.003	0.004	0.007	0.008	0.010	0.010
3.66	0.000	0.000	0.000	0.000	0.000	0.000	0.000	0.000	0.001	0.002	0.003	0.004	0.006	0.008	0.009	0.010
3.67	0.000	0.000	0.000	0.000	0.000	0.000	0.000	0.000	0.001	0.002	0.003	0.004	0.006	0.007	0.009	0.010
3.68	0.000	0.000	0.000	0.000	0.000	0.000	0.000	0.000	0.001	0.002	0.002	0.004	0.006	0.007	0.008	0.009
3.69	0.000	0.000	0.000	0.000	0.000	0.000	0.000	0.000	0.001	0.002	0.002	0.003	0.005	0.007	0.008	0.009
3.70	0.000	0.000	0.000	0.000	0.000	0.000	0.000	0.000	0.001	0.002	0.002	0.003	0.005	0.006	0.008	0.008
3.71	0.000	0.000	0.000	0.000	0.000	0.000	0.000	0.000	0.001	0.001	0.002	0.003	0.005	0.006	0.007	0.008
3.72	0.000	0.000	0.000	0.000	0.000	0.000	0.000	0.000	0.001	0.001	0.002	0.003	0.005	0.006	0.007	0.008
3.73	0.000	0.000	0.000	0.000	0.000	0.000	0.000	0.000	0.001	0.001	0.002	0.003	0.005	0.006	0.007	0.007
3.74	0.000	0.000	0.000	0.000	0.000	0.000	0.000	0.000	0.001	0.001	0.002	0.003	0.004	0.005	0.007	0.007
3.75	0.000	0.000	0.000	0.000	0.000	0.000	0.000	0.000	0.001	0.001	0.002	0.002	0.004	0.005	0.006	0.007
3.76	0.000	0.000	0.000	0.000	0.000	0.000	0.000	0.000	0.001	0.001	0.001	0.002	0.004	0.005	0.006	0.007
3.77	0.000	0.000	0.000	0.000	0.000	0.000	0.000	0.000	0.001	0.001	0.001	0.002	0.004	0.005	0.006	0.006
3.78	0.000	0.000	0.000	0.000	0.000	0.000	0.000	0.000	0.000	0.001	0.001	0.002	0.004	0.004	0.005	0.006
3.79	0.000	0.000	0.000	0.000	0.000	0.000	0.000	0.000	0.000	0.001	0.001	0.002	0.003	0.004	0.005	0.006
3.80	0.000	0.000	0.000	0.000	0.000	0.000	0.000	0.000	0.000	0.001	0.001	0.002	0.003	0.004	0.005	0.006
3.81	0.000	0.000	0.000	0.000	0.000	0.000	0.000	0.000	0.000	0.001	0.001	0.002	0.003	0.004	0.005	0.005
3.82	0.000	0.000	0.000	0.000	0.000	0.000	0.000	0.000	0.000	0.001	0.001	0.002	0.003	0.004	0.005	0.005
3.83	0.000	0.000	0.000	0.000	0.000	0.000	0.000	0.000	0.000	0.001	0.001	0.002	0.003	0.004	0.004	0.005
3.84	0.000	0.000	0.000	0.000	0.000	0.000	0.000	0.000	0.000	0.001	0.001	0.001	0.003	0.003	0.004	0.005
3.85	0.000	0.000	0.000	0.000	0.000	0.000	0.000	0.000	0.000	0.001	0.001	0.001	0.002	0.003	0.004	0.004
3.86	0.000	0.000	0.000	0.000	0.000	0.000	0.000	0.000	0.000	0.000	0.001	0.001	0.002	0.003	0.004	0.004
3.87	0.000	0.000	0.000	0.000	0.000	0.000	0.000	0.000	0.000	0.000	0.001	0.001	0.002	0.003	0.004	0.004
3.88	0.000	0.000	0.000	0.000	0.000	0.000	0.000	0.000	0.000	0.000	0.001	0.001	0.002	0.003	0.004	0.004
3.89	0.000	0.000	0.000	0.000	0.000	0.000	0.000	0.000	0.000	0.000	0.001	0.001	0.002	0.003	0.003	0.004
3.90	0.000	0.000	0.000	0.000	0.000	0.000	0.000	0.000	0.000	0.000	0.001	0.001	0.002	0.003	0.003	0.004

Source: Halpern, Siegmund, *The Assurance Sciences: An Introduction to Quality Control and Reliability*, Englewood Cliffs, N.J.: Prentice-Hall, Inc., 1978.

Reference

Lieberman, G. J. and G. J. Resnikoff, "Sampling Plans for Inspection by Variables," *Journal of the American Statistical Association*, Vol. L (1955), pp. 457–516.

VI.8 Variables Control Charts

A. Description

It has been recognized that manufacturing processes are subject to two types of variation: those due to chance or random causes, and those due to "assignable causes." In process control, attention is focused on detection of the latter of these, so that action can be taken to correct the process. Variables control charts are used to monitor inspection results based on measurements data. They are a graphical aid in conducting a hypothesis test that the units inspected come from a process that is operating in the absence of any assignable causes. This is referred to as being *in control.* Similarly, when assignable causes are present, the process is said to be *out of control.*

If an assignable cause is present, it may affect the process by changing the mean value of the quality measurements, or it may affect the variance of the measurements. Separate charts are used to examine the average (or mean) and the variability of the process. The chart used when considering the process average is called the $\overline{X}$ (read "X Bar") chart. Two different charts can be used for variability: the R chart and the S chart.

When the charts indicate that the process is out of control, action should be taken to identify and correct the assignable cause. Knowledge of whether the mean or the variability has been affected may be useful in these efforts. However, at times it may be impossible to identify a particular problem with the process. This may occur because the process has corrected itself. Alternatively, as can occur in any hypothesis-testing procedure, the point may have fallen beyond the limits due to random chance, and no assignable cause was present.

Historically, the R chart has been used much more widely than the S chart, as it requires less arithmetic manipulation of the data. The S chart is preferable on statistical grounds. With the current availability of electronic calculators for performing the necessary arithmetic, the S chart is recommended. A third alternative that has been reported in the literature is the σ chart, also referred to as the $S_{(rms)}$ chart in ANSI/ASQC Standard A1

[1978]. While the $S_{(\text{rms})}$ chart is statistically equivalent to the S chart with respect to hypothesis testing, the S chart is generally preferred.

Operation of the charts consist of the following steps, which are repeated at (usually) fixed intervals of time:

1. Take measurements on a random sample of n items, $X_1, X_2, \ldots, X_n$.
2. Compute the sample mean, $\overline{X} = \Sigma_{i=1}^{n} X_i / n$
3. a. Compute the sample standard deviation,

$$S = \sqrt{\left(\sum_{i=1}^{n} X_i^2 - n\overline{X}^2 \right) \Big/ (n-1)}$$

   or

   b. Compute the range (i.e., the difference between the largest and smallest values in the sample).
4. Plot the values found in steps 2 and 3 on the $\overline{X}$ and S (or R) charts, as illustrated by the $\overline{X}$ chart in the following figure. If points on either of the charts are outside of the control limits, the process is said to be out of control.

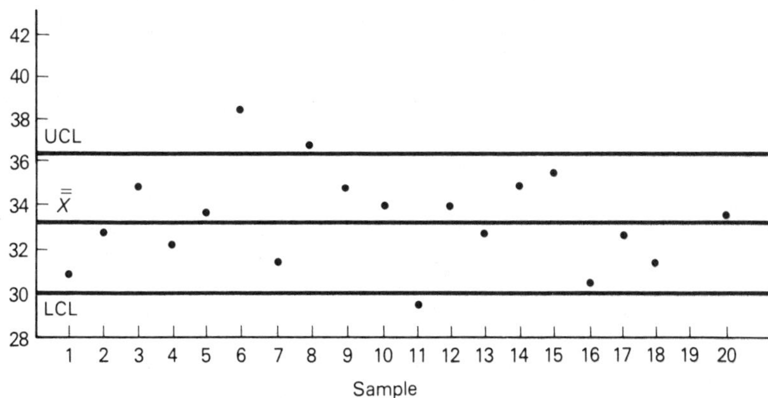

In addition to checking whether any single point falls outside of the control limits, the points on the chart can be analyzed for nonrandom patterns. A runs test, as described in Section III.3, is useful in this analysis.

To construct the charts, it is necessary to establish values for the control lines and control limits for each chart. The required procedures depend on which of two situations exist with respect to the desired values of the mean and variability of the process.

When the capabilities of the process are known (e.g., from historical experience or the equipment manufacturer's performance specifications), the values of the mean and variability when no assignable causes are present can be specified. These are referred to as standard values, and are denoted as $\overline{X}_0$ and S_0 (or R_0), respectively.

The reader is cautioned here that, since S is a biased estimate of the population standard deviation σ, and since standard values for variability will frequently be given in terms of σ, a conversion factor is required. (The reader might recall that S^2 is an unbiased estimate of σ^2; however, S is *not* an unbiased estimate of σ.) The relationships required are

$$S_0 = C_4 \sigma_0$$

or

$$R_0 = d_2 \sigma_0$$

where the values of C_4 and d_2 for various sample sizes are found in Exhibit VI.8–1.

If standard values are not available, data must be collected when the process is operating "correctly," and the target values of the mean and variability are estimated from a series of m samples by

$$\overline{\overline{X}} = (\overline{X}_1 + \overline{X}_2 + \cdots + \overline{X}_m)/m$$

and

$$\overline{S} = (S_1 + S_2 + \cdots + S_m)/m$$

or

$$\overline{R} = (R_1 + R_2 + \cdots + R_m)/m$$

The control chart limits are computed using various constants. The symbol A is used for charts for averages, the symbol B for S charts, and the symbol D for range charts. These symbols will be subscripted to provide values for computation of the upper and lower limits in the case where standards are given or in the case where no standards are given. Exhibit

VI.8–2 lists the formulas to be used for central lines and control limits for the charts.

The distance from the central line on a chart to the control limits is a specified multiple of the standard deviation of the quantity being plotted on the chart. Usually this multiple is chosen to have a value of three, which is the value used in the construction of Exhibit VI.8–1. This chart provides values for the A's, B's, and D's used in constructing the control chart limits. The necessary values for determining the limits are given for values of n from 2 to 25, since the standard deviations of the statistics are a function of the sample size.

B. Using the Tables

B–1. Values for $\overline{X}$ Charts

Suppose that samples of 5 items are being taken and the 3σ control chart limits for an $\overline{X}$ chart when standard values are given are desired. From Exhibit VI.8–2, we see that the central line will be $\overline{X}_0$, with limits at $\overline{X}_0 \pm A\sigma_0$. From Exhibit VI.8–1, the value of A for $n = 5$ is 1.342. If the standards had not been given, the central line would have had to be estimated with $\overline{\overline{X}}$ computed from previous data. The control chart limits would be $\overline{\overline{X}} \pm A_2\overline{R}$ if variability were being monitored with the range, or $\overline{\overline{X}} \pm A_3\overline{S}$ if the standard deviation was being used. For $n = 5$, $A_2 = 0.577$ and $A_3 = 1.427$.

B–2. Values for R Charts

Samples of 7 items are being taken, and the 3σ control chart limits are required for an R chart when the desired standard deviation of the process is a specified value. From Exhibit VI.8–2, the central line will be $d_2\sigma_0$, the lower control limit will be $D_1\sigma_0$, and the upper control limit will be $D_2\sigma_0$. From Exhibit VI.8–1, for $n = 7$, we find $d_2 = 2.704$, $D_1 = 0.204$, and $D_2 =$ 5.204.

If the desired value of standard deviation had not been specified, and $\overline{R}$ had been computed from previous data, the central line would be $\overline{R}$, and the control limits would be at $D_3\overline{R}$ and $D_4\overline{R}$. For $n = 7$, Exhibit VI.8–1 gives $D_3 = 0.076$ and $D_4 = 1.924$.

B–3. Values for S Charts

Assume samples of 6 items are to be used in the operation of an S chart and the 3σ control chart parameters are required when the desired value of the process standard deviation σ_0 is specified. From Exhibit VI.8–2, the central line is $c_4\sigma_0$, the lower control limit is $B_5\sigma_0$, and the upper control limit is $B_6\sigma_0$. From Exhibit VI.8–1, for $n=6$, we have $c_4=0.9515$, $B_5=0.029$, and $B_6=1.874$.

If σ_0 had not been specified and $\overline{S}$ had been computed from historical data, the central line would have been $\overline{S}$, and the control limits would have been at $B_3\overline{S}$ and $B_4\overline{S}$. For $n=6$, $B_3=0.030$ and $B_4=1.970$.

C. Examples of Control Chart Use

C–1. Standard Values Given

It is desired to set up the usual (3σ) $\overline{X}$ and S charts to monitor a process that fills boxes of cake mix. The quality characteristic of interest is the weight of material put into the boxes. The desired mean amount is 12.05 ounces, and the specified standard deviation that is expected is 0.02 ounces. Samples of $n=4$ are to be taken at half-hour intervals.

The central line on the $\overline{X}$ chart will be $\overline{X}_0=12.05$, and the control limits will be

$$\overline{X}\pm A\sigma_0 = 12.05 \pm 1.500(0.02)$$
$$= 12.05 \pm 0.0300$$

For the S chart, the central line will be $c_4\sigma_0=0.9213(.02)=0.0184$, and the control limits will be

$$B_5\sigma_0 = 0(0.02) = 0$$

and

$$B_6\sigma_0 = 2.088(0.02) = 0.0418$$

C–2. Data-Based Standards

Assume that the process described in Section C–1 is to be monitored with $\overline{X}$ and R charts, but that no standards are given. Historical data for 10 samples with four items in each sample are shown below. (In practice a minimum of 20 historical samples is recommended; 10 are used for illustrative purposes only.)

Sample No.	$\overline{X}_i$	R_i
1	12.047	0.019
2	12.054	0.034
3	12.052	0.026
4	12.031	0.022
5	12.028	0.037
6	12.058	0.012
7	12.029	0.019
8	12.051	0.029
9	12.027	0.013
10	12.060	0.009
Total	120.437	0.220
	$\overline{\overline{X}} = 12.0437$	$\overline{R} = 0.022$

The R chart will have its central line at $\overline{R} = 0.022$ and control limits at $D_3\overline{R} = 0(0.022) = 0$ and $D_4\overline{R} = 2.282(0.022) = 0.0502$. As all individual R_i's fall between the limits, it seems reasonable to assume that all data points were taken when the process was operating correctly with respect to variability. If any individual points had fallen outside the limits, the usual procedure is to discard those points and recompute $\overline{\overline{X}}$, $\overline{R}$, and the limits. This procedure presumes that points that fall outside the control limits were taken when an assignable cause had influenced the process. As the control chart parameters should be based only on data taken when the process is in control, discarding these points seems appropriate. However, it is recommended that efforts be made to verify that the process was in fact out of control when these points were collected. If it cannot be verified, it may be that the output from the process does not follow the assumed normal distribution, and caution should be exercised before adopting these control chart procedures. Only those points that are in control with respect to variability are used to construct the $\overline{X}$ chart.

The central line on the $\overline{X}$ chart is $\overline{\overline{X}} = 12.0437$, and the limits are $\overline{\overline{X}} \pm A_2\overline{R} = 12.0439 \pm (0.729)(0.022) = 12.0439 \pm 0.0164$. Again, all data points fall between the limits. If any points had fallen outside the limits, they would have been discarded (with the same reservations as noted for the $\overline{R}$ chart), and a new centerline and limits computed.

Reference

ANSI/ASQC Standard A1, "Definitions, Symbols, Formulas and Tables for Control Charts." American Society for Quality Control, Milwaukee, Wisconsin, 1978.

EXHIBIT VI.8–1

FACTORS FOR 3σ CONTROL CHARTS

Observations in Sample, n	X CHARTS			S CHARTS						R CHARTS						
	FACTORS FOR CONTROL LIMITS			FACTORS FOR CENTRAL LINE		FACTORS FOR CONTROL LIMITS				FACTORS FOR CENTRAL LINE		FACTORS FOR CONTROL LIMITS				
	A	A_2	A_3	c_4	$1/c_4$	B_3	B_4	B_5	B_6	d_2	$1/d_2$	d_3	D_1	D_2	D_3	D_4
2	2.121	1.880	2.659	0.7979	1.2533	0	3.267	0	2.606	1.128	0.8865	0.853	0	3.686	0	3.267
3	1.732	1.023	1.954	0.8862	1.1284	0	2.568	0	2.276	1.693	0.5907	0.888	0	4.358	0	2.574
4	1.500	0.729	1.628	0.9213	1.0854	0	2.266	0	2.088	2.059	0.4857	0.880	0	4.698	0	2.282
5	1.342	0.577	1.427	0.9400	1.0638	0	2.089	0	1.964	2.326	0.4299	0.864	0	4.918	0	2.114
6	1.225	0.483	1.287	0.9515	1.0510	0.030	1.970	0.029	1.874	2.534	0.3946	0.848	0	5.078	0	2.004
7	1.134	0.419	1.182	0.9594	1.0423	0.118	1.882	0.113	1.806	2.704	0.3698	0.833	0.204	5.204	0.076	1.924
8	1.061	0.373	1.099	0.9650	1.0363	0.185	1.815	0.179	1.751	2.847	0.3512	0.820	0.388	5.306	0.136	1.864
9	1.000	0.337	1.032	0.9693	1.0317	0.239	1.761	0.232	1.707	2.970	0.3367	0.808	0.547	5.393	0.184	1.816
10	0.949	0.308	0.975	0.9727	1.0281	0.284	1.716	0.276	1.669	3.078	0.3249	0.797	0.687	5.469	0.223	1.777
11	0.905	0.285	0.927	0.9754	1.0252	0.321	1.679	0.313	1.637	3.173	0.3152	0.787	0.811	5.535	0.256	1.744
12	0.866	0.266	0.886	0.9776	1.0229	0.354	1.646	0.346	1.610	3.258	0.3069	0.778	0.922	5.594	0.283	1.717
13	0.832	0.249	0.850	0.9794	1.0210	0.382	1.618	0.374	1.585	3.336	0.2998	0.770	1.025	5.647	0.307	1.693
14	0.802	0.235	0.817	0.9810	1.0194	0.406	1.594	0.399	1.563	3.407	0.2935	0.763	1.118	5.696	0.328	1.672
15	0.775	0.223	0.789	0.9823	1.0180	0.428	1.572	0.421	1.544	3.472	0.2880	0.756	1.203	5.741	0.347	1.653
16	0.750	0.212	0.763	0.9835	1.0168	0.448	1.552	0.440	1.526	3.532	0.2831	0.750	1.282	5.782	0.363	1.637
17	0.728	0.203	0.739	0.9845	1.0157	0.466	1.534	0.458	1.511	3.588	0.2787	0.744	1.356	5.820	0.378	1.622
18	0.707	0.194	0.718	0.9854	1.0148	0.482	1.518	0.475	1.496	3.640	0.2747	0.739	1.424	5.856	0.391	1.608
19	0.688	0.187	0.698	0.9862	1.0140	0.497	1.503	0.490	1.483	3.689	0.2711	0.734	1.487	5.891	0.403	1.597
20	0.671	0.180	0.680	0.9869	1.0133	0.510	1.490	0.504	1.470	3.735	0.2677	0.729	1.549	5.921	0.415	1.585
21	0.655	0.173	0.663	0.9876	1.0126	0.523	1.477	0.516	1.459	3.778	0.2647	0.724	1.605	5.951	0.425	1.575
22	0.640	0.167	0.647	0.9882	1.0119	0.534	1.466	0.528	1.448	3.819	0.2618	0.720	1.659	5.979	0.434	1.566
23	0.626	0.162	0.633	0.9887	1.0114	0.545	1.455	0.539	1.438	3.858	0.2592	0.716	1.710	6.006	0.443	1.557
24	0.612	0.157	0.619	0.9892	1.0109	0.555	1.445	0.549	1.429	3.895	0.2567	0.712	1.759	6.031	0.451	1.548
25	0.600	0.153	0.606	0.9896	1.0105	0.565	1.435	0.559	1.420	3.931	0.2544	0.708	1.806	6.056	0.459	1.541

*Source: Factors A_1, A_2, B_3, B_4, d_2, $1/d_2$, d_3, D_1, D_2, D_3, and D_4 from Table B2 of the *ASTM Manual on Quality Control of Materials*, 1951, Copyright, American Society for Testing and Materials, 1916 Race Street, Philadelphia, Pennsylvania 19103. Reprinted with permission.

Factors A_3, B_5, and B_6 from *ASQC Standard A1*, Table 1, 1978. Copyright, American Society for Quality Control, Inc. Reprinted by permission.

EXHIBIT VI.8–2

LIMIT FORMULAS FOR 3σ CONTROL CHARTS

	NO STANDARD GIVEN		STANDARD GIVEN	
Statistic	Central Line	3-Sigma Control Limits	Central Line	3-Sigma Control Limits
$\overline{X}$	$\overline{\overline{X}}$	$\overline{\overline{X}} \pm A_2\overline{R}, \overline{\overline{X}} \pm A_3\overline{S}$	$\overline{X}_0$ or μ	$\overline{X}_0 \pm A\sigma_0$
R	$\overline{R}$	$D_3\overline{R}, D_4\overline{R}$	R_0 or $d_2\sigma_0$	$D_1\sigma_0, D_2\sigma_0$
S	$\overline{S}$	$B_3\overline{S}, B_4\overline{S}$	S_0 or $c_4\sigma_0$	$B_5\sigma_0, B_6\sigma_0$

VI.9 Cumulative (Cusum) Control Charts

A. Description*

The cumulative (cusum) chart is used to maintain current control of a process. It may be at least as effective as other control charts, but is less expensive to operate. Its effectiveness comes from its ability to detect a change in the process average more quickly than other variables control charts, especially if the change is small. It is also possible to more easily detect the time at which the change occurred.

The cusum procedure for a one-sided scheme will be described in this section. If a two-sided scheme is desired, the reader is referred to Duncan [1974]. The one-sided scheme for protection against increases in the mean of the process operates by plotting the cumulative sums of $\overline{X}_t - k$, where k is a value larger than the target value for $\overline{X}$, and $\overline{X}_t$ is the sample mean observed at time t. When plotting cusums, only positive values and the first negative value need be shown, because negative values represent good quality. When the cusum falls below zero, a new series is begun. When the cusum exceeds the decision interval h, the process is out of control. Thus, a cusum scheme can be defined by n, the number in each sample, and h, the decision interval.

A one-sided scheme can also be used to detect shifts in the negative direction. In that case, k will be less than the target value, and the test will be whether $\Sigma(\overline{X}_t - k)$ has a negative value that falls below $-h$. Only

*Refer to the guide at the beginning of Section VI to determine the appropriate uses of the individual control procedures.

negative values and the first positive value need be shown, because positive values represent good quality.

B. Reading the Nomogram

The criterion for choosing the cusum scheme is the average run length (ARL). The ARL is the number of sample points that will, on the average, have to be plotted before the control scheme will detect a specified change in the process. It is dependent on the true quality level of the process as well as on n and h. Determination of the ARL is facilitated by a nomogram prepared by K. W. Kemp [1962] and shown as Exhibit VI.9–1.

Suppose that there is a quality level m_a that is considered to be an acceptable quality level and another quality level $m_r > m_a$ that is barely tolerable. A reference value k is midway between m_r and m_a. Assume that the standard deviation σ of X is known. We wish to find a cusum scheme with specified ARL's at m_a and m_r.

First, note that there are four scales on Exhibit VI.9–1. The scale labeled L_r gives the ARL at m_r. Likewise, the scale L_a gives the ARL at m_a. That leaves two scales to consider. Call $A = h\sqrt{n}/\sigma$ the scale that has both unknowns, h and n. The scale $B = |k - m|\sqrt{n}/\sigma$ has only one unknown. Consider $m = m_a$ and $m = m_r$. Since $|k - m| = k - m_a = m_r - k$, a line connecting the desired L_a and the desired L_r results in a single point on scale B. The only unknown, n, can readily be computed by setting $|k - m_a|\sqrt{n}/\sigma$ equal to the value read on the B scale.

Once n is determined, it is conveniently rounded, usually up, but if only slightly above an integer, it may be rounded down. Now, recompute the entry on the B scale using the integer value.

Connect the new value on the B scale to the desired value on the L_a scale, and note the resulting value on the L_r scale. This results in a value on the A scale. Since h is the only unknown, it can be determined, and the cusum scheme has been specified.

An alternative cusum scheme is obtained by connecting a point on the B scale to the desired value on the L_r scale and noting the value on the L_a scale. The result on the A scale is read, resulting in another cusum scheme.

Two additional cusum schemes may be obtained by rounding n in the other direction. In the end, there are four schemes from which to choose, with the choice made on the basis of how close the schemes come to the desired ARL values.

If n happened to be an integer, after reading scale B and solving for the unknown, the intersection on scale A can be used to determine h. In this case, the ARL's will be satisfied exactly; there are no alternative cusum schemes.

C. Using the Nomogram

Example C–1. We seek a one-sided cusum scheme for which the ARL will be about 400 when the process mean is about 80 (the acceptable level) and the ARL will be about 5 when the process mean is about 100 (the barely tolerable quality level). The process output is a normally distributed random variable. The standard deviation of the process is approximately 20.

First, set k as the median value between m_a and m_r, or

$$k = (100 + 80)/2 = 90$$

Now, we need values of h and n that will yield the desired ARL's. Since $k - m_a = m_r - k$, we connect the point 5 on the L_r scale of Exhibit VI.9–1 with the point 400 on the L_a scale. The intersection on the B scale is at about 0.722. Solving for n yields

$$(10)\sqrt{n}/20 = 0.722$$

and

$$n = 2.08$$

Rounding down to $n = 2$ gives

$$|k - m|\sqrt{n}/\sigma = 10\sqrt{2}/20 = 0.707$$

The line connecting 0.707 on the B scale and the point 400 on the L_a scale will intersect the A scale at 3.16. Solving for h yields

$$h\sqrt{2}/20 = 3.16$$

and

$$h = 44.69$$

The cusum scheme will be to compute $\Sigma(\bar{X}_t - 90)$. If this value becomes negative, start anew. If the summation exceeds 44.69, the process is out of control.

The line connecting the point 400 on the L_a scale and 3.16 on the A scale also intersects the L_r scale at 5.2. Thus, the scheme $k = 90$, $h = 44.69$, and $n = 2$ yields the desired ARL at $m = 80$, but a slightly worse ARL at $m = 100$ than that specified.

By connecting the points 0.707 on the B scale and 5 on the L_r scale, we could have found a scheme that holds the ARL at $m = 100$ but yields a different L_a at $m = 80$. That is, $L_a = 300$.

EXHIBIT VI.9–1

NOMOGRAM FOR DETERMINING *ARL* VALUES

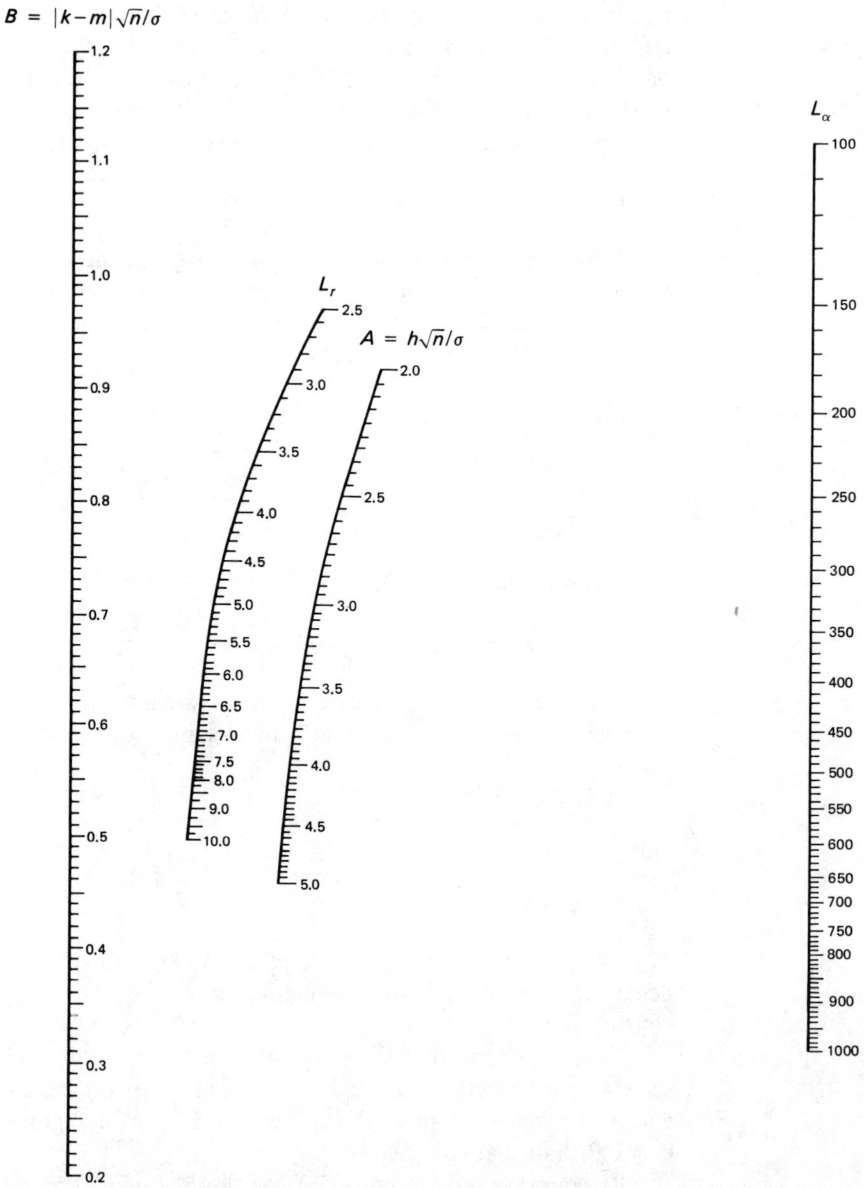

Source: Kemp, Kenneth W., "The Use of Cumulative Sums for Sampling Inspection Schemes," *Applied Statistics*, vol. XI, 1962, p. 23, With permission of the Royal Statistical Society.

Since $n = 2.08$, and was rounded down to 2, a conservative approach is to round n up to 3. Then we have

$$|k - m|\sqrt{n}/\sigma = 10\sqrt{3}/20 = 0.866$$

and a line connecting this point on the B scale with the point 400 on the L_a scale yields

$$h\sqrt{n}/\sigma = 2.6$$

on the A scale so that

$$h = 2.6(20)/\sqrt{3} = 30.02$$

The line also intersects the L_r line at the point 3.8, which is better than the called-for ARL at $m = 80$. Finally, connecting the points 0.866 on the B scale and 5 on the L_r scale yields an extremely large ARL at $m = 100$.

Of the four possibilities, the one coming closest to the desired ARL values is probably the first scheme, with $n = 2$ and $h = 44.69$.

References

Duncan, Acheson J., *Quality Control and Industrial Statistics*, 4th ed., Irwin, Homewood, Illinois, 1974.

Kemp, K. W., "The Use of Cumulative Sums for Sampling Inspection Schemes," *Applied Statistics*, Vol. XI (1962), p. 23.

VII

Random Numbers and Random Normal Numbers

VII.1 Random Numbers

A. Description

Random numbers have the following properties:

1. The set of random numbers is uniformly distributed between 0 and 1.
2. Successive random numbers are independent.

There are many techniques used to generate random numbers. Frequently used is the multiplicative congruential method, which produces a sequence of integers $X_1, X_2, \ldots$ between zero and $m-1$ according to the following recursive relationship:

$$X_{i+1} = aX_i \bmod m, \qquad i = 0, 1, 2, \ldots$$

The initial value, X_0, is called the seed, a is called the constant multiplier, and m is the modulus. To obtain random numbers between 0 and 1, set $R_i = X_i/m$, $i = 1, 2, \ldots$. Exhibit VII.1–1 contains random numbers generated using this technique.

Random numbers are used in discrete-event simulation, experimental design, and elsewhere.

B. Reading the Tables

Tables of random numbers generally have many thousands of entries. However, this Handbook can include only a small sample from such a table because of space limitations. Generally, discrete-event simulations are performed on a digital computer, and random numbers are generated within the routine (probably using the multiplicative congruential method). There are situations where a table of random numbers is needed, such as in a hand simulation or in randomly assigning subjects to experiments, and for this reason, a miniature table such as Exhibit VII.1–1 can be useful.

Exhibit VII.1–1 is actually a set of random integers. Random numbers are formed by placing a decimal point to the left of the selected value. The number of integers selected from the table is based on the accuracy of the underlying input distribution. Thus, if the probabilities associated with different events are expressed in hundredths, two-place integers would be selected.

In using a table of random numbers, begin at a random location. Just put your finger on a point selected at random. Then proceed in a random direction—up, down, left, right, diagonally, etc.—selecting the desired number of integers. An input distribution that has two-decimal-place accuracy may result in the random number stream .48, .40, .26, .84, ...

C. Using the Tables

C–1. Event Simulation

Suppose the number of daily arrivals to a job-shop is distributed as follows:

Arrivals/Day	Probability
0	.16
1	.32
2	.41
3	.10
4	.01

Generate random arrivals for ten workdays.

The first step is the assignment of random numbers according to the cumulative distribution function so that each event has the probability of occurrence specified by the input distribution. The result is as follows:

Arrivals/Day	Probability	Cumulative Probability	Random Number Assignment
0	.16	.16	.01–.16
1	.32	.48	.17–.48
2	.41	.89	.49–.89
3	.10	.99	.90–.99
4	.01	1.00	.00

Next, a set of 10 random numbers are obtained from Exhibit VII.1–1. These are compared with the random number assignment to generate the arrivals/day. The procedure is conducted as follows:

Day	Random Number (from the tables)	Arrivals
1	.60	2
2	.97	3
3	.26	1
4	.74	2
5	.37	1
6	.33	1
7	.52	2
8	.68	2
9	.03	0
10	.76	2

Example C–2. Experimental Design. Suppose there are three cloth-cutting machines that are being considered as potential replacements for the

EXHIBIT VII.1–1

Random Integers

25266	40490	55540	23419	29448	58200	72750	27332	31386	55885	88145	97681
37698	20271	40542	29584	56328	83551	38147	08664	79682	67694	78121	14877
86294	51710	21388	46447	09298	85448	30509	04343	24782	82329	79310	86242
52151	30700	36611	89860	88418	30887	74323	03686	96490	94760	94090	16144
76872	43019	64692	45869	37653	73719	41204	51562	09006	33892	28934	44419
28697	42777	79940	68740	80120	97980	35203	89748	14407	48000	19870	93207
80873	50329	49692	39306	87764	03361	40052	27147	67707	55082	89842	08468
13211	43668	27152	00549	05465	54200	35588	03134	40553	91416	90984	74828
98339	04705	13991	22120	39739	41214	39432	10791	08877	35448	09294	04378
04882	08084	13193	29122	21359	34143	14585	43981	56639	41023	55769	49806
04472	61049	28072	84981	69686	67060	60855	78787	90452	13755	68723	77529
65555	33436	75996	96100	12964	92337	54658	64818	87878	28281	03810	44857
28253	16861	35698	66865	32456	35257	65851	95049	41281	74280	35061	80333
71628	67151	28555	08482	79909	19172	26921	68772	70266	47597	38857	58610
86584	76666	79385	30661	95110	64569	04373	26773	37538	65509	22650	94819
93227	01630	81246	90743	47066	66667	82823	51968	78600	18615	43742	00535
58255	86732	89988	97775	57043	06230	60590	79849	34656	35221	65256	79320
84381	52930	85719	23041	08137	21758	99607	58433	48315	45275	30168	05518
40844	83953	62730	84695	42094	96287	66529	84209	57595	40482	02414	19689
31575	66270	66529	55820	03686	94910	21790	27051	38984	37194	36691	81964
86644	66871	59339	83633	36481	71735	63881	91385	76399	14464	86121	85853
05508	15468	62897	31593	22170	50932	85934	07146	34698	39444	90866	60223
81826	40159	36790	78124	95094	19027	26839	21056	17375	90048	51775	91247
26585	73975	55556	49795	20776	40280	35508	81970	67930	19387	39637	94121
85344	84314	49858	18985	07199	22307	38514	56448	30672	24240	97338	68164
75988	77846	80862	74230	74053	20515	98591	52354	61471	25366	24169	28432
18357	19901	80030	92513	33030	53281	49457	64831	75685	50569	24403	41040
39599	82358	04344	09574	47086	77205	10206	02220	58452	82268	45104	30607
19781	25496	81832	35225	20107	28039	88796	89874	66207	93156	62475	92383
14586	46043	91509	81494	43583	72906	76958	00266	03097	46427	33624	27331
94503	55242	99500	61184	07627	79720	36400	97847	89028	34265	04575	28799
34236	57573	63779	65082	16397	56374	34726	70413	90391	63544	81357	53571
56209	63103	31479	65551	96748	31300	65769	88196	68380	64115	21474	28187
32695	80831	13822	10116	60227	13060	83446	98045	27427	77435	30733	17582
13215	34758	34958	32784	68513	71293	95850	68686	48825	36476	87831	37720
03412	34802	90131	65710	99119	00013	28650	97382	67993	37899	56083	34082
22842	30266	02753	77158	47761	62812	90094	04601	36666	25248	58798	78280
14799	19883	30639	49388	72647	33753	63987	60633	60821	68528	88453	76690
51430	36336	92632	56025	92931	91141	02677	45340	74795	82562	61129	75461
74450	18977	66680	84663	60480	07758	31916	83670	28722	72172	20434	52750
99537	62418	61999	13422	41604	02270	05887	53821	21236	99835	00381	78338
48557	90147	40329	22467	64746	19968	01375	46520	09883	56898	39894	68882
59306	63246	07130	84882	21403	02705	70184	13871	05289	14175	56970	10742
50767	59174	60405	15257	28650	27755	82783	30202	70986	56384	11443	41287
71556	29029	95675	73840	58272	95202	80628	43273	96434	92532	54050	28972

current machine. The experimental design requires assigning 16 jobs to the existing and challenging machines at random so that each machine processes exactly four jobs. The machines will be rated on their performance. Exhibit VII.1–1 can be used to make the random assignments. First, assign the random numbers in accordance with the probability distribution as follows:

Machine	Probability	Cumulative Probability	Random Number Assignment
Existing	.25	.25	.01–.25
Challenger #1	.25	.50	.26–.50
Challenger #2	.25	.75	.51–.75
Challenger #3	.25	1.00	.76–.00

Suppose we want to assign the next 16 cutting jobs. The procedure requires obtaining 16 or more two-digit random numbers from the tables and comparing these to the random number assignments. The first random number is .57, which results in the assignment of Job 1 to Challenger #2. Now there are only three jobs that can be assigned to Challenger #2. Thus, we may have to "waste" some random numbers in order to ensure that each machine processes exactly four jobs. Such is the case for the 12th job. We eliminated the first random number, .68, because this would have been the fifth job assigned to Challenger #2.

Job	Random Number	Machine	Job	Random Number	Machine
1	.57	#2	9	.39	#1
2	.72	#2	10	.47	#1
3	.24	Existing	11	.91	#3
4	.70	#2	12	.68,.35	#1
5	.89	#3	13	.06	Existing
6	.69	#2	14	.93	#3
7	.22	Existing	15	.04	Existing
8	.76	#3	16	.48	#1

VII.2 Random Normal Numbers

A. Description

Random normal numbers are normally distributed with a mean of zero and a variance of one, or $N(0,1)$.

Many methods have been developed for generating random normal numbers (RNN). A method that generates approximate random normal numbers is given by

$$\text{RNN} = \frac{\sum_{i=1}^{n} R_i - .5n}{\sqrt{n/12}}$$

where R_i is the ith uniformly distributed random number (described in Section VII.1) and n is the number of uniformly distributed random numbers. It is convenient to let $n = 12$; then

$$\text{RNN} = \sum_{i=1}^{12} R_i - 6$$

Twelve uniformly distributed random numbers are summed. The value six is then subtracted from this sum. The result is an approximate random normal number.

Exhibit VII.2–1 alleviates the need for generating random normal numbers each time they are needed. Exhibit VII.2–1 might be just one page of many from a large table of random normal numbers. In a discrete simulation, if many random normal numbers are required, they may need to be generated in the computer using the approximate method above or an exact method as discussed in Banks and Carson [1984].

B. Reading the Tables

The correct procedure for reading the tables is to start at a random position, then proceed in a random direction, up, down, left, right, diagonally, etc. If a large number of RNN's is selected, approximately the same number of positive and negative values will occur, since half the area under the $N(0, 1)$ is negative and half is positive.

C. Using the Tables

The time X to process a job has been found to be normally distributed with a mean of 12 minutes and a variance of 9 minutes^2. Random processing times can be generated using the relationship

$$X = \sigma(\text{RNN}) + \mu = 3(\text{RNN}) + 12$$

where RNN's are obtained from Exhibit VII.2–1. Thus, if the first RNN is

EXHIBIT VII.2–1

Random Normal Numbers

-.622	.025	-.691	.503	.361	-.022	-1.738	-.071	1.528	-1.706
.192	.155	.037	-.101	-1.516	-.570	-.310	-.230	-1.014	1.686
-.719	1.438	-.172	-.067	1.061	.046	1.046	-.709	-1.391	-1.309
.529	-.819	.648	.078	-1.644	-.646	.544	-.335	-.514	-.525
-.276	-.973	-.503	1.052	.279	.105	.129	1.193	.890	.083
1.022	1.078	-.971	-.098	.087	1.478	.672	.412	.852	-.866
-.379	.577	.312	1.874	.881	-.651	-1.326	-.659	.629	-1.139
-.144	-1.879	.155	-.078	-.724	-.683	1.948	.136	.960	-.055
.118	.317	-.388	-.836	1.072	1.218	-.301	.109	.140	-1.225
-.309	1.228	-1.204	-.014	.834	-1.629	.971	.402	.375	-.028
.800	1.451	.423	1.179	-.591	.516	.571	.291	1.548	-.101
.738	.947	-1.187	-.650	-.983	-.944	-.247	1.022	.709	.778
1.134	.432	-.629	1.847	-.106	.034	-1.059	.563	-1.270	-1.697
-.559	-.990	-.507	1.112	1.094	-.162	.487	-.178	-.010	.559
-1.936	1.837	-.803	1.371	.844	1.020	.219	-.039	-.119	1.259
-.302	-1.564	.219	-1.546	2.070	-1.571	-.072	-.378	-.189	-.454
-.782	-.209	.643	.931	-.583	1.231	-.771	-.456	-.565	2.055
.569	1.332	-.369	-1.062	-1.850	.898	.441	-.831	-.043	-.567
.006	-.829	-1.063	.198	-1.115	-.326	-2.454	.713	-1.582	-2.291
-.320	.400	.334	-1.084	-.935	1.182	1.639	1.072	.360	-1.411
1.171	.916	-.014	-1.274	1.180	-.340	-1.380	.966	.944	.795
.746	-.242	-.320	-.683	-.312	-2.388	-.274	.395	1.031	.448
1.371	.506	-.173	1.616	-1.672	1.464	-.095	.770	.274	-1.459
1.615	-.097	-1.607	1.476	-1.980	-1.194	.367	-1.158	-.036	-.136
.803	.349	.956	.545	-.552	-.149	-.457	-2.533	-1.229	3.064
.334	-.203	.295	1.323	-.823	-.020	.174	1.171	.443	1.495
-.447	.646	.486	.064	-.470	.841	-.319	.671	-.924	2.257
-.160	-.881	-.553	-1.724	-.098	.079	-1.098	.090	.373	-.581
-1.308	2.233	-1.340	-1.791	.430	-.410	-.517	.966	1.802	-.589
-.774	1.066	1.637	-.412	-.163	-.024	-.208	-.057	-.978	1.689
-.830	.866	.305	1.462	.558	-.134	-.621	.774	.700	.639
.597	1.333	1.948	-.041	-2.089	.513	.901	.606	-.171	-1.315
1.241	-1.861	-1.149	-.607	-2.121	1.724	.556	1.503	1.112	-1.388
-.257	.150	-.670	-2.051	-.279	1.100	1.300	.619	-.251	.905
-.849	-.093	-.043	-1.459	.594	-.136	1.161	-1.646	-1.366	-2.032
-1.163	1.891	1.147	.810	-1.476	2.918	-.335	-.748	-3.012	.774
.926	-1.836	1.259	.716	-.385	.021	-2.755	-.286	-.694	1.357
-.021	1.438	.523	2.094	-.765	-.413	1.593	-.284	-2.283	.311
1.010	.679	.639	.279	-.225	-2.700	-.476	-.289	.273	-1.142
-.066	-2.456	-1.425	.201	-.656	-.590	.816	-.956	-.238	.707
.498	.766	.649	-1.459	.823	.196	.133	-2.063	.963	-.720
.892	1.406	1.215	-.233	-.815	-1.509	1.166	-.207	.456	1.231
-1.025	-.505	-.811	-.897	-.847	-.157	-.316	.356	.369	.974
-.772	.742	-1.047	.202	-.743	-1.777	-1.952	.076	-.073	1.719
-1.371	.229	-.088	.285	.046	.041	-.161	-.569	-1.872	-1.392

0.843, the resulting input (random processing time) would be given by

$$X = 3(0.843) + 12 = 14.529 \text{ minutes}$$

A simulation would involve the generation of many such input values.

Reference

Banks, J. and J. S. Carson, II, *Discrete-Event System Simulation*, Prentice-Hall, Englewood Cliffs, New Jersey, 1984.

Reliability

VIII.1 Reliability Testing (Handbook H108)

A. Description

This section concerns the statistical design of tests to investigate the probability that an item does not fail during a specified period of time. This is called the reliability of the item. Three types of testing procedures are commonly used:

1. *Termination on Occurrence of a Preassigned Number of Failures.* A sample of n items is put on test, and the testing is concluded when r items have failed. The times to failure for each item, $t_1, t_2, \ldots, t_r$, are recorded.
2. *Termination at a Preassigned Time.* A sample of n items is put on test, and the testing is concluded at some specified time T, or at the rth failure if it occurs before time T.
3. *Sequential Life Test.* A sample of n items is tested as above, but the decision to end testing depends on the accumulated test results.

Choice of which type of testing procedure to use may be based on constraints on the total time available before a decision is required or other budgetary or test requirements.

Under the assumption that the time to failure follows the exponential distribution, the reliability of an item is completely specified by its mean time to failure. In this case, demonstration that an item has a specified reliability, say R, for a particular application is achieved by showing that the item has the mean life θ that would achieve the specified reliability. The relationship between these parameters is

$$R = \exp(-T/\theta)$$

Handbook H108 [1960] provides tables of critical values of decision criteria and expected times to complete a test when testing is terminated on the occurrence of a preassigned number of failures. It also includes information on the effects of testing with replacement (i.e., replacing units that fail during the test) and tables for designing tests with specified consumer and producer risks. Comparable information for tests that are terminated at preassigned times and for sequential tests are also given. It is emphasized that these tables are valid only if the time to failure follows the exponential distribution.

Tables 2C–1(a) and 2C–1(b) from Handbook H108 for testing without replacement are partially reproduced in Exhibits VIII.1–1 and VIII.1–2, respectively. These show factors for computing test time T as a function of r, the critical number of failures, for testing that the mean time to failure is θ_0 with consumer's risk α equal to .01 and .05. The sample size is required to be a multiple of r.

Exhibit VIII.1–3 (taken from Table 2C–3 of Handbook H108) shows the sample sizes required to achieve specified consumer's risk α and producer's risk β when the true mean life is θ_1. Exhibit VIII.1–4 is identical to Exhibit VIII.1–3, except that it assumes that failed items have been replaced during testing.

B. Using the Tables

Example B–1. Find the test termination time if 45 items are to be tested to investigate the claim that the mean life of an item is 1000 hours. The test is to be stopped on the occurrence of the 15th failure and is to have a consumer's risk (probability of rejecting that the mean life is 1000 hours when the requirement is met) of .01. Testing is to be without replacement. Assuming that the time to failure follows an exponential distribution, we can use Exhibit VIII.1–1 with $r = 15$ to find that $T/\theta_0 = 0.199$. Since $\theta_0 = 1000$ hours, $T = 199$ hours. Forty-five items are placed on test, and if after 199 hours fewer than 15 have failed, the claim of a mean life of 1000 hours cannot be rejected.

Example B–2. How large a sample would have been required in Example B–1 to assure a probability of .10 or less of accepting the claim that the mean life was 1000 hours when in fact it was only 500 hours? Here $\theta_1/\theta_0 = 500/1000 = 1/2$, $\alpha = .01$, and $\beta = .10$. From Example B–1, $T = 199$ and $T/\theta_0 = 0.199$. In Exhibit VIII.1–3 only four values are given for T/θ_0. Since $1/5$ is close to 0.199, we will use that column. Thus, we find the required sample size to be approximately 109 if we are to achieve the desired protection levels.

Example B–3. How much is the sample size reduced in Example B–2 if items that fail during testing are replaced? Using Exhibit VIII.1–4 with $\theta_1/\theta_0 = 1/2$, $T/\theta_0 = 1/5$, $\alpha = .01$, and $\beta = .10$, we find $n = 93$. This represents a reduction of 16 units, or about 15 percent of the original sample size.

Reference

Handbook H108, Sampling Procedures and Tables for Life and Reliability Testing (Band on Exponential Distribution), Office of the Assistant Secretary of Defense, Washington, D.C., 1960.

EXHIBIT VIII.1–1

VALUES OF T/θ_0 FOR $\alpha = .01$

r	Sample size 2r	3r	4r	5r	6r	7r	8r	9r	10r	20r
1	0.005	0.003	0.003	0.002	0.002	0.001	0.001	0.001	0.001	0.0005
2	.043	.027	.020	.016	.013	.011	.010	.008	.008	.004
3	.089	.055	.040	.031	.026	.022	.019	.017	.015	.007
4	.131	.079	.057	.045	.037	.031	.027	.024	.021	.011
5	.165	.100	.072	.056	.046	.039	.034	.030	.027	.013
6	.195	.117	.084	.065	.054	.045	.039	.035	.031	.015
7	.219	.131	.094	.073	.060	.051	.044	.039	.035	.017
8	.241	.143	.103	.080	.065	.055	.048	.042	.038	.019
9	.260	.155	.110	.086	.070	.060	.052	.046	.041	.020
10	.276	.164	.117	.091	.075	.063	.055	.048	.043	.021
15	.337	.199	.142	.110	.090	.076	.066	.058	.052	.025
20	.377	.222	.158	.123	.101	.085	.074	.065	.058	.028
25	.406	.239	.170	.132	.108	.091	.079	.070	.062	.030
30	.428	.252	.179	.139	.114	.096	.083	.074	.066	.032
40	.460	.270	.192	.149	.122	.103	.089	.079	.070	.034
50	.482	.283	.201	.156	.128	.108	.094	.082	.074	.036
75	.518	.304	.216	.167	.137	.116	.100	.088	.079	.039
100	.540	.316	.225	.174	.142	.120	.104	.092	.082	.040

EXHIBIT VIII.1–2

VALUES OF T/θ_0 FOR $\alpha = .05$

r	Sample size 2r	3r	4r	5r	6r	7r	8r	9r	10r	20r
1	0.026	0.017	0.013	0.010	0.009	0.007	0.006	0.006	0.005	0.003
2	.104	.065	.048	.038	.031	.026	.023	.020	.018	.009
3	.168	.103	.075	.058	.048	.041	.036	.031	.028	.014
4	.217	.132	.095	.074	.061	.052	.045	.040	.036	.017
5	.254	.153	.110	.086	.071	.060	.052	.046	.041	.020
6	.284	.170	.122	.095	.078	.066	.057	.051	.045	.022
7	.309	.185	.132	.103	.084	.072	.062	.055	.049	.024
8	.330	.197	.141	.110	.090	.076	.066	.058	.052	.025
9	.348	.207	.148	.115	.094	.080	.069	.061	.055	.027
10	.363	.216	.154	.120	.098	.083	.072	.064	.057	.028
15	.417	.246	.175	.136	.112	.094	.082	.072	.065	.032
20	.451	.266	.189	.147	.120	.102	.088	.078	.070	.034
25	.475	.280	.199	.154	.126	.107	.093	.082	.073	.036
30	.493	.290	.206	.160	.131	.111	.096	.085	.076	.037
40	.519	.305	.216	.168	.137	.116	.101	.089	.079	.039
50	.536	.315	.223	.173	.142	.120	.104	.092	.082	.040
75	.564	.331	.235	.182	.149	.126	.109	.096	.086	.042
100	.581	.340	.242	.187	.153	.130	.112	.099	.089	.043

EXHIBIT VIII.1–3

Life Test Sampling Plans For Specified α, β, θ_1/θ_0, and T/θ_0 (Without Replacement)

		T/θ_0					T/θ_0					T/θ_0					T/θ_0				
		1/3	1/5	1/10	1/20		1/3	1/5	1/10	1/20		1/3	1/5	1/10	1/20		1/3	1/5	1/10	1/20	
θ_1/θ_0	r	n	n	n	n	r	n	n	n	n	r	n	n	n	n	r	n	n	n	n	θ_1/θ_0
		$\alpha = 0.01$		$\beta = 0.01$			$\alpha = 0.05$		$\beta = 0.01$			$\alpha = 0.10$		$\beta = 0.01$			$\alpha = 0.25$		$\beta = 0.01$		
2/3	136	403	622	1172	2275	95	289	447	843	1639	77	238	369	699	1358	52	168	261	496	965	2/3
1/2	46	119	182	340	657	33	90	138	258	499	26	73	112	210	407	17	51	79	149	289	1/2
1/3	19	41	61	113	216	13	30	45	83	160	11	27	40	75	145	7	19	29	54	105	1/3
1/5	9	15	22	39	74	7	13	20	36	69	5	10	14	26	51	3	6	10	18	36	1/5
1/10	5	6	9	15	28	4	6	9	15	29	3	5	7	12	23	2	3	5	10	20	1/10
		$\alpha = 0.01$		$\beta = 0.05$			$\alpha = 0.05$		$\beta = 0.05$			$\alpha = 0.10$		$\beta = 0.05$			$\alpha = 0.25$		$\beta = 0.05$		
2/3	101	291	448	842	1632	67	198	305	575	1116	52	156	242	456	886	32	101	156	296	576	2/3
1/2	35	87	132	245	472	23	59	90	168	326	18	48	73	137	265	11	31	48	91	177	1/2
1/3	15	30	45	82	157	10	21	32	59	113	8	18	27	50	97	5	12	19	36	69	1/3
1/5	8	13	18	33	62	5	8	12	22	41	4	7	10	19	36	2	3	5	10	20	1/5
1/10	4	4	6	10	18	3	4	5	9	17	2	2	3	6	11	2	3	5	10	20	1/10
		$\alpha = 0.01$		$\beta = 0.10$			$\alpha = 0.05$		$\beta = 0.10$			$\alpha = 0.10$		$\beta = 0.10$			$\alpha = 0.25$		$\beta = 0.10$		
2/3	83	234	359	675	1307	55	159	245	462	895	41	121	186	351	681	23	71	110	207	403	2/3
1/2	30	72	109	202	390	19	47	72	134	258	15	39	59	110	213	8	22	33	63	123	1/2
1/3	13	25	37	67	128	8	16	24	43	83	6	12	18	34	66	4	9	14	27	52	1/3
1/5	7	11	15	26	50	4	6	9	15	29	3	5	7	12	23	2	3	5	10	20	1/5
1/10	4	4	6	10	18	3	4	5	9	17	2	2	3	6	11	1	1	1	3	6	1/10
		$\alpha = 0.01$		$\beta = 0.25$			$\alpha = 0.05$		$\beta = 0.25$			$\alpha = 0.10$		$\beta = 0.25$			$\alpha = 0.25$		$\beta = 0.25$		
2/3	60	162	248	465	899	35	96	147	276	535	25	69	107	201	389	12	34	53	101	196	2/3
1/2	22	49	74	137	262	13	30	45	83	160	9	21	31	58	113	5	12	19	36	69	1/2
1/3	10	18	26	46	87	6	11	16	29	55	4	7	10	19	36	2	3	5	10	20	1/3
1/5	5	6	9	15	28	3	4	5	9	17	3	5	7	12	23	1	1	1	3	6	1/5
1/10	3	3	4	6	10	2	2	2	4	8	2	2	3	6	11	1	1	1	3	6	1/10

EXHIBIT VIII.1–4

Life Test Sampling Plans For Specified α, β, θ_1/θ_0, and T/θ_0 (With Replacement)

		T/θ_0					T/θ_0					T/θ_0					T/θ_0				
		1/3	1/5	1/10	1/20		1/3	1/5	1/10	1/20		1/3	1/5	1/10	1/20		1/3	1/5	1/10	1/20	
θ_1/θ_0	r	n	n	n	n	r	n	n	n	n	r	n	n	n	n	r	n	n	n	n	θ_1/θ_0
		$\alpha = 0.01$		$\beta = 0.01$			$\alpha = 0.05$		$\beta = 0.01$			$\alpha = 0.10$		$\beta = 0.01$			$\alpha = 0.25$		$\beta = 0.01$		
2/3	136	331	551	1103	2207	95	238	397	795	1591	77	197	329	659	1319	52	140	234	469	939	2/3
1/2	46	95	158	317	634	33	72	120	241	483	26	59	98	197	394	17	42	70	140	281	1/2
1/3	19	31	51	103	206	13	23	38	76	153	11	21	35	70	140	7	15	25	50	101	1/3
1/5	9	10	17	35	70	7	9	16	32	65	5	7	12	24	48	3	5	8	17	34	1/5
1/10	5	4	6	12	25	4	4	6	13	27	3	3	5	11	22	2	2	4	9	19	1/10
		$\alpha = 0.01$		$\beta = 0.05$			$\alpha = 0.05$		$\beta = 0.05$			$\alpha = 0.10$		$\beta = 0.05$			$\alpha = 0.25$		$\beta = 0.05$		
2/3	101	237	395	790	1581	67	162	270	541	1082	52	128	214	429	859	32	84	140	280	560	2/3
1/2	35	68	113	227	454	23	47	78	157	314	18	38	64	128	256	11	25	43	86	172	1/2
1/3	15	22	37	74	149	10	16	27	54	108	8	13	23	46	93	5	10	16	33	67	1/3
1/5	8	8	14	29	58	5	6	10	19	39	4	5	8	17	34	2	3	5	10	19	1/5
1/10	4	3	4	8	16	3	3	4	8	16	2	2	3	5	10	2	2	4	9	19	1/10
		$\alpha = 0.01$		$\beta = 0.10$			$\alpha = 0.05$		$\beta = 0.10$			$\alpha = 0.10$		$\beta = 0.10$			$\alpha = 0.25$		$\beta = 0.10$		
2/3	83	189	316	632	1265	55	130	216	433	867	41	99	165	330	660	23	58	98	196	392	2/3
1/2	30	56	93	187	374	19	37	62	124	248	15	30	51	102	205	8	17	29	59	119	1/2
1/3	13	18	30	60	121	8	11	19	39	79	6	9	15	31	63	4	7	12	25	50	1/3
1/5	7	7	11	23	46	4	4	7	13	27	3	4	6	11	22	2	3	4	9	19	1/5
1/10	4	2	4	8	16	3	3	4	8	16	2	2	2	5	10	1	1	2	3	5	1/10
		$\alpha = 0.01$		$\beta = 0.25$			$\alpha = 0.05$		$\beta = 0.25$			$\alpha = 0.10$		$\beta = 0.25$			$\alpha = 0.25$		$\beta = 0.25$		
2/3	60	130	217	434	869	35	77	129	258	517	25	56	94	188	376	12	28	47	95	190	2/3
1/2	22	37	62	125	251	13	23	38	76	153	9	16	27	54	108	5	10	16	33	67	1/2
1/3	10	12	20	41	82	6	7	13	26	52	4	5	8	17	34	2	2	4	9	19	1/3
1/5	5	4	7	13	25	3	3	4	8	16	3	3	5	11	22	1	1	2	3	6	1/5
1/10	3	2	2	4	8	2	1	2	3	7	2	1	2	5	10	1	1	1	2	5	1/10

VIII.2 Reliability, Maintainability, and Availability

A. Description

Availability, the probability that a system is in operating condition at any point in time, is a function of the system's failure rate and how long it takes to return the system to service once it has failed. When it is assumed that failure and service times are exponentially distributed random variables, this relationship can be expressed in terms of the mean time between failures (MTBF) and the mean time to repair (MTTR). Exhibit VIII.2–1 displays values of availability,

$$A = \text{MTBF}/(\text{MTTR} + \text{MTBF})$$

for selected values of A as a function of MTTR and MTBF.

B. Using the Figure

Any combination of values of MTBF and MTTR can result in a given availability. However, in many situations there are constraints placed on MTBF and MTTR. Exhibit VIII.2–1 allows the user to easily examine the trade-offs between reliability and maintainability.

Example B–1. Consider a system under development that is required to have an availability of .99, with a maximum MTTR of 5 hours and a minimum MTBF of 200 hours. A specific application of Exhibit VIII.2–1 is shown below. The maximum value of MTBF that could be used is found by reading MTBF at the point where the maximum value of MTTR intersects the $A = .99$ line. This value is found to be 500 hours. Likewise, the minimum value of MTTR is found by reading the value of MTTR where the MTBF = 200 line and the $A = .99$ line intersect. This value is 2.0 hours. The shaded area in the figure below represents all combinations of MTTR and MTBF that achieve an availability of .99 or more and fall within the limitations imposed on MTBF and MTTR.

EXHIBIT VIII.2–1

AVAILABILITY FOR GIVEN VALUES OF MTBF AND MTTR.

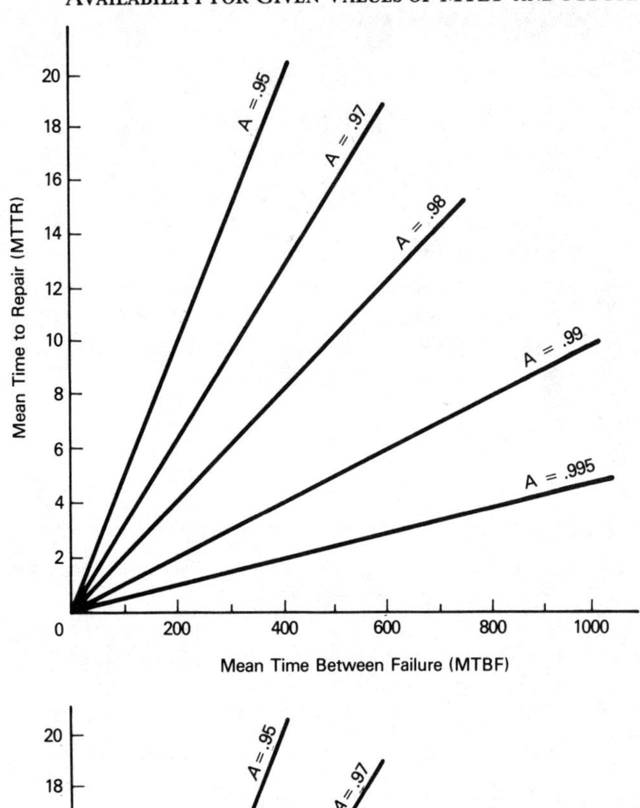

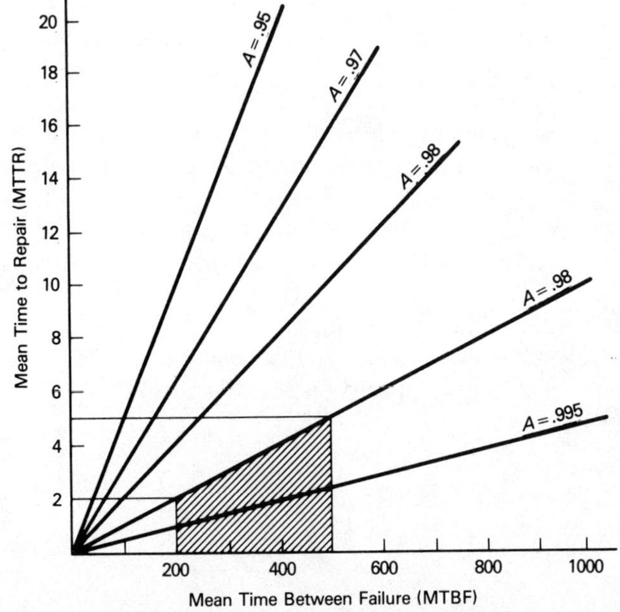

Waiting Line Models

IX.1 Measures for the M/M/s Queueing Model

A. Description

The expected number in the system L in an M/M/s queueing model is one of several related measures of effectiveness. The notation M/M/s indicates a Poisson arrival process, exponentially distributed service times, and s servers. Although not shown directly in the abbreviated notation, an infinite waiting line capacity and an infinite calling population are implied. However, a calling population does not have to be infinite if the exit of a unit to join the queueing system does not affect the arrival distribution. The expected number in the system L is related to the expected time in the system W by the equation

$$L = \lambda W$$

where λ is the average arrival rate [Little, 1961].

A similar equation relates the expected waiting line length L_Q and the expected waiting time in the queue W_Q, viz.,

$$L_Q = \lambda W_Q$$

All of the measures are related through the equations

$$W = W_Q + 1/\mu$$
$$L = L_Q + \lambda/\mu$$

where μ is the service rate. The first of these two equations states that the expected time in the system is the sum of the expected time waiting in the queue plus the expected service time. The second equation states that the expected number in the system is the sum of the expected number waiting in the queue plus the expected number being served (which is equal to the expected number of busy servers).

Other measures of interest are the probability that the system is idle, P_0, and the probability that all servers are busy, P_B. The two measures are related by

$$P_B = \frac{(s\rho)^s P_0}{s!(1-\rho)}$$

where

$$\rho = \lambda/(s\mu)$$

The utilization factor, ρ, is one of the input values for the two graphs appearing as Exhibits IX.1–1 and IX.1–2. For the queueing system to be stable over a long time period, $\rho < 1$. Otherwise the queue length will grow without bound, a situation referred to as an explosive system.

B. Reading the Graphs

Exhibits IX.1–1 and IX.1–2 have the same two inputs, ρ and s. The first input, ρ, is the server utilization and can be computed as shown above. The second input is s, the number of servers. The output is L or P_0, depending on which Exhibit is being used. Thus, $\rho = 0.6$ and $s = 3$ results in $L = 3$ in Exhibit IX.1–1 and $P_0 = .15$ in Exhibit IX.1–2.

C. Using the Graphs

Example C–1. Attendants manage a tool crib while mechanics, assumed to be from an infinite calling population, arrive for service. The arrivals occur according to a Poisson process at a rate of 2 per minute, and the average service time is 40 seconds, exponentially distributed. There are two tool crib attendants.

From the data, $\lambda = 2$ per minute and $\mu = 60/40 = 3/2$ per minute. The value of ρ is then given by

$$\rho = \frac{2}{(2)(3/2)} = 0.667$$

which is less than unity. Entering the horizontal axis gives $L = 2.4$ from Exhibit IX.1–1 and $P_0 = .2$ from Exhibit IX.1–2. Then

$$W = L/\lambda = 2.4/2 = 1.2 \text{ minutes}$$

Now W_Q and L_Q can be found. First,

$$W_Q = W - 1/\mu = 1.2 - 0.667 = 0.533 \text{ minutes}$$

Next,

$$L_Q = L - \lambda/\mu = 2.4 - 1.33 = 1.067 \text{ mechanics}$$

Note that the expected number of busy servers is given by

$$\lambda/\mu = \frac{2}{(3/2)} = 1.333 \text{ servers}$$

Finally, the probability that all servers are busy (the probability of an arrival having to wait) is given by

$$P_B = \frac{[2(2/3)]^2(.2)}{2!(1-2/3)} = .533$$

Reference

Little, J. D. C., "A Proof for the Queueing Formula $L = \lambda W$," *Operations Research*, 16 (1961), pp. 651–65.

EXHIBIT IX.1–1

EXPECTED NUMBER IN THE SYSTEM

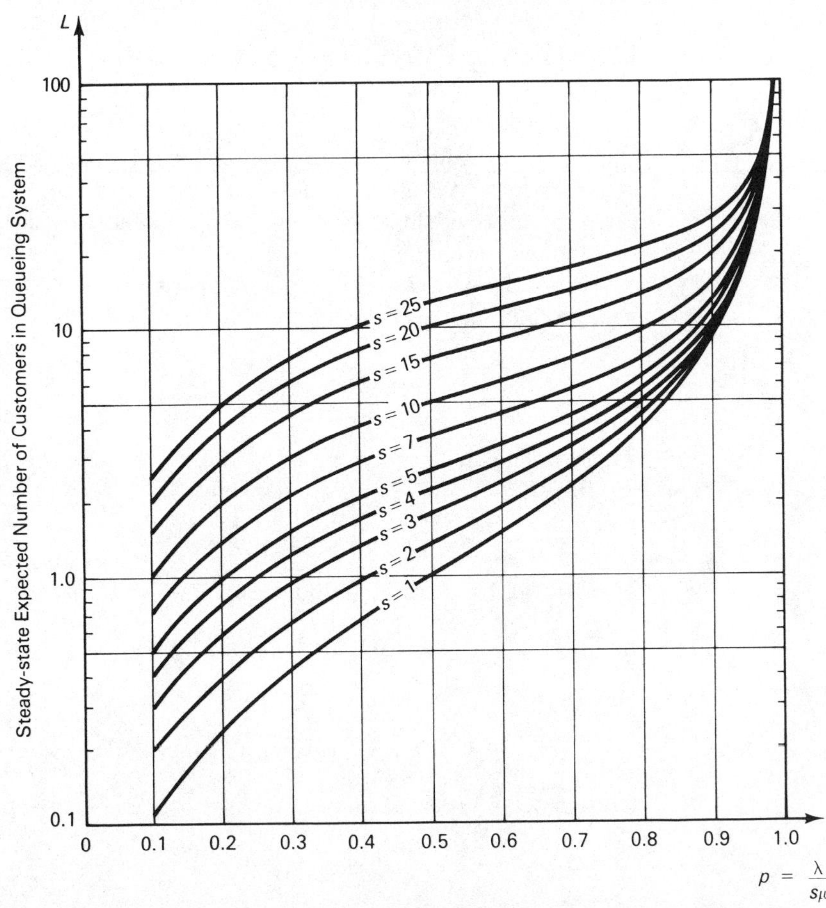

Source: Hillier, F. S. and G. J. Lieberman, *Introduction to Operations Research*, 3rd ed., p. 423, © 1980. With permission of Holden-Day, San Francisco.

EXHIBIT IX.1–2

PROBABILITY OF AN EMPTY SYSTEM

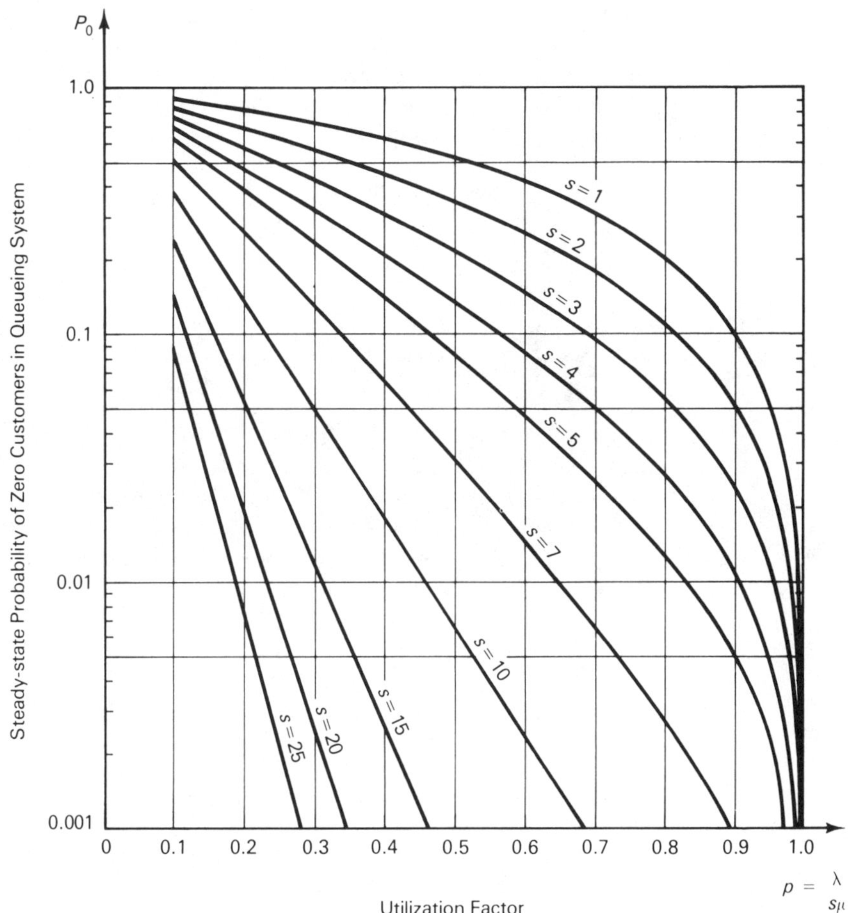

Source: Hillier, F. S. and G. J. Lieberman, *Introduction to Operations Research*, 3rd ed., p. 422, © 1980. With permission of Holden-Day, San Francisco.

IX.2 Measures for a Finite Calling Population

A. Description

In many practical problems there is a finite population of units that may call for service. If this population is small, the arrival of a unit for service can affect the distribution of arrivals for those members that remain. A bank of machines that break down and require repair, machines that require servicing during their operation, and mechanics that line up at a cage for parts or tools are examples of populations that are finite and may be small.

In this section, tables for solving problems that follow the Poisson arrival process and have exponentially distributed service times are described. There are s servers and a calling population of size N. Peck and Hazelwood [1958] and others have tabulated factors for the solution of these problems. A sample page from Peck and Hazelwood appears in Exhibit IX.2–1. Also, Buffa [1963] has developed a number of useful graphs for solving finite calling population problems for various combinations of s and N. Exhibits IX.2–2 through IX.2–4 are attributed to Buffa.

B. Reading the Tables

Peck and Hazelwood's tables are indexed first on the population size N, where $(4 \leq N \leq 250)$, then by a service factor X, and finally by the number of servers s. On the example page from the tables, shown in Exhibit IX.2–1, the user reads an efficiency factor F and the conditional probability D that if a unit calls for service it will have to wait.The value of the service factor X is given by

$$X = \frac{1/\mu}{1/\lambda + 1/\mu} = \frac{\lambda}{\lambda + \mu}$$

where

$1/\mu$ = Mean service time

$1/\lambda$ = Mean run time, or the time between calls for service for an element in the population

The measures for the system are functions of input values N and X, and the tabulated value F.

Example B–1. Two workers are responsible for 10 milling machines. The machines run for an average of 20 minutes, then require an average of 5 minutes for service. Both times are exponentially distributed. In this example, $1/\mu = 5$ and $1/\lambda = 20$ so that

$$X = 5/(5+20) = .200$$

The values of D and F are read from Exhibit IX.2–1 as .692 and .854, respectively. The probability is .692 that if a unit calls for service it will have to wait.

C. Using the Tables

The efficiency factor F is the proportion of the population not waiting for service (in the queue), or

$$F=(N-L_Q)/N$$

where L_Q is the mean number waiting for service. Solving for L_Q yields

$$L_Q=N(1-F)$$

The average waiting time in the queue, W_Q, is given by

$$W_Q=\left[L_Q(1/\mu+1/\lambda)\right]/(N-L_Q)$$

Other measures which can be determined are the average number being serviced, H, as

$$H=FNX$$

and J, the number of units neither waiting in the queue nor in service, where

$$J=NF(1-X)$$

Example C–1. Consider the data given in Example B–1. Using the tabulated value of $F=.854$, determine the measures of effectiveness. The average number of units waiting for service is given by

$$L_Q=10(1-.854)=1.46$$

The average waiting time in the queue can then be determined by

$$W_Q=\frac{1.46(5+20)}{10-1.46}=4.27$$

Now, the average number of units being serviced is given by

$$H=.854(10)(.200)=1.708$$

Since the units must be running, waiting to be serviced, or in service, the average number of units running is

$$J=10-1.708-1.46=6.832$$

This can be checked, by using the factor F, as

$$J = 10(.854)(.8) = 6.832$$

D. Using the Figures

Exhibits IX.2–2, IX.2–3, and IX.2–4 pertain to finite queueing when $s = 1$, 2, 4, or 8 and $N = 1$, 4, 8, and 16. Interpolation is required for situations between these values of s and N.

Again, consider the data given in Example B–1, where $X = .200$. First, consider the case where there is only one worker. Interpolating between eight and twelve machines in Exhibit IX.2–2, it is seen that approximately 5 of the machines can be expected to be running. From Exhibit IX.2–3, the repair crew can be expected to be busy 96 percent of the time. Finally, $W_Q X\mu$ is read as 1.0 from Exhibit IX.2–4, yielding $W_Q = 25$ minutes.

Suppose now that there are two workers as in Example B–1. Using Exhibit IX.2–2, and interpolating between the plots for eight and twelve machines, yields the same result, 6.8 machines, as the mean number running. It is not possible to obtain the same accuracy using the figures as using the tables. From Exhibit IX.2–3, the workers are busy approximately 83 percent of the time. Lastly, using Exhibit IX.2–4, the value of $W_Q X\mu$ is about 0.165, yielding a $W_Q = 4.125$ minutes.

References

Buffa, Ellwood S., *Operations Management*, Second Ed., John Wiley, New York, 1963.

Peck, L. G. and R. N. Hazelwood, *Finite Queueing Tables*, John Wiley, New York, 1958.

EXHIBIT IX.2-1

SELECTED PAGE FROM FINITE QUEUEING TABLES

POPULATION SIZE $N = 10$											
X	s	D	F	X	s	D	F	X	s	D	F
.064	2	.119	.995	.125	3	.100	.994	.180	2	.614	.890
	1	.547	.940		2	.369	.962		1	.975	.549
.066	2	.126	.995		1	.878	.737	.190	5	.016	.999
	1	.562	.936	.130	4	.022	.999		4	.078	.995
.068	3	.020	.999		3	.110	.994		3	.269	.973
	2	.133	.994		2	.392	.958		2	.654	.873
	1	.577	.931		1	.893	.718		1	.982	.522
.070	3	.022	.999	.135	4	.025	.999	.200	5	.020	.999
	2	.140	.994		3	.121	.993		4	.092	.994
	1	.591	.926		2	.415	.952		3	.300	.968
.075	3	.026	.999		1	.907	.699		2	.692	.854
	2	.158	.992	.140	4	.028	.999		1	.987	.497
	1	.627	.913		3	.132	.991	.210	5	.025	.999
.080	3	.031	.999		2	.437	.947		4	.108	.992
	2	.177	.990		1	.919	.680		3	.333	.961
	1	.660	.899	.145	4	.032	.999		2	.728	.835
.085	3	.037	.999		3	.144	.990		1	.990	.474
	2	.196	.988		2	.460	.941	.220	5	.030	.998
	1	.692	.883		1	.929	.662		4	.124	.990
.090	3	.043	.998	.150	4	.036	.998		3	.366	.954
	2	.216	.986		3	.156	.989		2	.761	.815
.090	1	.722	.867		2	.483	.935		1	.993	.453
.095	3	.049	.998		1	.939	.644	.230	5	.037	.998
	2	.237	.984	.155	4	.040	.998		4	.142	.988
	1	.750	.850		3	.169	.987		3	.400	.947
.100	3	.056	.998		2	.505	.928		2	.791	.794
	2	.258	.981		1	.947	.627		1	.995	.434
	1	.776	.832	.160	4	.044	.998	.240	5	.044	.997
.105	3	.064	.997		3	.182	.986		4	.162	.986
	2	.279	.978		2	.528	.921		3	.434	.938
	1	.800	.814		1	.954	.610		2	.819	.774
.110	3	.072	.997	.165	4	.049	.997		1	.996	.416
	2	.301	.974		3	.195	.984	.250	6	.010	.999
	1	.822	.795		2	.550	.914		5	.052	.997
.115	3	.081	.996		1	.961	.594		4	.183	.983
	2	.324	.971	.170	4	.054	.997		3	.469	.929
	1	.843	.776		3	.209	.982		2	.844	.753
.120	4	.016	.999		2	.571	.906		1	.997	.400
	3	.090	.995		1	.966	.579	.260	6	.013	.999
	2	.346	.967	.180	5	.013	.999		5	.060	.996
	1	.861	.756		4	.066	.996		4	.205	.980
.125	4	.019	.999		3	.238	.978		3	.503	.919

Source: Peck, L. G. and R. N. Hazelwood, *Finite Queueing Tables*, John Wiley, New York, 1958. Reproduced with Permission.

EXHIBIT IX.2–2

Mean Number Running

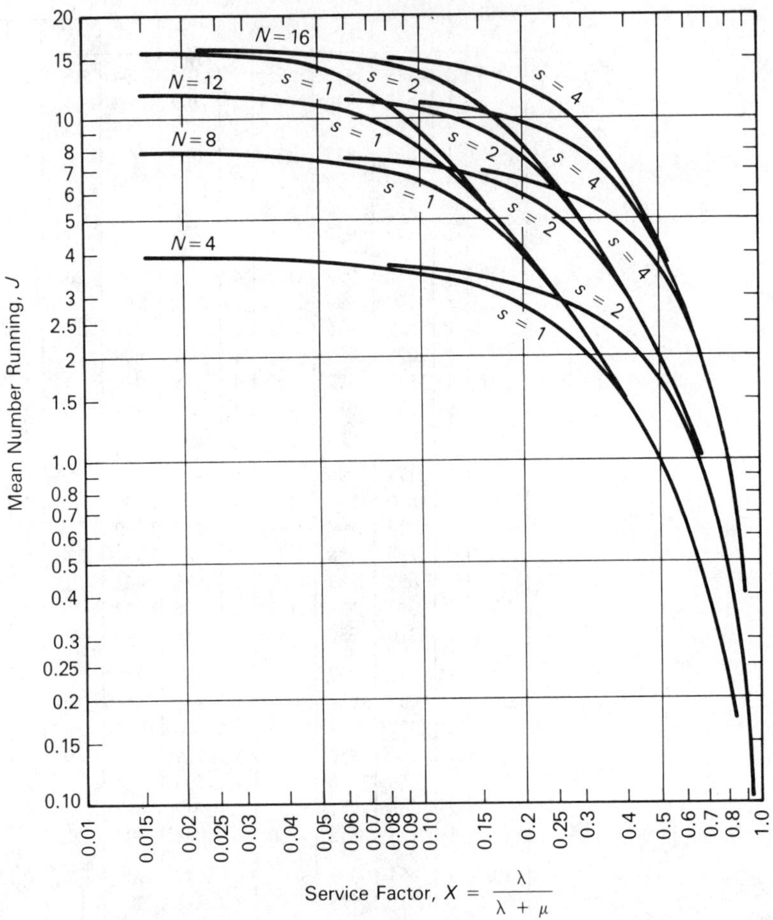

Source: Buffa, Elwood S., *Operations Management: Problems and Models*, 2nd ed., New York: John Wiley & Sons, Inc., 1963. Reproduced with permission.

EXHIBIT IX.2–3

Proportion of Busy Servers

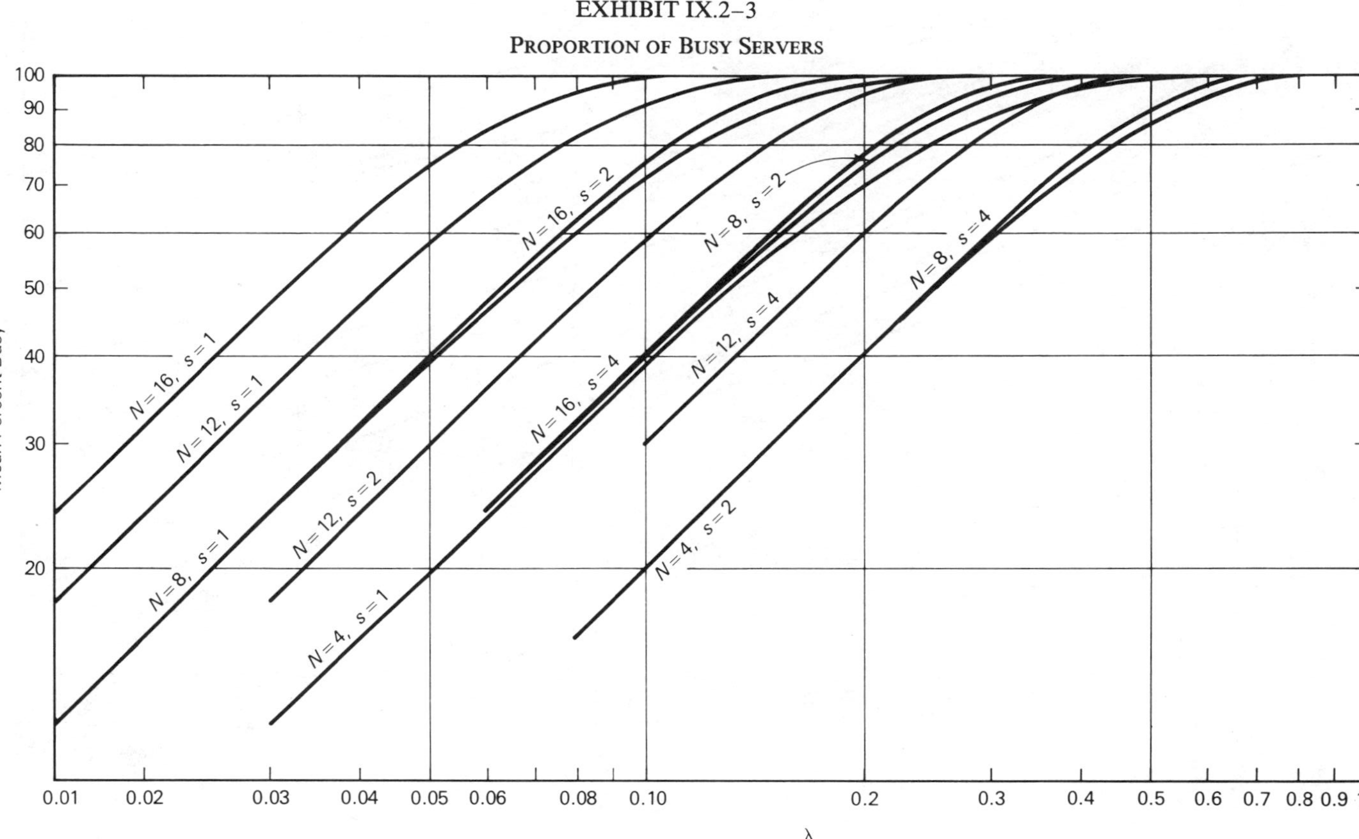

Source: Buffa, Elwood S., *Operations Management: Problems and Models*, 2nd ed., New York: John Wiley & Sons, Inc., 1963. Reproduced with permission.

EXHIBIT IX.2–4

WAITING TIME × ($X\mu$)

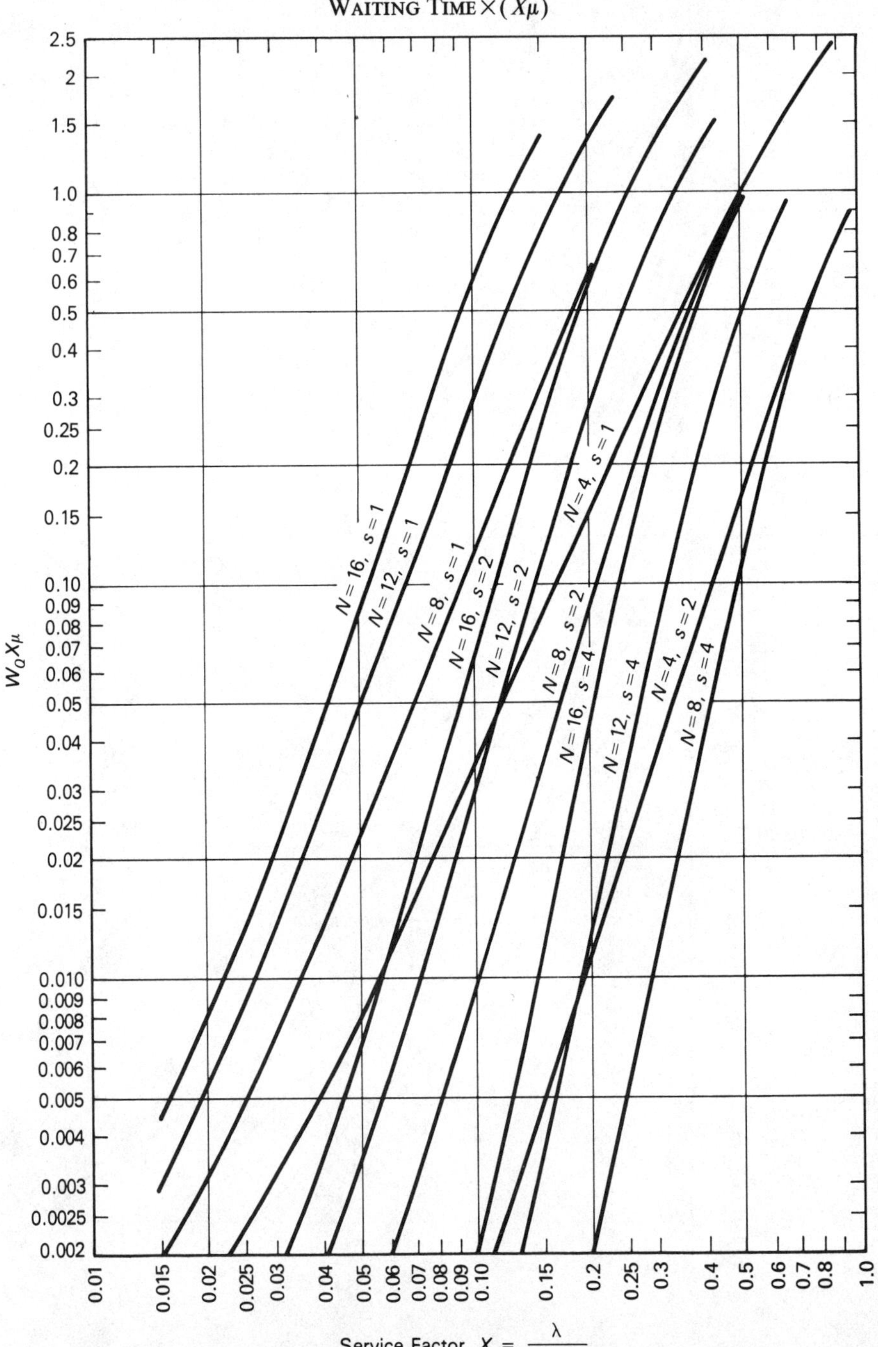

Source: Buffa, Elwood S., *Operations Management: Problems and Models*, 2nd ed., New York: John Wiley & Sons, Inc., 1963. Reproduced with permission.

X

Production–Inventory Systems

X.1 Manufacturing Progress

A. Description

Evidence demonstrates that the number of direct labor hours required to produce a unit of product decreases as the production run continues. A manufacturing progress function expresses the anticipated reduction, which can be used to determine the item cost for manufacturing.

The manufacturing progress function described in this section is based on a constant percentage improvement as production quantities double. Most progress functions rest on this assumption and differ only in the percentage improvement between doubled production quantities. In application, there are usually three possible interests: determining the unit, cumulative, and average values of direct labor hours for various production quantities.

The number of direct labor hours to produce the nth unit Y_n is given by

$$Y_n = Kn^X$$

where

$n =$ unit number

$K =$ direct labor hours to produce the first unit

$X = \ln\phi/\ln 2 = 1.4427 \ln\phi$

$\phi =$ slope parameter of the manufacturing progress function

Example A–1. The Number of Hours to Produce the *n*th Unit. Consider a case where there is an 80 percent manufacturing progress function, with the first unit requiring 8000 direct labor hours. The number of direct labor hours to produce the eighth unit is given by

$$Y_8 = (8000)8^{1.4427 \ln .80}$$
$$= 4096 \text{ hours}$$

The cumulative number T_N of direct labor hours to produce N units is approximated by

$$T_N = \frac{K}{1+X}\left[(N+.5)^{(1+X)} - .5^{(1+X)}\right]$$

Example A–2. The Number of Labor Hours to Produce *N* Units. The number of direct labor hours to produce the first four units described in Example *A*–1 is given by

$$T_4 = \frac{8000}{.678}[4.5^{.678} - .5^{.678}] = 25{,}339 \text{ hours}$$

The exact value is 25,136, so that the approximation is certainly adequate. As N increases, the approximation improves.

The average direct labor hours V_N to produce each of N units is simply T_N/N.

Example A–3. The Average Number of Labor Hours to Produce Each of *N* Units. The average number of labor hours to produce each unit in Example *A*–2 is given by

$$V_4 = 25{,}136/4 = 6284 \text{ hours}$$

Application of the manufacturing progress function is facilitated by Exhibits X.1–1 and X.1–2. These Exhibits give unit and cumulative values for selected slope parameters, with the first unit at one direct labor hour. The table of unit values, Exhibit X.1–1, is based on the value of n^X, where n and X are as previously defined. The cumulative values in Exhibits X.1–2 were obtained by summing the unit values. The average values can be found by dividing the cumulative values by N.

The direct labor hours to produce the nth unit, from Exhibit X.1–1, or the total direct labor hours to produce N units, from Exhibit X.1–2, requires multiplying the applicable tabular value by K. For example, if $K = 100$ direct labor hours, multiply the tabular value for the specified value of N by 100.

B. Using the Tables

Example B–1. Direct Labor Hours to Produce the *N*th Unit. It is known that 100 direct labor hours were required to produce the first unit and that manufacturing progress is at the 90 percent level. How many direct labor hours will be required to produce the 10th unit? The tabular value in Exhibit X.1–1 is given as .7047. Thus, it is estimated that 70.47 hours will be required to produce the 10th unit.

Example B–2. Total Direct Labor Hours to Produce *N* Units. The total hours can be found for Example B–1 by multiplying the tabular value in Exhibit X.1–2, 7.994, by 100, or 799.4 hours.

Example B–3. Average Direct Labor Hours to Produce Each of *N* Units. The average number of hours to produce each unit in Example B–2 is given by 799.4/10 = 79.94 hours/unit.

EXHIBIT X.1–1

Manufacturing Progress Unit Values

Unit Number n	ϕ = Slope Parameter							
	.70	.75	.80	.85	.90	.95	.975	.99
1	1.0000	1.0000	1.0000	1.0000	1.0000	1.0000	1.0000	1.0000
2	.7000	.7500	.8000	.8500	.9000	.9500	.9750	.9900
3	.5682	.6338	.7021	.7729	.8462	.9219	.9607	.9842
4	.4900	.5625	.6400	.7225	.8100	.9025	.9506	.9801
5	.4368	.5127	.5956	.6857	.7830	.8877	.9429	.9769
6	.3977	.4754	.5617	.6570	.7616	.8758	.9367	.9744
7	.3674	.4459	.5345	.6337	.7439	.8659	.9314	.9722
8	.3430	.4219	.5120	.6141	.7290	.8574	.9269	.9703
9	.3228	.4017	.4929	.5974	.7161	.8499	.9229	.9686
10	.3058	.3846	.4765	.5828	.7047	.8433	.9193	.9672
11	.2912	.3696	.4621	.5699	.6946	.8374	.9161	.9658
12	.2784	.3565	.4493	.5584	.6854	.8320	.9132	.9646
13	.2672	.3449	.4379	.5480	.6771	.8271	.9106	.9635
14	.2572	.3344	.4276	.5386	.6696	.8226	.9081	.9625
15	.2482	.3250	.4182	.5300	.6626	.8184	.9058	.9615
16	.2401	.3164	.4096	.5220	.6561	.8145	.9037	.9606
17	.2327	.3085	.4017	.5146	.6501	.8109	.9017	.9598
18	.2260	.3013	.3944	.5078	.6445	.8074	.8998	.9590
19	.2198	.2946	.3876	.5014	.6392	.8042	.8980	.9582
20	.2141	.2884	.3812	.4954	.6342	.8012	.8964	.9575
21	.2087	.2826	.3753	.4898	.6295	.7983	.8948	.9568
22	.2038	.2772	.3697	.4844	.6251	.7955	.8932	.9562
23	.1992	.2722	.3644	.4794	.6209	.7929	.8918	.9556
24	.1949	.2674	.3595	.4747	.6169	.7904	.8904	.9550
25	.1908	.2629	.3548	.4701	.6131	.7880	.8891	.9544
26	.1870	.2587	.3503	.4658	.6094	.7858	.8878	.9539
27	.1834	.2546	.3461	.4617	.6059	.7836	.8866	.9533
28	.1800	.2508	.3421	.4578	.6026	.7815	.8854	.9528
29	.1768	.2472	.3382	.4541	.5994	.7794	.8843	.9523
30	.1737	.2437	.3346	.4505	.5963	.7775	.8832	.9519
31	.1708	.2405	.3310	.4470	.5933	.7756	.8821	.9514
32	.1681	.2373	.3277	.4437	.5905	.7738	.8811	.9510
33	.1654	.2343	.3244	.4405	.5877	.7720	.8801	.9506
34	.1629	.2314	.3213	.4374	.5851	.7703	.8791	.9502
35	.1605	.2286	.3184	.4345	.5825	.7687	.8782	.9498
36	.1582	.2260	.3155	.4316	.5800	.7671	.8773	.9494
37	.1560	.2234	.3127	.4289	.5776	.7655	.8764	.9490
38	.1538	.2210	.3100	.4262	.5753	.7640	.8756	.9486
39	.1518	.2186	.3075	.4236	.5730	.7625	.8748	.9483
40	.1498	.2163	.3050	.4211	.5708	.7611	.8739	.9479

EXHIBIT X.1-1—CONTINUED

Unit Number n	ϕ = Slope Parameter							
	.70	.75	.80	.85	.90	.95	.975	.99
41	.1479	.2141	.3026	.4187	.5687	.7597	.8732	.9476
42	.1461	.2120	.3002	.4163	.5666	.7584	.8724	.9472
43	.1444	.2099	.2979	.4140	.5646	.7570	.8716	.9469
44	.1427	.2079	.2958	.4118	.5626	.7558	.8709	.9466
45	.1410	.2060	.2936	.4096	.5607	.7545	.8702	.9463
46	.1394	.2041	.2915	.4075	.5588	.7533	.8695	.9460
47	.1379	.2023	.2895	.4055	.5570	.7521	.8688	.9457
48	.1364	.2005	.2876	.4035	.5552	.7509	.8681	.9454
49	.1350	.1988	.2857	.4015	.5535	.7498	.8675	.9451
50	.1336	.1972	.2838	.3996	.5518	.7486	.8668	.9449
55	.1272	.1895	.2753	.3908	.5438	.7434	.8638	.9436
60	.1216	.1828	.2676	.3829	.5367	.7386	.8611	.9424
65	.1167	.1768	.2608	.3758	.5302	.7342	.8586	.9413
70	.1123	.1715	.2547	.3693	.5243	.7302	.8563	.9403
75	.1084	.1666	.2491	.3634	.5188	.7265	.8541	.9393
80	.1049	.1622	.2440	.3579	.5137	.7231	.8521	.9384
85	.1017	.1582	.2393	.3529	.5090	.7198	.8502	.9376
90	.0987	.1545	.2349	.3482	.5046	.7168	.8484	.9368
95	.0960	.1511	.2308	.3438	.5005	.7139	.8468	.9361
100	.0935	.1479	.2271	.3397	.4966	.7112	.8452	.9354
110	.0890	.1421	.2202	.3322	.4894	.7062	.8422	.9341
120	.0851	.1371	.2141	.3255	.4830	.7017	.8396	.9329
130	.0817	.1326	.2087	.3194	.4772	.6975	.8371	.9319
140	.0786	.1286	.2038	.3139	.4718	.6937	.8349	.9309
150	.0759	.1250	.1993	.3089	.4669	.6902	.8328	.9299
160	.0734	.1217	.1952	.3042	.4623	.6869	.8308	.9291
170	.0712	.1187	.1914	.2999	.4581	.6838	.8290	.9282
180	.0691	.1159	.1879	.2959	.4541	.6809	.8272	.9275
190	.0672	.1133	.1847	.2922	.4504	.6782	.8256	.9267
200	.0655	.1109	.1816	.2887	.4469	.6757	.8240	.9261
225	.0616	.1056	.1749	.2809	.4390	.6698	.8205	.9245
250	.0584	.1011	.1691	.2740	.4320	.6646	.8174	.9231
275	.0556	.0972	.1639	.2680	.4258	.6599	.8145	.9218
300	.0531	.0937	.1594	.2625	.4202	.6557	.8119	.9206
325	.0510	.0907	.1554	.2577	.4151	.6518	.8096	.9196
350	.0491	.0879	.1517	.2532	.4105	.6482	.8074	.9186
375	.0474	.0854	.1484	.2492	.4062	.6449	.8053	.9177
400	.0458	.0832	.1453	.2454	.4022	.6419	.8034	.9168
450	.0431	.0792	.1399	.2387	.3951	.6363	.8000	.9152
500	.0408	.0758	.1352	.2329	.3888	.6314	.7969	.9138

EXHIBIT X.1–2

Manufacturing Progress Cumulative Values

Unit Number N	ϕ = Slope Parameter							
	.70	.75	.80	.85	.90	.95	.975	.99
1	1.000	1.000	1.000	1.000	1.000	1.000	1.000	1.000
2	1.700	1.750	1.800	1.850	1.900	1.950	1.975	1.990
3	2.268	2.384	2.502	2.623	2.746	2.872	2.936	2.974
4	2.758	2.946	3.142	3.345	3.556	3.774	3.886	3.954
5	3.195	3.459	3.738	4.031	4.339	4.662	4.829	4.931
6	3.593	3.934	4.299	4.688	5.101	5.538	5.766	5.906
7	3.960	4.380	4.834	5.322	5.845	6.404	6.697	6.878
8	4.303	4.802	5.346	5.936	6.574	7.261	7.624	7.848
9	4.626	5.204	5.839	6.533	7.290	8.111	8.547	8.817
10	4.932	5.589	6.315	7.116	7.994	8.954	9.466	9.784
11	5.223	5.958	6.777	7.686	8.689	9.792	10.382	10.750
12	5.501	6.315	7.227	8.244	9.374	10.624	11.296	11.714
13	5.769	6.660	7.665	8.792	10.052	11.451	12.206	12.678
14	6.026	6.994	8.092	9.331	10.721	12.274	13.114	13.640
15	6.274	7.319	8.511	9.861	11.384	13.092	14.020	14.602
16	6.514	7.635	8.920	10.383	12.040	13.907	14.924	15.562
17	6.747	7.944	9.322	10.898	12.690	14.717	15.826	16.522
18	6.973	8.245	9.716	11.405	13.334	15.525	16.725	17.481
19	7.192	8.540	10.104	11.907	13.974	16.329	17.623	18.439
20	7.407	8.828	10.485	12.402	14.608	17.130	18.520	19.397
21	7.615	9.111	10.860	12.892	15.237	17.929	19.415	20.354
22	7.819	9.388	11.230	13.376	15.862	18.724	20.308	21.310
23	8.018	9.660	11.594	13.856	16.483	19.517	21.200	22.265
24	8.213	9.928	11.954	14.331	17.100	20.307	22.090	23.220
25	8.404	10.191	12.309	14.801	17.713	21.095	22.979	24.175
30	9.305	11.446	14.020	17.091	20.727	25.003	27.406	28.939
35	10.133	12.618	15.643	19.294	23.666	28.864	31.807	33.692
40	10.902	13.723	17.193	21.425	26.543	32.684	36.185	38.435
45	11.625	14.773	18.684	23.496	29.366	36.469	40.543	43.170
50	12.307	15.776	20.122	25.513	32.142	40.224	44.884	47.897
60	13.574	17.666	22.868	29.414	37.574	47.653	53.520	57.331
70	14.738	19.430	25.471	33.166	42.871	54.992	62.104	66.743
80	15.819	21.092	27.957	36.795	48.054	62.254	70.643	76.135
90	16.833	22.671	30.346	40.320	53.140	69.450	79.143	85.511
100	17.791	24.179	32.651	43.754	58.141	76.586	87.610	94.871
150	21.972	30.934	43.234	59.888	82.156	111.573	129.530	141.492
200	25.482	36.801	52.720	74.789	104.964	145.693	170.935	187.885
300	31.342	46.943	69.663	102.230	148.204	212.177	252.686	280.198
400	36.260	55.748	84.849	127.569	189.268	277.012	333.429	372.057
500	40.577	63.675	98.847	151.450	228.785	340.647	413.432	463.582

X.2 Economic Order Quantity

A. Description

The economic order quantity, or lot size equation, is given by

$$\text{EOQ} = \sqrt{2AD/IC}$$

where

EOQ = Economic order quantity (units)
A = Cost of ordering (dollars per order)
D = Annual demand (units per year)
I = Inventory carrying cost (stated as a decimal fraction of average inventory value on an annual basis)
C = Item cost (dollars per unit)

The economic order quantity equation minimizes the annual cost for an inventory item where the relevant costs are those for ordering and holding only.

To facilitate the use of the order quantity equation, consider the separation of the portion under the square root into two parts as

$$\text{EOQ} = \sqrt{2A/I} \cdot \sqrt{D/C}$$

The first square root term is characteristic of a specific firm, class of items, or suppliers, while the second is characteristic of a given item in inventory. The first part is relatively constant for a specific user and may be identified by the index number

$$K = \sqrt{2A/I}$$

Then the economic order quantity equation becomes

$$\text{EOQ} = K\sqrt{D/C}$$

Many firms are unable to use the EOQ model since the required data is not readily available. The EOQ treatment in this section is based on the assumption that the cost of ordering and the inventory carrying costs for a firm are rather constant. Furthermore, demand is also assumed to be rather constant over time and known with reasonable certainty. These assumptions enhance the possible use of scientific inventory management for most firms by requiring a minimum amount of data.

Another use of the simplified equation given above is in the initial approximation of order quantities. Thus, even if all of the necessary data is unavailable, an estimate of the order quantity could be made.

Since demand data are usually monthly,

$$\text{EOQ} = K\sqrt{12M/C}$$

where

$M =$ Monthly demand (units)

To implement the use of this last equation, an index number must be chosen. This requires careful analysis at the outset. If the improper number is selected, procurement quantities may be too high or too low. Typically, index values will be between 8 and 12.

The index numbers can apply to all items, to classes of items, to specific suppliers, or some other strata as desired. Thus, a firm may use several different values of K in determining order quantities for different items.

To further facilitate the use of the simplified economic order quantity equation, the nomograph shown in Exhibit X.2–1 has been prepared.

B. Reading the Nomograph

There are three scales on the nomograph. The scales are M/C, the monthly sales-to-cost ratio; K, the index number; and EOQ, the economic order quantity. The inputs are usually M/C and K. A line connecting these two points crosses the EOQ scale at the desired value.

C. Using the Nomograph

Example C–1. Given *M*, *C*, and *K*. If the monthly sales are 1200 units for an item that costs \$100, what is the economic order quantity for a $K = 10$? The M/C ratio is $1200/100 = 12$. Connecting $M/C = 12$ and $K = 10$ gives an EOQ = 120 units.

Example C–2. Given *M*, *C*, and EOQ, Impute *K*. A firm may desire to impute the value of K for a number of items given the current inventory policy. If the K values are vastly different and/or unusually high or low, the inventory policy may be altered to obtain a smaller total cost. Consider a case in which annual sales are 12,000 units for an item that costs \$5 per unit. Then $M/C = 1000/5 = 200$. If the order quantity for this item is 600 units, connecting the scales for M/C and EOQ results in a K of approximately 12.

EXHIBIT X.2-1
EOQ NOMOGRAPH

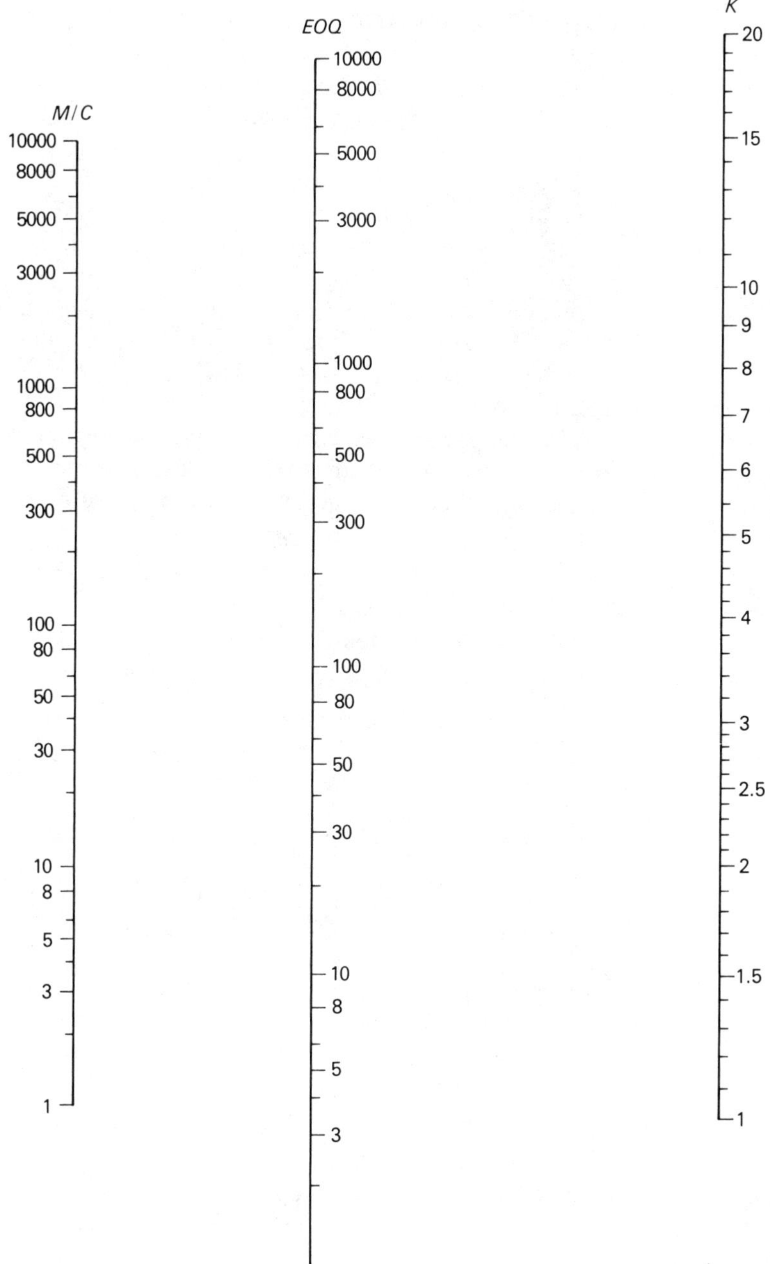

X.3. Reorder Points

A. Description

The distribution of lead time demand is a convolution of the distribution of lead time and the distribution of demand. (The time between placement and receipt of an order is called the lead time.) The average lead time demand is a product of the average lead time and the average rate of demand, assuming that demand and lead time are independent. Thus, an average lead time of two weeks and an average rate of demand of 10 units per week results in an average lead time demand of 20 units.

Safety stock may be added to the average lead time demand to obtain the reorder point. The amount of safety stock added to the average lead time demand is related to the risk of running out of inventory during the lead time.

In many cases, lead time demand is Poisson distributed. For large average values of lead time demand, this distribution is well approximated by the normal distribution. Then, the reorder point can be determined from

$$\text{ROP} = \bar{D}\,\bar{T} + Z\sqrt{\bar{D}\,\bar{T}}$$

where

ROP = Reorder point

$\bar{D}$ = Average rate of demand

$\bar{T}$ = Average lead time

Z = Number of standard deviations required to obtain desired protection

In the above example, let the average lead time demand be Poisson distributed with $\bar{D} = 10$ units per week and $\bar{T} = 2$ weeks. If 95-percent protection from a stockout is desired (on the average a shortage will occur in only 5 percent of the reorder cycles), the appropriate Z is 1.645. Using the previous equation, the ROP = 27.4, or, rounding to the nearest integer, 27. Several selected values of Z are given below.

Z	Protection Level
1.282	90 %
1.645	95 %
1.960	97.5%
2.326	99%
2.575	99.5%

Exhibit X.3–1 is a graph that facilitates the computation of reorder points. The stockout protection levels on the graph are 95 percent and 99 percent. Using the ROP equation and the appropriate Z values, additional graphs can be constructed to meet a specific application.

B. Reading the Graph

The average lead time demand is computed and used as the input for the horizontal axis in Exhibit X.3–1. Read up to the line pertaining to the desired level of protection. Then read the reorder point to the left on the vertical axis.

C. Using the Graph

Example C–1. Obtaining the ROP. If the average rate of demand is 12 units per day and the average lead time is 5 days, the average lead time demand is 60 units. (Assume that the lead time demand is Poisson distributed.) To obtain 99-percent protection, reorder when the stock position reaches 78 units, as shown in Exhibit X.3–1.

Example C–2. Obtaining the Protection Level. The average lead time demand for an item is 100 units and is Poisson distributed. The firm's ROP policy for this item has been to reorder when the amount in inventory reaches 120. The protection level can be found by the intersection of the two given values in Exhibit X.3–1, or by interpolation, about 98 percent.

Example C–3. Obtaining the Average Lead Time. What average lead time can be tolerated if the average daily demand is 5 units and a stockout protection of 95 percent is desired when the reorder point has been established at 100 units? Using the ROP as an input in Exhibit X.3–1, the intersection on the 95-percent protection level shows an average lead time demand of 85 units. Then $5\overline{T} = 85$, so $\overline{T} = 17$ days. A supplier whose average lead time exceeds this value will face a higher than 5 percent risk of a stockout (a lower protection level). (Again, we assume that lead time demand is Poisson distributed.)

Example C–4. Determining the Units Required to Achieve Different Levels of Protection. For a Poisson distributed lead time demand whose average is 120 units, the reorder point is increased by 16 units to increase the protection level from 95 to 99 percent. The increase is determined by evaluating the ROP's between the referenced protection levels at the stated average lead time demand in Exhibit X.3–1. Increases between protection levels are nonlinear.

EXHIBIT X.3–1

NOMOGRAM FOR COMPUTATION OF REORDER POINTS

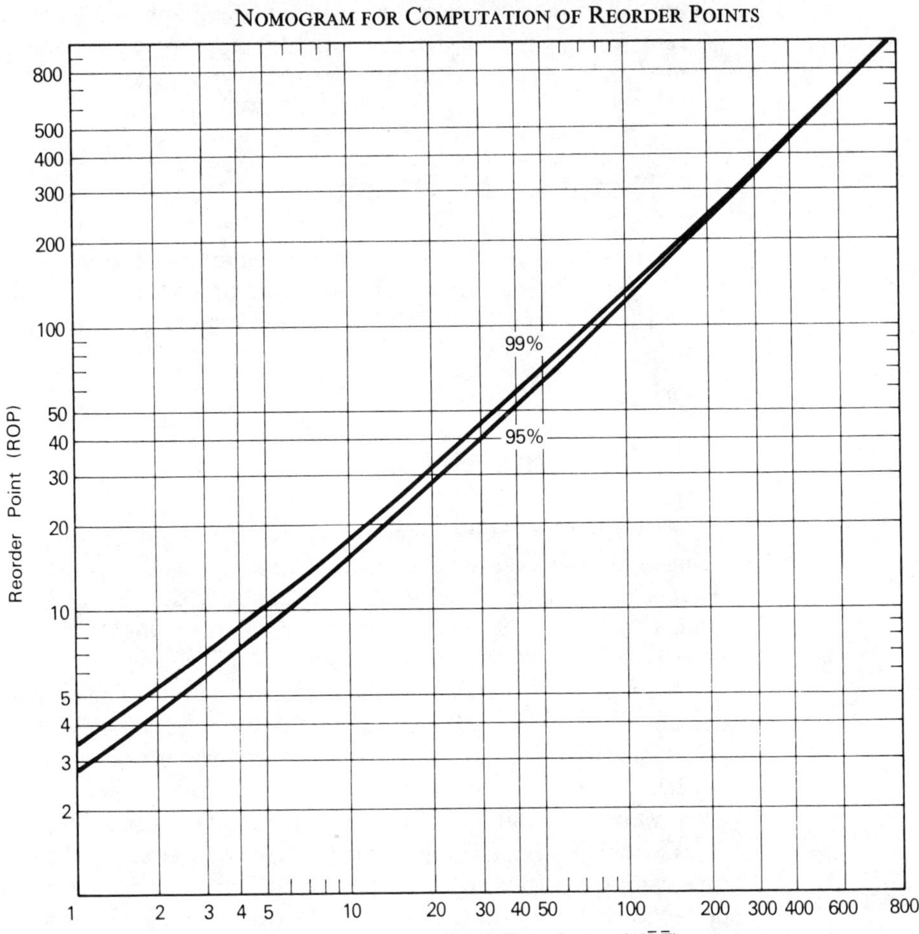

XI

Engineering Economy

XI. Compound Interest Factors

A. Description

Interest factors are used to relate the worth of money at various points in time. The worth of money is assumed to be a function of its earning power, represented by an interest rate i, and not a function of inflation. The interest rate is the amount, expressed as a percent of the original worth, by which the worth would change in one interest period. An interest period can be any length of time, months and years being the most common. If the interest period is a year, the interest rate is referred to as the *annual* interest rate. When the worth of money is considered over a number of periods, the increase in the worth during the first period(s) also increases in worth during the remaining periods. The interest in this case is said to be *compounded*. If the interest rate is to be compounded at intervals other than at each interest period, the interest rate before accounting for this compounding is referred to as the *nominal* rate, and after accounting for this as the *effective* interest rate.

Three types of money/time flows are considered here:

1. P, a principal amount at the current point in time
2. A, a single payment in a series of several equal payments made at the end of each interest period
3. F, a future sum at the end of some number of periods in the future, equal to the principal amount plus compounded interest.

Exhibit XI.1 provides factors that relate each pair of the three quantities P, F, and A for given interest rates and number of periods, n. The usual names given these factors and their relationships are as follows:

Given	To Find	Multiply Given Value by the Factor[1]	Where the Factor is Called
P	F	$F/P\ i, n$	Single-payment compound-amount factor
F	P	$P/F\ i, n$	Single-payment present-worth factor
A	F	$F/A\ i, n$	Equal-payment-series compound-amount factor
F	A	$A/F\ i, n$	Equal-payment-series sinking-fund factor
A	P	$P/A\ i, n$	Equal-payment-series present-worth factor
P	A	$A/P\ i, n$	Equal-payment-series capital-recovery factor

[1]For continuous compounding substitute r for i.

While the interest periods are considered to be discrete for money flow purposes, it is possible to consider the interest to be compounded an infinite number of times per interest period. This is referred to as *continuous compounding*, and Exhibit XI.2 is provided for this case. The interest rate considered is r, the rate for the discrete interest period, or the nominal rate.

B. Reading the Tables

Find the single-payment present-worth factor, where $i = .12$ and $n = 10$ for discrete compounding. The entry in Exhibit XI.1–7 is 0.3220. For continuous compounding, where $r = .12$ and $n = 10$, this is found to be 0.3012 in Exhibit XI.2–7.

C. Using the Tables

Example C–1. Find the future worth of $1000 if invested for 20 years at an interest rate of 12 percent per year compounded yearly. The single-payment compound-amount factor for discrete compounding, from Exhibit XI.1–7 with $i = 12\%$ and $n = 20$ is 9.646. Thus $F = P \cdot (F/P\ 12, 20) =$ $1000(9.646) = $9646.

Example C–2. Repeating Example C–1 for continuous compounding, we find the single-payment compound-amount factor in Exhibit XI.2–7 to be 11.023. Thus, $F =$ $1000(11.023) = $11,023.

Example C–3. How much money would be available for a child at age 18 if at the first birthday and on each birthday through age 18, the child's parents added $100 to a fund that earned 12 percent annual interest, compounded continuously? From Exhibit XI.2–7, the equal-payment series compound-amount factor for continuous compounding with $r = 12\%$ and $n = 18$ is 60.167. Thus, $F = A \cdot (F/A\ 12, 18) =$ $100(60.167) = $6016.70.

Example C–4. A $1000 diamond ring is debited to your charge account. Find the total interest paid if you wish to make monthly payments so that the balance is paid off at the end of two years. The finance charges to the account are 18 percent per effective year, compounded monthly. The effective interest rate per month is 18 per cent per year/(12 months per year), or 1.5 percent per month. From Exhibit XI.1–3, the equal-payment series capital-recovery factor for $i = 1.5\%$ and $n = 24$ months is 0.0499. Thus, the monthly payments will be $A = P \cdot (A/P\ 1.5, 24) =$ $1000 (0.0499) = $49.90 per month. The total amount paid is ($49.90/month)(24 months) = $1197.60. The interest paid is $1197.60 − $1000.00 = $197.60.

EXHIBIT XI.1–1

Interest Factors for Discrete Compounding

($i = .005$)

r	Single Payment		Equal Payment Series			
	Compound-amount Factor	Present-worth Factor	Compound-amount Factor	Sinking-fund Factor	Present-worth Factor	Capital-recovery Factor
	To Find F Given P F/P i,n	To Find P Given F P/F i,n	To Find F Given A F/A i,n	To Find A Given F A/F i,n	To Find P Given A P/A i,n	To Find A Given P A/P i,n
1	1.005	.9950	1.000	1.0000	.9950	1.0050
2	1.010	.9901	2.005	.4988	1.9851	.5038
3	1.015	.9851	3.015	.3317	2.9702	.3367
4	1.020	.9802	4.030	.2481	3.9505	.2531
5	1.025	.9754	5.050	.1980	4.9259	.2030
6	1.030	.9705	6.076	.1646	5.8964	.1696
7	1.036	.9657	7.106	.1407	6.8621	.1457
8	1.041	.9609	8.141	.1228	7.8230	.1278
9	1.046	.9561	9.182	.1089	8.7791	.1139
10	1.051	.9513	10.228	.0978	9.7304	.1028
11	1.056	.9466	11.279	.0887	10.6770	.0937
12	1.062	.9419	12.336	.0811	11.6189	.0861
13	1.067	.9372	13.397	.0746	12.5562	.0796
14	1.072	.9326	14.464	.0691	13.4887	.0741
15	1.078	.9279	15.537	.0644	14.4166	.0694
16	1.083	.9233	16.614	.0602	15.3399	.0652
17	1.088	.9187	17.697	.0565	16.2586	.0615
18	1.094	.9141	18.786	.0532	17.1728	.0582
19	1.099	.9096	19.880	.0503	18.0824	.0553
20	1.105	.9051	20.979	.0477	18.9874	.0527
21	1.110	.9006	22.084	.0453	19.8880	.0503
22	1.116	.8961	23.194	.0431	20.7841	.0481
23	1.122	.8916	24.310	.0411	21.6757	.0461
24	1.127	.8872	25.432	.0393	22.5629	.0443
30	1.161	.8610	32.280	.0310	27.7941	.0360
36	1.197	.8356	39.336	.0254	32.8710	.0304
42	1.233	.8110	46.607	.0215	37.7983	.0265
48	1.270	.7871	54.098	.0185	42.5803	.0235
54	1.309	.7639	61.817	.0162	47.2214	.0212
60	1.349	.7414	69.770	.0143	51.7256	.0193
72	1.432	.6983	86.409	.0116	60.3395	.0166
84	1.520	.6577	104.074	.0096	68.4530	.0146
96	1.614	.6195	122.829	.0081	76.0952	.0131
108	1.714	.5835	142.740	.0070	83.2934	.0120
120	1.819	.5496	163.879	.0061	90.0735	.0111
132	1.932	.5177	186.323	.0054	96.4596	.0104
144	2.051	.4876	210.150	.0048	102.4747	.0098
156	2.177	.4593	235.447	.0042	108.1404	.0092
168	2.312	.4326	262.305	.0038	113.4770	.0088
180	2.454	.4075	290.819	.0034	118.5035	.0084

EXHIBIT XI.1–2

Interest Factors for Discrete Compounding

($i = .01$)

n	Single Payment		Equal Payment Series			
	Compound-amount Factor	Present-worth Factor	Compound-amount Factor	Sinking-fund Factor	Present-worth Factor	Capital-recovery Factor
	To Find F Given P F/P i,n	To Find P Given F P/F i,n	To Find F Given A F/A i,n	To Find A Given F A/F i,n	To Find P Given A P/A i,n	To Find A Given P A/P i,n
1	1.010	.9901	1.000	1.0000	.9901	1.0100
2	1.020	.9803	2.010	.4975	1.9704	.5075
3	1.030	.9706	3.030	.3300	2.9410	.3400
4	1.041	.9610	4.060	.2463	3.9020	.2563
5	1.051	.9515	5.101	.1960	4.8534	.2060
6	1.062	.9420	6.152	.1625	5.7955	.1725
7	1.072	.9327	7.214	.1386	6.7282	.1486
8	1.083	.9235	8.286	.1207	7.6517	.1307
9	1.094	.9143	9.369	.1067	8.5660	.1167
10	1.105	.9053	10.462	.0956	9.4713	.1056
11	1.116	.8963	11.567	.0865	10.3676	.0965
12	1.127	.8874	12.683	.0788	11.2551	.0888
13	1.138	.8787	13.809	.0724	12.1337	.0824
14	1.149	.8700	14.947	.0669	13.0037	.0769
15	1.161	.8613	16.097	.0621	13.8651	.0721
16	1.173	.8528	17.258	.0579	14.7179	.0679
17	1.184	.8444	18.430	.0543	15.5623	.0643
18	1.196	.8360	19.615	.0510	16.3983	.0610
19	1.208	.8277	20.811	.0481	17.2260	.0581
20	1.220	.8195	22.019	.0454	18.0456	.0554
21	1.232	.8114	23.239	.0430	18.8570	.0530
22	1.245	.8034	24.472	.0409	19.6604	.0509
23	1.257	.7954	25.716	.0389	20.4558	.0489
24	1.270	.7876	26.973	.0371	21.2434	.0471
30	1.348	.7419	34.785	.0287	25.8077	.0387
36	1.431	.6989	43.077	.0232	30.1075	.0332
42	1.519	.6584	51.879	.0193	34.1581	.0293
48	1.612	.6203	61.223	.0163	37.9740	.0263
54	1.711	.5843	71.141	.0141	41.5687	.0241
60	1.817	.5504	81.670	.0122	44.9550	.0222
72	2.047	.4885	104.710	.0096	51.1504	.0196
84	2.307	.4335	130.672	.0077	56.6485	.0177
96	2.599	.3847	159.927	.0063	61.5277	.0163
108	2.929	.3414	192.893	.0052	65.8578	.0152
120	3.300	.3030	230.039	.0043	69.7005	.0143
132	3.719	.2689	271.896	.0037	73.1108	.0137
144	4.191	.2386	319.062	.0031	76.1372	.0131
156	4.722	.2118	372.209	.0027	78.8229	.0127
168	5.321	.1879	432.097	.0023	81.2064	.0123
180	5.996	.1668	499.580	.0020	83.3217	.0120

EXHIBIT XI.1–3

INTEREST FACTORS FOR DISCRETE COMPOUNDING

($i = .015$)

	Single Payment		Equal Payment Series			
n	Compound-amount Factor	Present-worth Factor	Compound-amount Factor	Sinking-fund Factor	Present-worth Factor	Capital-recovery Factor
	To Find *F* Given *P* *F/P i,n*	To Find *P* Given *F* *P/F i,n*	To Find *F* Given *A* *F/A i,n*	To Find *A* Given *F* *A/F i,n*	To Find *P* Given *A* *P/A i,n*	To Find *A* Given *P* *A/P i,n*
1	1.015	.9852	1.000	1.0000	.9852	1.0150
2	1.030	.9707	2.015	.4963	1.9559	.5113
3	1.046	.9563	3.045	.3284	2.9122	.3434
4	1.061	.9422	4.091	.2444	3.8544	.2594
5	1.077	.9283	5.152	.1941	4.7826	.2091
6	1.093	.9145	6.230	.1605	5.6972	.1755
7	1.110	.9010	7.323	.1366	6.5982	.1516
8	1.126	.8877	8.433	.1186	7.4859	.1336
9	1.143	.8746	9.559	.1046	8.3605	.1196
10	1.161	.8617	10.703	.0934	9.2222	.1084
11	1.178	.8489	11.863	.0843	10.0711	.0993
12	1.196	.8364	13.041	.0767	10.9075	.0917
13	1.214	.8240	14.237	.0702	11.7315	.0852
14	1.232	.8118	15.450	.0647	12.5434	.0797
15	1.250	.7999	16.682	.0599	13.3432	.0749
16	1.269	.7880	17.932	.0558	14.1313	.0708
17	1.288	.7764	19.201	.0521	14.9076	.0671
18	1.307	.7649	20.489	.0488	15.6726	.0638
19	1.327	.7536	21.797	.0459	16.4262	.0609
20	1.347	.7425	23.124	.0432	17.1686	.0582
21	1.367	.7315	24.471	.0409	17.9001	.0559
22	1.388	.7207	25.838	.0387	18.6208	.0537
23	1.408	.7100	27.225	.0367	19.3309	.0517
24	1.430	.6995	28.634	.0349	20.0304	.0499
30	1.563	.6398	37.539	.0266	24.0158	.0416
36	1.709	.5851	47.276	.0212	27.6607	.0362
42	1.869	.5351	57.923	.0173	30.9941	.0323
48	2.043	.4894	69.565	.0144	34.0426	.0294
54	2.234	.4475	82.295	.0122	36.8305	.0272
60	2.443	.4093	96.215	.0104	39.3803	.0254
72	2.921	.3423	128.077	.0078	43.8447	.0228
84	3.493	.2863	166.173	.0060	47.5786	.0210
96	4.176	.2395	211.720	.0047	50.7017	.0197
108	4.993	.2003	266.178	.0038	53.3137	.0188
120	5.969	.1675	331.288	.0030	55.4985	.0180
132	7.137	.1401	409.135	.0024	57.3257	.0174
144	8.533	.1172	502.211	.0020	58.8540	.0170
156	10.202	.0980	613.494	.0016	60.1323	.0166
168	12.198	.0820	746.545	.0013	61.2014	.0163
180	14.584	.0686	905.625	.0011	62.0956	.0161

EXHIBIT XI.1–4

Interest Factors for Discrete Compounding

($i = .02$)

	Single Payment		Equal Payment Series			
n	Compound-amount Factor	Present-worth Factor	Compound-amount Factor	Sinking-fund Factor	Present-worth Factor	Capital-recovery Factor
	To Find *F* Given *P* *F/P i,n*	To Find *P* Given *F* *P/F i,n*	To Find *F* Given *A* *F/A i,n*	To Find *A* Given *F* *A/F i,n*	To Find *P* Given *A* *P/A i,n*	To Find *A* Given *P* *A/P i,n*
1	1.020	.9804	1.000	1.0000	.9804	1.0200
2	1.040	.9612	2.020	.4950	1.9416	.5150
3	1.061	.9423	3.060	.3268	2.8839	.3468
4	1.082	.9238	4.122	.2426	3.8077	.2626
5	1.104	.9057	5.204	.1922	4.7135	.2122
6	1.126	.8880	6.308	.1585	5.6014	.1785
7	1.149	.8706	7.434	.1345	6.4720	.1545
8	1.172	.8535	8.583	.1165	7.3255	.1365
9	1.195	.8368	9.755	.1025	8.1622	.1225
10	1.219	.8203	10.950	.0913	8.9826	.1113
11	1.243	.8043	12.169	.0822	9.7868	.1022
12	1.268	.7885	13.412	.0746	10.5753	.0946
13	1.294	.7730	14.680	.0681	11.3484	.0881
14	1.319	.7579	15.974	.0626	12.1062	.0826
15	1.346	.7430	17.293	.0578	12.8493	.0778
16	1.373	.7284	18.639	.0537	13.5777	.0737
17	1.400	.7142	20.012	.0500	14.2919	.0700
18	1.428	.7002	21.412	.0467	14.9920	.0667
19	1.457	.6864	22.841	.0438	15.6785	.0638
20	1.486	.6730	24.297	.0412	16.3514	.0612
21	1.516	.6598	25.783	.0388	17.0112	.0588
22	1.546	.6468	27.299	.0366	17.6580	.0566
23	1.577	.6342	28.845	.0347	18.2922	.0547
24	1.608	.6217	30.422	.0329	18.9139	.0529
30	1.811	.5521	40.568	.0246	22.3965	.0446
36	2.040	.4902	51.994	.0192	25.4888	.0392
42	2.297	.4353	64.862	.0154	28.2348	.0354
48	2.587	.3865	79.354	.0126	30.6731	.0326
54	2.913	.3432	95.673	.0105	32.8383	.0305
60	3.281	.3048	114.052	.0088	34.7609	.0288
72	4.161	.2403	158.057	.0063	37.9841	.0263
84	5.277	.1895	213.867	.0047	40.5255	.0247
96	6.693	.1494	284.647	.0035	42.5294	.0235
108	8.488	.1178	374.413	.0027	44.1095	.0227
120	10.765	.0929	488.258	.0020	45.3554	.0220
132	13.653	.0732	632.641	.0016	46.3378	.0216
144	17.315	.0578	815.754	.0012	47.1123	.0212
156	21.960	.0455	1047.986	.0010	47.7231	.0210
168	27.850	.0359	1342.512	.0007	48.2047	.0207
180	35.321	.0283	1716.042	.0006	48.5844	.0206

EXHIBIT XI.1–5

INTEREST FACTORS FOR DISCRETE COMPOUNDING
($i = .025$)

	Single Payment		Equal Payment Series			
n	Compound-amount Factor	Present-worth Factor	Compound-amount Factor	Sinking-fund Factor	Present-worth Factor	Capital-recovery Factor
	To Find *F* Given *P* *F/P i,n*	To Find *P* Given *F* *P/F i,n*	To Find *F* Given *A* *F/A i,n*	To Find *A* Given *F* *A/F i,n*	To Find *P* Given *A* *P/A i,n*	To Find *A* Given *P* *A/P i,n*
1	1.025	.9756	1.000	1.0000	.9756	1.0250
2	1.051	.9518	2.025	.4938	1.9274	.5188
3	1.077	.9286	3.076	.3251	2.8560	.3501
4	1.104	.9060	4.153	.2408	3.7620	.2658
5	1.131	.8839	5.256	.1902	4.6458	.2152
6	1.160	.8623	6.388	.1565	5.5081	.1815
7	1.189	.8413	7.547	.1325	6.3494	.1575
8	1.218	.8207	8.736	.1145	7.1701	.1395
9	1.249	.8007	9.955	.1005	7.9709	.1255
10	1.280	.7812	11.203	.0893	8.7521	.1143
11	1.312	.7621	12.483	.0801	9.5142	.1051
12	1.345	.7436	13.796	.0725	10.2578	.0975
13	1.379	.7254	15.140	.0660	10.9832	.0910
14	1.413	.7077	16.519	.0605	11.6909	.0855
15	1.448	.6905	17.932	.0558	12.3814	.0808
16	1.485	.6736	19.380	.0516	13.0550	.0766
17	1.522	.6572	20.865	.0479	13.7122	.0729
18	1.560	.6412	22.386	.0447	14.3534	.0697
19	1.599	.6255	23.946	.0418	14.9789	.0668
20	1.639	.6103	25.545	.0391	15.5892	.0641
21	1.680	.5954	27.183	.0368	16.1845	.0618
22	1.722	.5809	28.863	.0346	16.7654	.0596
23	1.765	.5667	30.584	.0327	17.3321	.0577
24	1.809	.5529	32.349	.0309	17.8850	.0559
30	2.098	.4767	43.903	.0228	20.9303	.0478
36	2.433	.4111	57.301	.0175	23.5563	.0425
42	2.821	.3545	72.840	.0137	25.8206	.0387
48	3.271	.3057	90.860	.0110	27.7732	.0360
54	3.794	.2636	111.757	.0089	29.4568	.0339
60	4.400	.2273	135.992	.0074	30.9087	.0324
72	5.917	.1690	196.689	.0051	33.2401	.0301
84	7.958	.1257	278.321	.0036	34.9736	.0286
96	10.703	.0934	388.106	.0026	36.2626	.0276
108	14.394	.0695	535.755	.0019	37.2210	.0269
120	19.358	.0517	734.326	.0014	37.9337	.0264
132	26.035	.0384	1001.382	.0010	38.4636	.0260
144	35.014	.0286	1360.544	.0007	38.8576	.0257
156	47.089	.0212	1843.575	.0005	39.1506	.0255
168	63.330	.0158	2493.199	.0004	39.3684	.0254
180	85.172	.0117	3366.872	.0003	39.5304	.0253

EXHIBIT XI.1–6

Interest Factors for Discrete Compounding

($i = .06$)

	Single Payment		Equal Payment Series			
n	Compound-amount Factor	Present-worth Factor	Compound-amount Factor	Sinking-fund Factor	Present-worth Factor	Capital-recovery Factor
	To Find F Given P $F/P\ i,n$	To Find P Given F $P/F\ i,n$	To Find F Given A $F/A\ i,n$	To Find A Given F $A/F\ i,n$	To Find P Given A $P/A\ i,n$	To Find A Given P $A/P\ i,n$
1	1.060	.9434	1.000	1.0000	.9434	1.0600
2	1.124	.8900	2.060	.4854	1.8334	.5454
3	1.191	.8396	3.184	.3141	2.6730	.3741
4	1.262	.7921	4.375	.2286	3.4651	.2886
5	1.338	.7473	5.637	.1774	4.2124	.2374
6	1.419	.7050	6.975	.1434	4.9173	.2034
7	1.504	.6651	8.394	.1191	5.5824	.1791
8	1.594	.6274	9.897	.1010	6.2098	.1610
9	1.689	.5919	11.491	.0870	6.8017	.1470
10	1.791	.5584	13.181	.0759	7.3601	.1359
11	1.898	.5268	14.972	.0668	7.8869	.1268
12	2.012	.4970	16.870	.0593	8.3838	.1193
13	2.133	.4688	18.882	.0530	8.8527	.1130
14	2.261	.4423	21.015	.0476	9.2950	.1076
15	2.397	.4173	23.276	.0430	9.7122	.1030
16	2.540	.3936	25.673	.0390	10.1059	.0990
17	2.693	.3714	28.213	.0354	10.4773	.0954
18	2.854	.3503	30.906	.0324	10.8276	.0924
19	3.026	.3305	33.760	.0296	11.1581	.0896
20	3.207	.3118	36.786	.0272	11.4699	.0872
21	3.400	.2942	39.993	.0250	11.7641	.0850
22	3.604	.2775	43.392	.0230	12.0416	.0830
23	3.820	.2618	46.996	.0213	12.3034	.0813
24	4.049	.2470	50.816	.0197	12.5504	.0797
25	4.292	.2330	54.865	.0182	12.7834	.0782
26	4.549	.2198	59.156	.0169	13.0032	.0769
27	4.822	.2074	63.706	.0157	13.2105	.0757
28	5.112	.1956	68.528	.0146	13.4062	.0746
29	5.418	.1846	73.640	.0136	13.5907	.0736
30	5.743	.1741	79.058	.0126	13.7648	.0726
31	6.088	.1643	84.802	.0118	13.9291	.0718
32	6.453	.1550	90.890	.0110	14.0840	.0710
33	6.841	.1462	97.343	.0103	14.2302	.0703
34	7.251	.1379	104.184	.0096	14.3681	.0696
35	7.686	.1301	111.435	.0090	14.4982	.0690
36	8.147	.1227	119.121	.0084	14.6210	.0684
37	8.636	.1158	127.268	.0079	14.7368	.0679
38	9.154	.1092	135.904	.0074	14.8460	.0674
39	9.704	.1031	145.058	.0069	14.9491	.0669
40	10.286	.0972	154.762	.0065	15.0463	.0665

EXHIBIT XI.1–7

INTEREST FACTORS FOR DISCRETE COMPOUNDING

($i = .12$)

	Single Payment		Equal Payment Series			
n	Compound-amount Factor	Present-worth Factor	Compound-amount Factor	Sinking-fund Factor	Present-worth Factor	Capital-recovery Factor
	To Find F Given P F/P i,n	To Find P Given F P/F i,n	To Find F Given A F/A i,n	To Find A Given F A/F i,n	To Find P Given A P/A i,n	To Find A Given P A/P i,n
1	1.120	.8929	1.000	1.0000	.8929	1.1200
2	1.254	.7972	2.120	.4717	1.6901	.5917
3	1.405	.7118	3.374	.2963	2.4018	.4163
4	1.574	.6355	4.779	.2092	3.0373	.3292
5	1.762	.5674	6.353	.1574	3.6048	.2774
6	1.974	.5066	8.115	.1232	4.1114	.2432
7	2.211	.4523	10.089	.0991	4.5638	.2191
8	2.476	.4039	12.300	.0813	4.9676	.2013
9	2.773	.3606	14.776	.0677	5.3282	.1877
10	3.106	.3220	17.549	.0570	5.6502	.1770
11	3.479	.2875	20.655	.0484	5.9377	.1684
12	3.896	.2567	24.133	.0414	6.1944	.1614
13	4.363	.2292	28.029	.0357	6.4235	.1557
14	4.887	.2046	32.393	.0309	6.6282	.1509
15	5.474	.1827	37.280	.0268	6.8109	.1468
16	6.130	.1631	42.753	.0234	6.9740	.1434
17	6.866	.1456	48.884	.0205	7.1196	.1405
18	7.690	.1300	55.750	.0179	7.2497	.1379
19	8.613	.1161	63.440	.0158	7.3658	.1358
20	9.646	.1037	72.052	.0139	7.4694	.1339
21	10.804	.0926	81.699	.0122	7.5620	.1322
22	12.100	.0826	92.503	.0108	7.6446	.1308
23	13.552	.0738	104.603	.0096	7.7184	.1296
24	15.179	.0659	118.155	.0085	7.7843	.1285
25	17.000	.0588	133.334	.0075	7.8431	.1275
26	19.040	.0525	150.334	.0067	7.8957	.1267
27	21.325	.0469	169.374	.0059	7.9426	.1259
28	23.884	.0419	190.699	.0052	7.9844	.1252
29	26.750	.0374	214.583	.0047	8.0218	.1247
30	29.960	.0334	241.333	.0041	8.0552	.1241
31	33.555	.0298	271.293	.0037	8.0850	.1237
32	37.582	.0266	304.848	.0033	8.1116	.1233
33	42.092	.0238	342.429	.0029	8.1354	.1229
34	47.143	.0212	384.521	.0026	8.1566	.1226
35	52.800	.0189	431.663	.0023	8.1755	.1223
36	59.136	.0169	484.463	.0021	8.1924	.1221
37	66.232	.0151	543.599	.0018	8.2075	.1218
38	74.180	.0135	609.831	.0016	8.2210	.1216
39	83.081	.0120	684.010	.0015	8.2330	.1215
40	93.051	.0107	767.091	.0013	8.2438	.1213

EXHIBIT XI.1–8

INTEREST FACTORS FOR DISCRETE COMPOUNDING

($i = .18$)

n	Single Payment		Equal Payment Series			
	Compound-amount Factor	Present-worth Factor	Compound-amount Factor	Sinking-fund Factor	Present-worth Factor	Capital-recovery Factor
	To Find *F* Given *P* *F/P i,n*	To Find *P* Given *F* *P/F i,n*	To Find *F* Given *A* *F/A i,n*	To Find *A* Given *F* *A/F i,n*	To Find *P* Given *A* *P/A i,n*	To Find *A* Given *P* *A/P i,n*
1	1.180	.8475	1.000	1.0000	.8475	1.1800
2	1.392	.7182	2.180	.4587	1.5656	.6387
3	1.643	.6086	3.572	.2799	2.1743	.4599
4	1.939	.5158	5.215	.1917	2.6901	.3717
5	2.288	.4371	7.154	.1398	3.1272	.3198
6	2.700	.3704	9.442	.1059	3.4976	.2859
7	3.185	.3139	12.142	.0824	3.8115	.2624
8	3.759	.2660	15.327	.0652	4.0776	.2452
9	4.435	.2255	19.086	.0524	4.3030	.2324
10	5.234	.1911	23.521	.0425	4.4941	.2225
11	6.176	.1619	28.755	.0348	4.6560	.2148
12	7.288	.1372	34.931	.0286	4.7932	.2086
13	8.599	.1163	42.219	.0237	4.9095	.2037
14	10.147	.0985	50.818	.0197	5.0081	.1997
15	11.974	.0835	60.965	.0164	5.0916	.1964
16	14.129	.0708	72.939	.0137	5.1624	.1937
17	16.672	.0600	87.068	.0115	5.2223	.1915
18	19.673	.0508	103.740	.0096	5.2732	.1896
19	23.214	.0431	123.414	.0081	5.3162	.1881
20	27.393	.0365	146.628	.0068	5.3527	.1868
21	32.324	.0309	174.021	.0057	5.3837	.1857
22	38.142	.0262	206.345	.0048	5.4099	.1848
23	45.008	.0222	244.487	.0041	5.4321	.1841
24	53.109	.0188	289.494	.0035	5.4509	.1835
25	62.669	.0160	342.603	.0029	5.4669	.1829
26	73.949	.0135	405.272	.0025	5.4804	.1825
27	87.260	.0115	479.221	.0021	5.4919	.1821
28	102.967	.0097	566.481	.0018	5.5016	.1818
29	121.501	.0082	669.447	.0015	5.5098	.1815
30	143.371	.0070	790.948	.0013	5.5168	.1813
31	169.177	.0059	934.319	.0011	5.5227	.1811
32	199.629	.0050	1103.496	.0009	5.5277	.1809
33	235.563	.0042	1303.125	.0008	5.5320	.1808
34	277.964	.0036	1538.688	.0006	5.5356	.1806
35	327.997	.0030	1816.652	.0006	5.5386	.1806
36	387.037	.0026	2144.649	.0005	5.5412	.1805
37	456.703	.0022	2531.686	.0004	5.5434	.1804
38	538.910	.0019	2988.389	.0003	5.5452	.1803
39	635.914	.0016	3527.299	.0003	5.5468	.1803
40	750.378	.0013	4163.213	.0002	5.5482	.1802

EXHIBIT XI.1–9

INTEREST FACTORS FOR DISCRETE COMPOUNDING

($i = .24$)

	Single Payment		Equal Payment Series			
n	Compound-amount Factor	Present-worth Factor	Compound-amount Factor	Sinking-fund Factor	Present-worth Factor	Capital-recovery Factor
	To Find F Given P F/P i,n	To Find P Given F P/F i,n	To Find F Given A F/A i,n	To Find A Given F A/F i,n	To Find P Given A P/A i,n	To Find A Given P A/P i,n
1	1.240	.8065	1.000	1.0000	.8065	1.2400
2	1.538	.6504	2.240	.4464	1.4568	.6864
3	1.907	.5245	3.778	.2647	1.9813	.5047
4	2.364	.4230	5.684	.1759	2.4043	.4159
5	2.932	.3411	8.048	.1242	2.7454	.3642
6	3.635	.2751	10.980	.0911	3.0205	.3311
7	4.508	.2218	14.615	.0684	3.2423	.3084
8	5.590	.1789	19.123	.0523	3.4212	.2923
9	6.931	.1443	24.712	.0405	3.5655	.2805
10	8.594	.1164	31.643	.0316	3.6819	.2716
11	10.657	.0938	40.238	.0249	3.7757	.2649
12	13.215	.0757	50.895	.0196	3.8514	.2596
13	16.386	.0610	64.110	.0156	3.9124	.2556
14	20.319	.0492	80.496	.0124	3.9616	.2524
15	25.196	.0397	100.815	.0099	4.0013	.2499
16	31.243	.0320	126.011	.0079	4.0333	.2479
17	38.741	.0258	157.253	.0064	4.0591	.2464
18	48.039	.0208	195.994	.0051	4.0799	.2451
19	59.568	.0168	244.033	.0041	4.0967	.2441
20	73.864	.0135	303.601	.0033	4.1103	.2433
21	91.592	.0109	377.465	.0026	4.1212	.2426
22	113.574	.0088	469.056	.0021	4.1300	.2421
23	140.831	.0071	582.630	.0017	4.1371	.2417
24	174.631	.0057	723.461	.0014	4.1428	.2414
25	216.542	.0046	898.092	.0011	4.1474	.2411
26	268.512	.0037	1114.634	.0009	4.1511	.2409
27	332.955	.0030	1383.146	.0007	4.1542	.2407
28	412.864	.0024	1716.101	.0006	4.1566	.2406
29	511.952	.0020	2128.965	.0005	4.1585	.2405
30	634.820	.0016	2640.916	.0004	4.1601	.2404
31	787.177	.0013	3275.736	.0003	4.1614	.2403
32	976.099	.0010	4062.913	.0002	4.1624	.2402
33	1210.363	.0008	5039.012	.0002	4.1632	.2402
34	1500.850	.0007	6249.375	.0002	4.1639	.2402
35	1861.054	.0005	7750.225	.0001	4.1644	.2401
36	2307.707	.0004	9611.279	.0001	4.1649	.2401
37	2861.557	.0003	11918.986	.0001	4.1652	.2401
38	3548.330	.0003	14780.543	.0001	4.1655	.2401
39	4399.930	.0002	18328.873	.0001	4.1657	.2401
40	5455.913	.0002	22728.803	.0000	4.1659	.2400

EXHIBIT XI.1–10

Interest Factors for Discrete Compounding

($i = .30$)

n	Single Payment		Equal Payment Series			
	Compound-amount Factor	Present-worth Factor	Compound-amount Factor	Sinking-fund Factor	Present-worth Factor	Capital-recovery Factor
	To Find F Given P F/P i,n	To Find P Given F P/F i,n	To Find F Given A F/A i,n	To Find A Given F A/F i,n	To Find P Given A P/A i,n	To Find A Given P A/P i,n
1	1.300	.7692	1.000	1.0000	.7692	1.3000
2	1.690	.5917	2.300	.4348	1.3609	.7348
3	2.197	.4552	3.990	.2506	1.8161	.5506
4	2.856	.3501	6.187	.1616	2.1662	.4616
5	3.713	.2693	9.043	.1106	2.4356	.4106
6	4.827	.2072	12.756	.0784	2.6427	.3784
7	6.275	.1594	17.583	.0569	2.8021	.3569
8	8.157	.1226	23.858	.0419	2.9247	.3419
9	10.604	.0943	32.015	.0312	3.0190	.3312
10	13.786	.0725	42.619	.0235	3.0915	.3235
11	17.922	.0558	56.405	.0177	3.1473	.3177
12	23.298	.0429	74.327	.0135	3.1903	.3135
13	30.288	.0330	97.625	.0102	3.2233	.3102
14	39.374	.0254	127.913	.0078	3.2487	.3078
15	51.186	.0195	167.286	.0060	3.2682	.3060
16	66.542	.0150	218.472	.0046	3.2832	.3046
17	86.504	.0116	285.014	.0035	3.2948	.3035
18	112.455	.0089	371.518	.0027	3.3037	.3027
19	146.192	.0068	483.973	.0021	3.3105	.3021
20	190.050	.0053	630.165	.0016	3.3158	.3016
21	247.065	.0040	820.215	.0012	3.3198	.3012
22	321.184	.0031	1067.280	.0009	3.3230	.3009
23	417.539	.0024	1388.464	.0007	3.3254	.3007
24	542.801	.0018	1806.003	.0006	3.3272	.3006
25	705.641	.0014	2348.803	.0004	3.3286	.3004
26	917.333	.0011	3054.444	.0003	3.3297	.3003
27	1192.533	.0008	3971.778	.0003	3.3305	.3003
28	1550.293	.0006	5164.311	.0002	3.3312	.3002
29	2015.381	.0005	6714.604	.0001	3.3317	.3001
30	2619.996	.0004	8729.985	.0001	3.3321	.3001
31	3405.994	.0003	11349.981	.0001	3.3324	.3001
32	4427.793	.0002	14755.975	.0001	3.3326	.3001
33	5756.130	.0002	19183.768	.0001	3.3328	.3001
34	7482.970	.0001	24939.899	.0000	3.3329	.3000
35	9727.860	.0001	32422.868	.0000	3.3330	.3000
36	12646.219	.0001	42150.729	.0000	3.3331	.3000
37	16440.084	.0001	54796.947	.0000	3.3331	.3000
38	21372.109	.0000	71237.031	.0000	3.3332	.3000
39	27783.742	.0000	92609.141	.0000	3.3332	.3000
40	36118.865	.0000	120392.883	.0000	3.3332	.3000

EXHIBIT XI.2–1

INTEREST FACTORS FOR CONTINUOUS COMPOUNDING
($r = .005$)

	Single Payment		Equal Payment Series			
n	Compound-amount Factor	Present-worth Factor	Compound-amount Factor	Sinking-fund Factor	Present-worth Factor	Capital-recovery Factor
	To Find *F* Given *P* *F/P r,n*	To Find *P* Given *F* *P/F r,n*	To Find *F* Given *A* *F/A r,n*	To Find *A* Given *F* *A/F r,n*	To Find *P* Given *A* *P/A r,n*	To Find *A* Given *P* *A/P r,n*
1	1.005	.9950	1.000	1.0000	.9950	1.0050
2	1.010	.9900	2.005	.4988	1.9851	.5038
3	1.015	.9851	3.015	.3317	2.9702	.3367
4	1.020	.9802	4.030	.2481	3.9504	.2531
5	1.025	.9753	5.050	.1980	4.9257	.2030
6	1.030	.9704	6.076	.1646	5.8961	.1696
7	1.036	.9656	7.106	.1407	6.8617	.1457
8	1.041	.9608	8.142	.1228	7.8225	.1278
9	1.046	.9560	9.183	.1089	8.7785	.1139
10	1.051	.9512	10.229	.0978	9.7298	.1028
11	1.057	.9465	11.280	.0887	10.6762	.0937
12	1.062	.9418	12.336	.0811	11.6180	.0861
13	1.067	.9371	13.398	.0746	12.5551	.0796
14	1.073	.9324	14.465	.0691	13.4875	.0741
15	1.078	.9277	15.538	.0644	14.4152	.0694
16	1.083	.9231	16.616	.0602	15.3383	.0652
17	1.089	.9185	17.699	.0565	16.2568	.0615
18	1.094	.9139	18.788	.0532	17.1708	.0582
19	1.100	.9094	19.882	.0503	18.0801	.0553
20	1.105	.9048	20.982	.0477	18.9850	.0527
21	1.111	.9003	22.087	.0453	19.8853	.0503
22	1.116	.8958	23.198	.0431	20.7811	.0481
23	1.122	.8914	24.314	.0411	21.6725	.0461
24	1.127	.8869	25.436	.0393	22.5594	.0443
30	1.162	.8607	32.286	.0310	27.7888	.0360
36	1.197	.8353	39.345	.0254	32.8637	.0304
42	1.234	.8106	46.619	.0215	37.7885	.0265
48	1.271	.7866	54.114	.0185	42.5678	.0235
54	1.310	.7634	61.838	.0162	47.2059	.0212
60	1.350	.7408	69.797	.0143	51.7069	.0193
72	1.433	.6977	86.449	.0116	60.3137	.0166
84	1.522	.6570	104.132	.0096	68.4193	.0146
96	1.616	.6188	122.907	.0081	76.0529	.0131
108	1.716	.5827	142.844	.0070	83.2419	.0120
120	1.822	.5488	164.013	.0061	90.0123	.0111
132	1.935	.5169	186.491	.0054	96.3884	.0104
144	2.054	.4868	210.360	.0048	102.3931	.0098
156	2.181	.4584	235.704	.0042	108.0482	.0093
168	2.316	.4317	262.616	.0038	113.3740	.0088
180	2.460	.4066	291.191	.0034	118.3896	.0084

EXHIBIT XI.2–2

Interest Factors for Continuous Compounding

$(r = .01)$

n	Single Payment		Equal Payment Series			
	Compound-amount Factor	Present-worth Factor	Compound-amount Factor	Sinking-fund Factor	Present-worth Factor	Capital-recovery Factor
	To Find F Given P F/P r,n	To Find P Given F P/F r,n	To Find F Given A F/A r,n	To Find A Given F A/F r,n	To Find P Given A P/A r,n	To Find A Given P A/P r,n
1	1.010	.9900	1.000	1.0000	.9900	1.0101
2	1.020	.9802	2.010	.4975	1.9702	.5076
3	1.030	.9704	3.030	.3300	2.9407	.3401
4	1.041	.9608	4.061	.2463	3.9015	.2563
5	1.051	.9512	5.102	.1960	4.8527	.2061
6	1.062	.9418	6.153	.1625	5.7945	.1726
7	1.073	.9324	7.215	.1386	6.7269	.1487
8	1.083	.9231	8.287	.1207	7.6500	.1307
9	1.094	.9139	9.370	.1067	8.5639	.1168
10	1.105	.9048	10.465	.0956	9.4688	.1056
11	1.116	.8958	11.570	.0864	10.3646	.0965
12	1.127	.8869	12.686	.0788	11.2515	.0889
13	1.139	.8781	13.814	.0724	12.1296	.0824
14	1.150	.8694	14.952	.0669	12.9990	.0769
15	1.162	.8607	16.103	.0621	13.8597	.0722
16	1.174	.8521	17.264	.0579	14.7118	.0680
17	1.185	.8437	18.438	.0542	15.5555	.0643
18	1.197	.8353	19.623	.0510	16.3908	.0610
19	1.209	.8270	20.821	.0480	17.2177	.0581
20	1.221	.8187	22.030	.0454	18.0364	.0554
21	1.234	.8106	23.251	.0430	18.8470	.0531
22	1.246	.8025	24.485	.0408	19.6495	.0509
23	1.259	.7945	25.731	.0389	20.4441	.0489
24	1.271	.7866	26.990	.0371	21.2307	.0471
30	1.350	.7408	34.811	.0287	25.7888	.0388
36	1.433	.6977	43.117	.0232	30.0815	.0332
42	1.522	.6570	51.936	.0193	34.1241	.0293
48	1.616	.6188	61.300	.0163	37.9314	.0264
54	1.716	.5827	71.243	.0140	41.5169	.0241
60	1.822	.5488	81.802	.0122	44.8936	.0223
72	2.054	.4868	104.917	.0095	51.0686	.0196
84	2.316	.4317	130.980	.0076	56.5453	.0177
96	2.612	.3829	160.365	.0062	61.4027	.0163
108	2.945	.3396	193.497	.0052	65.7108	.0152
120	3.320	.3012	230.854	.0043	69.5318	.0144
132	3.743	.2671	272.973	.0037	72.9206	.0137
144	4.221	.2369	320.462	.0031	75.9263	.0132
156	4.759	.2101	374.006	.0027	78.5921	.0127
168	5.366	.1864	434.376	.0023	80.9565	.0124
180	6.050	.1653	502.444	.0020	83.0535	.0120

EXHIBIT XI.2–3

Interest Factors for Continuous Compounding

($r = .015$)

n	Single Payment		Equal Payment Series			
	Compound-amount Factor	Present-worth Factor	Compound-amount Factor	Sinking-fund Factor	Present-worth Factor	Capital-recovery Factor
	To Find F Given P F/P r,n	To Find P Given F P/F r,n	To Find F Given A F/A r,n	To Find A Given F A/F r,n	To Find P Given A P/A r,n	To Find A Given P A/P r,n
1	1.015	.9851	1.000	1.0000	.9851	1.0151
2	1.030	.9704	2.015	.4963	1.9556	.5114
3	1.046	.9560	3.046	.3283	2.9116	.3435
4	1.062	.9418	4.092	.2444	3.8533	.2595
5	1.078	.9277	5.153	.1940	4.7811	.2092
6	1.094	.9139	6.231	.1605	5.6950	.1756
7	1.111	.9003	7.325	.1365	6.5953	.1516
8	1.127	.8869	8.436	.1185	7.4822	.1336
9	1.145	.8737	9.564	.1046	8.3560	.1197
10	1.162	.8607	10.708	.0934	9.2167	.1085
11	1.179	.8479	11.870	.0842	10.0646	.0994
12	1.197	.8353	13.049	.0766	10.8998	.0917
13	1.215	.8228	14.247	.0702	11.7227	.0853
14	1.234	.8106	15.462	.0647	12.5332	.0798
15	1.252	.7985	16.696	.0599	13.3318	.0750
16	1.271	.7866	17.948	.0557	14.1184	.0708
17	1.290	.7749	19.219	.0520	14.8933	.0671
18	1.310	.7634	20.510	.0488	15.6567	.0639
19	1.330	.7520	21.820	.0458	16.4087	.0609
20	1.350	.7408	23.149	.0432	17.1495	.0583
21	1.370	.7298	24.499	.0408	17.8793	.0559
22	1.391	.7189	25.870	.0387	18.5982	.0538
23	1.412	.7082	27.261	.0367	19.3065	.0518
24	1.433	.6977	28.673	.0349	20.0041	.0500
30	1.568	.6376	37.604	.0266	23.9774	.0417
36	1.716	.5827	47.377	.0211	27.6087	.0362
42	1.878	.5326	58.070	.0172	30.9274	.0323
48	2.054	.4868	69.770	.0143	33.9605	.0294
54	2.248	.4449	82.571	.0121	36.7326	.0272
60	2.460	.4066	96.579	.0104	39.2660	.0255
72	2.945	.3396	128.675	.0078	43.6976	.0229
84	3.525	.2837	167.102	.0060	47.3991	.0211
96	4.221	.2369	213.107	.0047	50.4909	.0198
108	5.053	.1979	268.185	.0037	53.0734	.0188
120	6.050	.1653	334.125	.0030	55.2304	.0181
132	7.243	.1381	413.069	.0024	57.0322	.0175
144	8.671	.1153	507.583	.0020	58.5371	.0171
156	10.381	.0963	620.737	.0016	59.7941	.0167
168	12.429	.0805	756.206	.0013	60.8441	.0164
180	14.880	.0672	918.393	.0011	61.7211	.0162

EXHIBIT XI.2–4

INTEREST FACTORS FOR CONTINUOUS COMPOUNDING

$(r = .02)$

	Single Payment		Equal Payment Series			
n	Compound-amount Factor	Present-worth Factor	Compound-amount Factor	Sinking-fund Factor	Present-worth Factor	Capital-recovery Factor
	To Find *F* Given *P* *F/P r,n*	To Find *P* Given *F* *P/F r,n*	To Find *F* Given *A* *F/A r,n*	To Find *A* Given *F* *A/F r,n*	To Find *P* Given *A* *P/A r,n*	To Find *A* Given *P* *A/P r,n*
1	1.020	.9802	1.000	1.0000	.9802	1.0202
2	1.041	.9608	2.020	.4950	1.9410	.5152
3	1.062	.9418	3.061	.3267	2.8828	.3469
4	1.083	.9231	4.123	.2426	3.8059	.2628
5	1.105	.9048	5.206	.1921	4.7107	.2123
6	1.127	.8869	6.311	.1584	5.5976	.1786
7	1.150	.8694	7.439	.1344	6.4670	.1546
8	1.174	.8521	8.589	.1164	7.3191	.1366
9	1.197	.8353	9.763	.1024	8.1544	.1226
10	1.221	.8187	10.960	.0912	8.9731	.1114
11	1.246	.8025	12.181	.0821	9.7756	.1023
12	1.271	.7866	13.427	.0745	10.5623	.0947
13	1.297	.7711	14.699	.0680	11.3333	.0882
14	1.323	.7558	15.995	.0625	12.0891	.0827
15	1.350	.7408	17.319	.0577	12.8299	.0779
16	1.377	.7261	18.668	.0536	13.5561	.0738
17	1.405	.7118	20.046	.0499	14.2678	.0701
18	1.433	.6977	21.451	.0466	14.9655	.0668
19	1.462	.6839	22.884	.0437	15.6494	.0639
20	1.492	.6703	24.346	.0411	16.3197	.0613
21	1.522	.6570	25.838	.0387	16.9768	.0589
22	1.553	.6440	27.360	.0365	17.6208	.0568
23	1.584	.6313	28.913	.0346	18.2521	.0548
24	1.616	.6188	30.497	.0328	18.8709	.0530
30	1.822	.5488	40.696	.0246	22.3346	.0448
36	2.054	.4868	52.196	.0192	25.4066	.0394
42	2.316	.4317	65.162	.0153	28.1313	.0355
48	2.612	.3829	79.782	.0125	30.5478	.0327
54	2.945	.3396	96.265	.0104	32.6911	.0306
60	3.320	.3012	114.850	.0087	34.5921	.0289
72	4.221	.2369	159.430	.0063	37.7733	.0265
84	5.366	.1864	216.102	.0046	40.2758	.0248
96	6.821	.1466	288.147	.0035	42.2444	.0237
108	8.671	.1153	379.734	.0026	43.7929	.0228
120	11.023	.0907	496.164	.0020	45.0110	.0222
132	14.013	.0714	644.175	.0016	45.9692	.0218
144	17.814	.0561	832.335	.0012	46.7229	.0214
156	22.646	.0442	1071.532	.0009	47.3158	.0211
168	28.789	.0347	1375.611	.0007	47.7822	.0209
180	36.598	.0273	1762.172	.0006	48.1491	.0208

EXHIBIT XI.2–5

Interest Factors for Continuous Compounding

$(r = .025)$

n	Single Payment		Equal Payment Series			
	Compound-amount Factor	Present-worth Factor	Compound-amount Factor	Sinking-fund Factor	Present-worth Factor	Capital-recovery Factor
	To Find *F* Given *P* *F/P r,n*	To Find *P* Given *F* *P/F r,n*	To Find *F* Given *A* *F/A r,n*	To Find *A* Given *F* *A/F r,n*	To Find *P* Given *A* *P/A r,n*	To Find *A* Given *P* *A/P r,n*
1	1.025	.9753	1.000	1.0000	.9753	1.0253
2	1.051	.9512	2.025	.4938	1.9265	.5191
3	1.078	.9277	3.077	.3250	2.8543	.3504
4	1.105	.9048	4.154	.2407	3.7591	.2660
5	1.133	.8825	5.260	.1901	4.6416	.2154
6	1.162	.8607	6.393	.1564	5.5023	.1817
7	1.191	.8395	7.555	.1324	6.3418	.1577
8	1.221	.8187	8.746	.1143	7.1605	.1397
9	1.252	.7985	9.967	.1003	7.9590	.1256
10	1.284	.7788	11.220	.0891	8.7378	.1144
11	1.317	.7596	12.504	.0800	9.4974	.1053
12	1.350	.7408	13.820	.0724	10.2382	.0977
13	1.384	.7225	15.170	.0659	10.9607	.0912
14	1.419	.7047	16.554	.0604	11.6654	.0857
15	1.455	.6873	17.973	.0556	12.3527	.0810
16	1.492	.6703	19.428	.0515	13.0230	.0768
17	1.530	.6538	20.920	.0478	13.6768	.0731
18	1.568	.6376	22.450	.0445	14.3144	.0699
19	1.608	.6219	24.018	.0416	14.9363	.0670
20	1.649	.6065	25.626	.0390	15.5429	.0643
21	1.690	.5916	27.275	.0367	16.1344	.0620
22	1.733	.5769	28.965	.0345	16.7114	.0598
23	1.777	.5627	30.698	.0326	17.2741	.0579
24	1.822	.5488	32.475	.0308	17.8229	.0561
30	2.117	.4724	44.124	.0227	20.8426	.0480
36	2.460	.4066	57.657	.0173	23.4417	.0427
42	2.858	.3499	73.381	.0136	25.6788	.0389
48	3.320	.3012	91.649	.0109	27.6043	.0362
54	3.857	.2592	112.874	.0089	29.2616	.0342
60	4.482	.2231	137.534	.0073	30.6880	.0326
72	6.050	.1653	199.472	.0050	32.9724	.0303
84	8.166	.1225	283.079	.0035	34.6648	.0288
96	11.023	.0907	395.936	.0025	35.9185	.0278
108	14.880	.0672	548.278	.0018	36.8473	.0271
120	20.086	.0498	753.918	.0013	37.5354	.0266
132	27.113	.0369	1031.504	.0010	38.0451	.0263
144	36.598	.0273	1406.204	.0007	38.4227	.0260
156	49.402	.0202	1911.998	.0005	38.7025	.0258
168	66.686	.0150	2594.747	.0004	38.9097	.0257
180	90.017	.0111	3516.362	.0003	39.0633	.0256

EXHIBIT XI.2–6

INTEREST FACTORS FOR CONTINUOUS COMPOUNDING

($r = .06$)

	Single Payment		Equal Payment Series			
n	Compound-amount Factor	Present-worth Factor	Compound-amount Factor	Sinking-fund Factor	Present-worth Factor	Capital-recovery Factor
	To Find F Given P F/P r,n	To Find P Given F P/F r,n	To Find F Given A F/A r,n	To Find A Given F A/F r,n	To Find P Given A P/A r,n	To Find A Given P A/P r,n
1	1.062	.9418	1.000	1.0000	.9418	1.0618
2	1.127	.8869	2.062	.4850	1.8287	.5468
3	1.197	.8353	3.189	.3135	2.6640	.3754
4	1.271	.7866	4.387	.2280	3.4506	.2898
5	1.350	.7408	5.658	.1767	4.1914	.2386
6	1.433	.6977	7.008	.1427	4.8891	.2045
7	1.522	.6570	8.441	.1185	5.5461	.1803
8	1.616	.6188	9.963	.1004	6.1649	.1622
9	1.716	.5827	11.579	.0864	6.7477	.1482
10	1.822	.5488	13.295	.0752	7.2965	.1371
11	1.935	.5169	15.117	.0662	7.8133	.1280
12	2.054	.4868	17.052	.0586	8.3001	.1205
13	2.181	.4584	19.106	.0523	8.7585	.1142
14	2.316	.4317	21.288	.0470	9.1902	.1088
15	2.460	.4066	23.604	.0424	9.5968	.1042
16	2.612	.3829	26.064	.0384	9.9797	.1002
17	2.773	.3606	28.676	.0349	10.3402	.0967
18	2.945	.3396	31.449	.0318	10.6798	.0936
19	3.127	.3198	34.393	.0291	10.9997	.0909
20	3.320	.3012	37.520	.0267	11.3009	.0885
21	3.525	.2837	40.840	.0245	11.5845	.0863
22	3.743	.2671	44.366	.0225	11.8516	.0844
23	3.975	.2516	48.109	.0208	12.1032	.0826
24	4.221	.2369	52.084	.0192	12.3401	.0810
25	4.482	.2231	56.305	.0178	12.5633	.0796
26	4.759	.2101	60.786	.0165	12.7734	.0783
27	5.053	.1979	65.545	.0153	12.9713	.0771
28	5.366	.1864	70.598	.0142	13.1577	.0760
29	5.697	.1755	75.964	.0132	13.3332	.0750
30	6.050	.1653	81.661	.0122	13.4985	.0741
31	6.424	.1557	87.711	.0114	13.6542	.0732
32	6.821	.1466	94.135	.0106	13.8008	.0725
33	7.243	.1381	100.956	.0099	13.9389	.0717
34	7.691	.1300	108.198	.0092	14.0689	.0711
35	8.166	.1225	115.889	.0086	14.1913	.0705
36	8.671	.1153	124.055	.0081	14.3067	.0699
37	9.207	.1086	132.726	.0075	14.4153	.0694
38	9.777	.1023	141.934	.0070	14.5176	.0689
39	10.381	.0963	151.710	.0066	14.6139	.0684
40	11.023	.0907	162.091	.0062	14.7046	.0680

EXHIBIT XI.2–7

Interest Factors for Continuous Compounding

($r = .12$)

n	Single Payment		Equal Payment Series			
	Compound-amount Factor	Present-worth Factor	Compound-amount Factor	Sinking-fund Factor	Present-worth Factor	Capital-recovery Factor
	To Find F Given P F/P r,n	To Find P Given F P/F r,n	To Find F Given A F/A r,n	To Find A Given F A/F r,n	To Find P Given A P/A r,n	To Find A Given P A/P r,n
1	1.127	.8869	1.000	1.0000	.8869	1.1275
2	1.271	.7866	2.127	.4700	1.6735	.5975
3	1.433	.6977	3.399	.2942	2.3712	.4217
4	1.616	.6188	4.832	.2070	2.9900	.3344
5	1.822	.5488	6.448	.1551	3.5388	.2826
6	2.054	.4868	8.270	.1209	4.0256	.2484
7	2.316	.4317	10.325	.0969	4.4573	.2244
8	2.612	.3829	12.641	.0791	4.8402	.2066
9	2.945	.3396	15.253	.0656	5.1798	.1931
10	3.320	.3012	18.197	.0550	5.4810	.1824
11	3.743	.2671	21.518	.0465	5.7481	.1740
12	4.221	.2369	25.261	.0396	5.9850	.1671
13	4.759	.2101	29.482	.0339	6.1952	.1614
14	5.366	.1864	34.241	.0292	6.3815	.1567
15	6.050	.1653	39.606	.0252	6.5468	.1527
16	6.821	.1466	45.656	.0219	6.6934	.1494
17	7.691	.1300	52.477	.0191	6.8235	.1466
18	8.671	.1153	60.167	.0166	6.9388	.1441
19	9.777	.1023	68.838	.0145	7.0411	.1420
20	11.023	.0907	78.615	.0127	7.1318	.1402
21	12.429	.0805	89.638	.0112	7.2123	.1387
22	14.013	.0714	102.067	.0098	7.2836	.1373
23	15.800	.0633	116.080	.0086	7.3469	.1361
24	17.814	.0561	131.880	.0076	7.4030	.1351
25	20.086	.0498	149.694	.0067	7.4528	.1342
26	22.646	.0442	169.780	.0059	7.4970	.1334
27	25.534	.0392	192.426	.0052	7.5362	.1327
28	28.789	.0347	217.960	.0046	7.5709	.1321
29	32.460	.0308	246.749	.0041	7.6017	.1315
30	36.598	.0273	279.209	.0036	7.6290	.1311
31	41.264	.0242	315.807	.0032	7.6533	.1307
32	46.525	.0215	357.071	.0028	7.6747	.1303
33	52.457	.0191	403.597	.0025	7.6938	.1300
34	59.145	.0169	456.054	.0022	7.7107	.1297
35	66.686	.0150	515.200	.0019	7.7257	.1294
36	75.189	.0133	581.886	.0017	7.7390	.1292
37	84.775	.0118	657.075	.0015	7.7508	.1290
38	95.583	.0105	741.850	.0013	7.7613	.1288
39	107.770	.0093	837.433	.0012	7.7706	.1287
40	121.510	.0082	945.203	.0011	7.7788	.1286

EXHIBIT XI.2–8

INTEREST FACTORS FOR CONTINUOUS COMPOUNDING

($r = .18$)

n	Single Payment		Equal Payment Series			
	Compound-amount Factor	Present-worth Factor	Compound-amount Factor	Sinking-fund Factor	Present-worth Factor	Capital-recovery Factor
	To Find F Given P F/P r,n	To Find P Given F P/F r,n	To Find F Given A F/A r,n	To Find A Given F A/F r,n	To Find P Given A P/A r,n	To Find A Given P A/P r,n
1	1.197	.8353	1.000	1.0000	.8353	1.1972
2	1.433	.6977	2.197	.4551	1.5329	.6523
3	1.716	.5827	3.631	.2754	2.1157	.4727
4	2.054	.4868	5.347	.1870	2.6024	.3843
5	2.460	.4066	7.401	.1351	3.0090	.3323
6	2.945	.3396	9.861	.1014	3.3486	.2986
7	3.525	.2837	12.805	.0781	3.6323	.2753
8	4.221	.2369	16.331	.0612	3.8692	.2585
9	5.053	.1979	20.551	.0487	4.0671	.2459
10	6.050	.1653	25.604	.0391	4.2324	.2363
11	7.243	.1381	31.654	.0316	4.3705	.2288
12	8.671	.1153	38.897	.0257	4.4858	.2229
13	10.381	.0963	47.568	.0210	4.5821	.2182
14	12.429	.0805	57.949	.0173	4.6626	.2145
15	14.880	.0672	70.378	.0142	4.7298	.2114
16	17.814	.0561	85.258	.0117	4.7859	.2089
17	21.328	.0469	103.072	.0097	4.8328	.2069
18	25.534	.0392	124.399	.0080	4.8720	.2053
19	30.569	.0327	149.933	.0067	4.9047	.2039
20	36.598	.0273	180.503	.0055	4.9320	.2028
21	43.816	.0228	217.101	.0046	4.9548	.2018
22	52.457	.0191	260.917	.0038	4.9739	.2011
23	62.803	.0159	313.374	.0032	4.9898	.2004
24	75.189	.0133	376.177	.0027	5.0031	.1999
25	90.017	.0111	451.366	.0022	5.0142	.1994
26	107.770	.0093	541.383	.0018	5.0235	.1991
27	129.024	.0078	649.153	.0015	5.0312	.1988
28	154.470	.0065	778.177	.0013	5.0377	.1985
29	184.934	.0054	932.647	.0011	5.0431	.1983
30	221.406	.0045	1117.581	.0009	5.0476	.1981
31	265.072	.0038	1338.988	.0007	5.0514	.1980
32	317.348	.0032	1604.059	.0006	5.0546	.1978
33	379.935	.0026	1921.408	.0005	5.0572	.1977
34	454.865	.0022	2301.342	.0004	5.0594	.1977
35	544.572	.0018	2756.207	.0004	5.0612	.1976
36	651.971	.0015	3300.779	.0003	5.0628	.1975
37	780.551	.0013	3952.750	.0003	5.0641	.1975
38	934.489	.0011	4733.301	.0002	5.0651	.1974
39	1118.787	.0009	5667.790	.0002	5.0660	.1974
40	1339.431	.0007	6786.577	.0001	5.0668	.1974

EXHIBIT XI.2–9

Interest Factors for Continuous Compounding

($r = .24$)

	Single Payment		Equal Payment Series			
n	Compound-amount Factor	Present-worth Factor	Compound-amount Factor	Sinking-fund Factor	Present-worth Factor	Capital-recovery Factor
	To Find F Given P $F/P\ r,n$	To Find P Given F $P/F\ r,n$	To Find F Given A $F/A\ r,n$	To Find A Given F $A/F\ r,n$	To Find P Given A $P/A\ r,n$	To Find A Given P $A/P\ r,n$
1	1.271	.7866	1.000	1.0000	.7866	1.2712
2	1.616	.6188	2.271	.4403	1.4054	.7115
3	2.054	.4868	3.887	.2572	1.8922	.5285
4	2.612	.3829	5.942	.1683	2.2751	.4395
5	3.320	.3012	8.553	.1169	2.5763	.3882
6	4.221	.2369	11.874	.0842	2.8132	.3555
7	5.366	.1864	16.094	.0621	2.9996	.3334
8	6.821	.1466	21.460	.0466	3.1462	.3178
9	8.671	.1153	28.281	.0354	3.2615	.3066
10	11.023	.0907	36.952	.0271	3.3522	.2983
11	14.013	.0714	47.975	.0208	3.4236	.2921
12	17.814	.0561	61.988	.0161	3.4797	.2874
13	22.646	.0442	79.803	.0125	3.5239	.2838
14	28.789	.0347	102.449	.0098	3.5586	.2810
15	36.598	.0273	131.238	.0076	3.5859	.2789
16	46.525	.0215	167.836	.0060	3.6074	.2772
17	59.145	.0169	214.362	.0047	3.6243	.2759
18	75.189	.0133	273.507	.0037	3.6376	.2749
19	95.583	.0105	348.696	.0029	3.6481	.2741
20	121.510	.0082	444.279	.0023	3.6563	.2735
21	154.470	.0065	565.790	.0018	3.6628	.2730
22	196.370	.0051	720.260	.0014	3.6679	.2726
23	249.635	.0040	916.630	.0011	3.6719	.2723
24	317.348	.0032	1166.265	.0009	3.6750	.2721
25	403.429	.0025	1483.613	.0007	3.6775	.2719
26	512.859	.0019	1887.042	.0005	3.6795	.2718
27	651.971	.0015	2399.900	.0004	3.6810	.2717
28	828.818	.0012	3051.871	.0003	3.6822	.2716
29	1053.634	.0009	3880.689	.0003	3.6831	.2715
30	1339.431	.0007	4934.322	.0002	3.6839	.2715
31	1702.750	.0006	6273.753	.0002	3.6845	.2714
32	2164.620	.0005	7976.503	.0001	3.6849	.2714
33	2751.771	.0004	10141.123	.0001	3.6853	.2713
34	3498.187	.0003	12892.894	.0001	3.6856	.2713
35	4447.067	.0002	16391.081	.0001	3.6858	.2713
36	5653.330	.0002	20838.148	.0000	3.6860	.2713
37	7186.791	.0001	26491.477	.0000	3.6861	.2713
38	9136.202	.0001	33678.268	.0000	3.6862	.2713
39	11614.389	.0001	42814.470	.0000	3.6863	.2713
40	14764.782	.0001	54428.858	.0000	3.6864	.2713

EXHIBIT XI.2–10

Interest Factors for Continuous Compounding

($r = .30$)

n	Single Payment		Equal Payment Series			
	Compound-amount Factor	Present-worth Factor	Compound-amount Factor	Sinking-fund Factor	Present-worth Factor	Capital-recovery Factor
	To Find F Given P F/P r,n	To Find P Given F P/F r,n	To Find F Given A F/A r,n	To Find A Given F A/F r,n	To Find P Given A P/A r,n	To Find A Given P A/P r,n
1	1.350	.7408	1.000	1.0000	.7408	1.3499
2	1.822	.5488	2.350	.4256	1.2896	.7754
3	2.460	.4066	4.172	.2397	1.6962	.5896
4	3.320	.3012	6.632	.1508	1.9974	.5007
5	4.482	.2231	9.952	.1005	2.2205	.4503
6	6.050	.1653	14.433	.0693	2.3858	.4191
7	8.166	.1225	20.483	.0488	2.5083	.3987
8	11.023	.0907	28.649	.0349	2.5990	.3848
9	14.880	.0672	39.672	.0252	2.6662	.3751
10	20.086	.0498	54.552	.0183	2.7160	.3682
11	27.113	.0369	74.638	.0134	2.7529	.3633
12	36.598	.0273	101.750	.0098	2.7802	.3597
13	49.402	.0202	138.349	.0072	2.8004	.3571
14	66.686	.0150	187.751	.0053	2.8154	.3552
15	90.017	.0111	254.437	.0039	2.8265	.3538
16	121.510	.0082	344.454	.0029	2.8348	.3528
17	164.022	.0061	465.965	.0021	2.8409	.3520
18	221.406	.0045	629.987	.0016	2.8454	.3514
19	298.867	.0033	851.393	.0012	2.8487	.3510
20	403.429	.0025	1150.261	.0009	2.8512	.3507
21	544.572	.0018	1553.689	.0006	2.8530	.3505
22	735.095	.0014	2098.261	.0005	2.8544	.3503
23	992.275	.0010	2833.356	.0004	2.8554	.3502
24	1339.431	.0007	3825.631	.0003	2.8562	.3501
25	1808.042	.0006	5165.062	.0002	2.8567	.3501
26	2440.602	.0004	6973.104	.0001	2.8571	.3500
27	3294.468	.0003	9413.706	.0001	2.8574	.3500
28	4447.067	.0002	12708.174	.0001	2.8577	.3499
29	6002.912	.0002	17155.241	.0001	2.8578	.3499
30	8103.084	.0001	23158.153	.0000	2.8579	.3499
31	10938.019	.0001	31261.237	.0000	2.8580	.3499
32	14764.782	.0001	42199.257	.0000	2.8581	.3499
33	19930.370	.0001	56964.038	.0000	2.8582	.3499
34	26903.186	.0000	76894.409	.0000	2.8582	.3499
35	36315.503	.0000	103797.595	.0000	2.8582	.3499
36	49020.801	.0000	140113.097	.0000	2.8582	.3499
37	66171.160	.0000	189133.898	.0000	2.8583	.3499
38	89321.723	.0000	255305.059	.0000	2.8583	.3499
39	120571.715	.0000	344626.782	.0000	2.8583	.3499
40	162754.791	.0000	465198.497	.0000	2.8583	.3499

XII Human Factors Engineering

XII.1 Applied Anthropometry

A. Description

Anthropometry refers to physical measurement of human subjects, and applied anthropometry indicates that the measures are to be used in design (of a workstation, for example). Voluminous anthropometric data are available. However, this section will contain only an illustration of some of the measures that have been reported.

The data generally fall into two categories: static and functional. *Static*, or *structural*, dimensions are taken with the subject in fixed, standardized positions. Many positions of the body have been measured and documented. The *NASA Anthropometric Source Book, Volume II* [1978], for example, illustrates 973 such measurements. Some of these NASA type measurements are for rather specific purposes, viz., designing earphones. However, some measurements have more generic appeal.

The *functional*, or *dynamic*, body dimensions are taken under conditions in which the body is involved in some physical movement. Functional body measurements are probably more useful than static measures for design problems because people, in most life circumstances, are in motion, not stationary. Further, functional measures are useful because in motion, several body members move. For example, in reaching, not only does the arm move, but the shoulders lean forward, and the torso may bend forward or rotate.

B. Example of Static Measures

Eleven structural body dimensions and weights of adults are given in Exhibit XII.1–1. These data come from a survey by the United States Public Health Service [1965] of a representative sample of 6672 adult males and females. For each of the twelve measures, data on the 5th, 50th and 95th percentiles are given. The age range was from 18 years to 79 years. Since weight and height vary with age, this factor should be considered in using the data for design purposes. There are many different anthropometric data sets, and these vary greatly. For example, male United States Air Force fliers range in stature (5th percentile to 95th percentile) from 66 cm to 74 cm, whereas Japanese civilians range from 61.5 cm to 69 cm. Again, caution is suggested in using any anthropometric data. Also, be apprised that static measures are dynamic in time! World War II draftees were much larger than World War I draftees; and Korean War draftees were even bigger.

C. Workspace Design

C–1. Workspace Envelope

Human workspace can consist of many physical conditions. Increasingly, however, work activities are carried out while in a seated position, the operator working from a fixed location. The space within which the operator works is referred to as the workspace envelope. Many different types of data that are relevant to designing a workspace envelope have been collected.

Roth, Ayoub, and Halcomb [1977] presented a device called the Ayoub Reach Anthropometer to measure the functional arm reach of subjects at various lateral angles from a dead-ahead seated position and at levels ranging from $-60°$ to $+ 90°$ from a seat reference point. The arm reaches of subjects were measured under both restrained and unrestrained conditions.

The nature of the manual tasks to be performed influences the boundaries of the workspace envelope. If the subject has to push a button or flip a switch, a fingertip motion is required with only a slight decrease in the envelope. However, the requirements for twisting knobs could decrease the envelope by approximately two inches (5 to 6 cm) [Bullock, 1974]. Using the hand in grasping or gripping would reduce the workspace by approximately four inches (10 cm).

Even different hand grasp actions influence the workspace envelope. Also, the clothing worn by subjects can limit the effective size of the workspace envelope. For example, Sanders [1977] found that a winter coat can reduce a vehicle operator's reach by approximately two inches (5 cm).

The dimensions for the right-hand side of the maximum envelope for male and female workers are shown in Exhibits XII.1–2 and XII.1–3. The left side can be treated as a mirror image of the right side. The dimensions in the Exhibits are expressed in terms of two coordinates. Each column represents a height above the working surface. The first column describes the maximum reach in a plane one inch above and parallel to the working surface. The rows are measurements along the front edge of the workplace. Thus, Exhibit XII.1–2 shows that for a point nine inches to the right of the centerline of the operator's body and one inch above the worktable surface, a male can reach 18 1/16 inches forward of the front edge of the workplace.

The row labeled "Intercept" shows the point at which the curve actually crosses the front edge of the workplace. A physical model of the maximum reach envelope for females and males can be built and used in workplace design problems.

C–2. Workplace Height

The correct height of the workplace depends on the nature of the work being performed. Most manual tasks are best performed at elbow height. The recommendations shown below assume that ordinary manual tasks are being performed. If the work requires fine visual detail, it will be necessary to raise the work above elbow height, closer to the eye.

The dimensions of sit-stand workplaces are shown in Exhibits XII.1–4 and XII.1–5 [Davis and Miller, 1971]. A sit-stand workplace is generally more desirable than either a sit or a stand workplace. If a sit-stand workplace is to be suitable for use by all operators, it must be provided with an adjustable-height chair and an adjustable footrest. Standing workplaces can be built as shown in Exhibits XII.1–4 and XII.1–5 but with the footrests omitted. However, the workplace for a standing job will be significantly improved if it is made adjustable in height. When this is done, the distance from the floor to the top of the working surface should be variable, from 40 to 46 inches for males and from 36 to 42 inches for females.

Workplaces where the operator will always be seated can be built with a lower working surface. These workplaces can also be provided with adjustable footrests. The dimensions recommended for female and male operators are shown in Exhibits XII.1–6 and XII.1–7.

If it is not possible to provide an adjustable footrest for a sitting workplace, the height of the workplace must be lower than the dimensions shown in Exhibits XII.1–6 and XII.1–7. Under these circumstances, the workplace should be 26 inches high for males and 24 inches high for females. The chair for males should be adjustable from 15 to 21 inches, the chair for females from 13 to 19 inches. The depth of the seat well must be increased to 29 inches for males and 28 inches for females. This type of workplace is, however, less satisfactory than one having an adjustable footrest.

References

Bullock, M. I. "The Determination of Functional Arm Reach Boundaries for Operation of Manual Controls," *Ergonomics*, Vol. 17, No. 3 (1974), pp. 375–388.

Davis, H. L. and C. I. Miller, "Human Productivity and Work Design," in Maynard, H. B., ed., *Industrial Engineering Handbook*, Third Edition, McGraw-Hill, New York, 1971.

NASA, *Anthropometric Source Book*: (*Vol. II*), *A Handbook of Anthropometric Data*, NASA Publication No. 1024, 1978.

Roth, J. T., M. M. Ayoub, and C. G. Halcomb, "Seating Console and Workplace Design: Seated Operator Reach Profiles," *Proceedings of the Human Factors Society*, 21st Annual Meeting, 1977 pp. 83–87.

Sanders, M. S., "Anthropometric Survey of Truck and Bus Drivers: Anthropometry, Control Reach and Control Force," Canyon Research Group, Inc., Westlake Village, California, 1977.

United States Public Health Service, "Weight, Height and Selected Body Dimensions of Adults: United States, 1960–1962," USPHS Publications 1000, Ser. 11, No. 8, 1965.

EXHIBIT XII.1–1

SELECTED STRUCTURAL BODY DIMENSIONS AND WEIGHTS OF ADULTS

	Dimensions (Inches)						Dimensions (Centimeters)[2]					
	Male, Percentile			Female, Percentile			Male, Percentile			Female, Percentile		
Body Feature	5th	50th	95th	5th	50th	95th	5th	50th	95th	5th	50th	95th
1. Height	63.6	68.3	72.8	59.0	62.9	67.1	162	173	185	150	160	170
2. Sitting height, erect	33.2	35.7	38.0	30.9	33.4	35.7	84	91	97	79	85	91
3. Sitting height, normal	31.6	34.1	36.6	29.6	32.3	34.7	80	87	93	75	82	88
4. Knee height	19.3	21.4	23.4	17.9	19.6	21.5	49	54	59	46	50	55
5. Popliteal height	15.5	17.3	19.3	14.0	15.7	17.5	39	44	49	36	40	45
6. Elbow-rest height	7.4	9.5	11.6	7.1	9.2	11.0	19	24	30	18	23	28
7. Thigh-clearance height	4.3	5.7	6.9	4.1	5.4	6.9	11	15	18	10	14	18
8. Buttock-knee length	21.3	23.3	25.2	20.4	22.4	24.6	54	59	64	52	57	63
9. Buttock-popliteal length	17.3	19.5	21.6	17.0	18.9	21.0	44	50	55	43	48	53
10. Elbow-to-elbow breadth	13.7	16.5	19.9	12.3	15.1	19.3	35	42	51	31	38	49
11. Seat breadth	12.2	14.0	15.9	12.3	14.3	17.1	31	36	40	31	36	43
12. Weight[1]	120	166	217	104	137	199	58	75	98	47	62	90

[1]Weight given in pounds (first six columns) and kilograms (last six columns).

[2]Centimeter values rounded to whole numbers.

Source: U.S. Public Health Service, 1965.

EXHIBIT XII.1–2

MAXIMUM REACH OF RIGHT HAND (MALE)

Distance Along Front Edge of Workplace	Height Above Worktable Surface						
	1″	6″	11″	16″	21″	26″	31″
0″ (center line)	18″	19 1/3″	19 3/8″	18 15/16″	16 3/16″	14 3/8″	8 7/8″
3″ right	18 1/2	19 1/2	19 3/4	19 3/8	17 1/2	14 7/8	9 1/2
6″ right	18 3/16	19 1/2	19 3/4	19 1/2	17 9/16	14 13/16	9 3/8
9″ right	18 1/16	19 1/3	19 7/8	19 1/4	17 5/16	13 1/3	8 3/4
12″ right	17 1/4	18 1/2	18 13/16	18 1/2	16 9/16	11 1/2	6 3/8
15″ right	15 15/16	17 3/8	17 5/8	17 1/4	15 1/16	8 11/16	4
18″ right	14 1/2	15 1/2	15 7/8	15 1/2	13	5 1/4	
21″ right	11 1/2	13	13 2/3	13	10 5/16		
24″ right	7 1/2	9 5/8	10 1/8	9 1/3	6		
27″ right		3 3/4	5 1/8	3 7/8			
Intercept	26 7/8	28 1/3	28 15/16	28 3/8	26 3/16	23	17 1/2

Source: Maynard, H. B., ed., *Industrial Engineering Handbook*, 3rd. ed., McGraw-Hill, New York, 1977, p. 7–97.

EXHIBIT XII.1–3

MAXIMUM REACH OF RIGHT HAND (FEMALE)

Distance Along Front Edge of Workplace	Height Above Worktable Surface						
	1″	6″	11″	16″	21″	26″	31″
0″ (centerline)	14 1/2″	15 5/8″	15 3/8″	15 7/16″	13 1/2″	10 7/8″	5 7/16″
3″ right	15	15 7/8	16 1/8	15 7/8	13 15/16	11 1/8	5 7/8
6″ right	14 3/4	15 3/4	16	15 3/4	14	10 15/16	5 1/4
9″ right	14	15 1/4	15 9/16	15 5/16	13 1/2	10 1/4	3 5/8
12″ right	12 7/8	14 1/4	14 5/8	14 1/4	12 1/8	8 1/2	7/8
15″ right	11 3/16	12 1/2	13	12 5/8	10 1/8	6	
18″ right	8 1/2	9 7/8	10 1/2	9 13/16	7	3/4	
21″ right	3 7/8	6 1/8	6 7/8	5 1/2	1 1/2		
Intercept	22 3/16	23 9/16	23 7/8	23 1/4	21 9/16	18 1/4	12 5/8

Source: Same as Exhibit XII.1–2, p. 7-96.

EXHIBIT XII.1–4
Sit-Stand Workplace for Males

Minimum Overhead Clearance – 80″

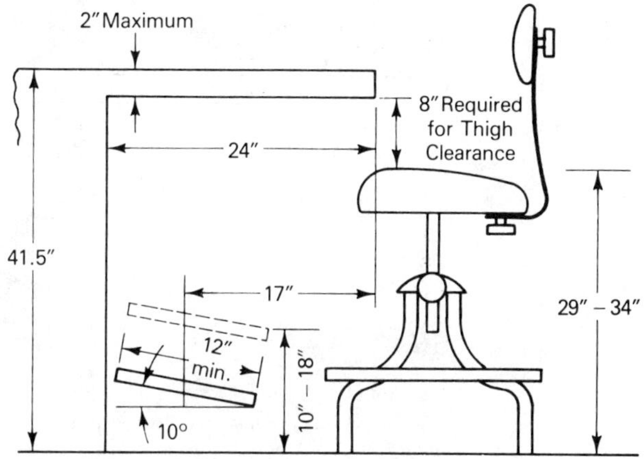

Minimum Seating Well Width – 24″

Source: Same as Exhibit XII.1–2, p. 7–97.

EXHIBIT XII.1–5
Sit-Stand Workplace for Females

Minimum Overhead Clearance – 76″

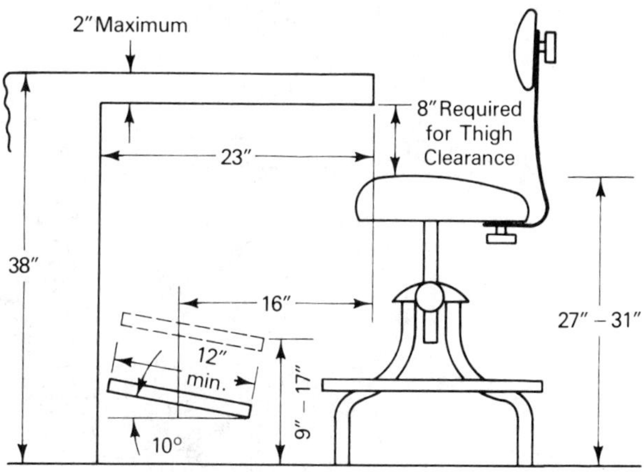

Minimum Seating Well Width – 24″

Source: Same As Exhibit XII.1–2, p. 7–97.

EXHIBIT XII.1–6

SITTING WORKPLACE FOR MALES

Minimum Overhead Clearance – 80″

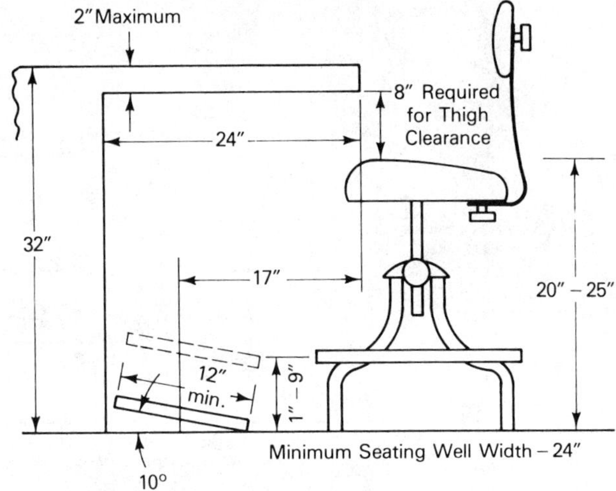

Source: Same as Exhibit XII.1–2, p. 7–98.

EXHIBIT XII.1–7

SITTING WORKPLACE FOR FEMALES

Minimum Overhead Clearance – 76″

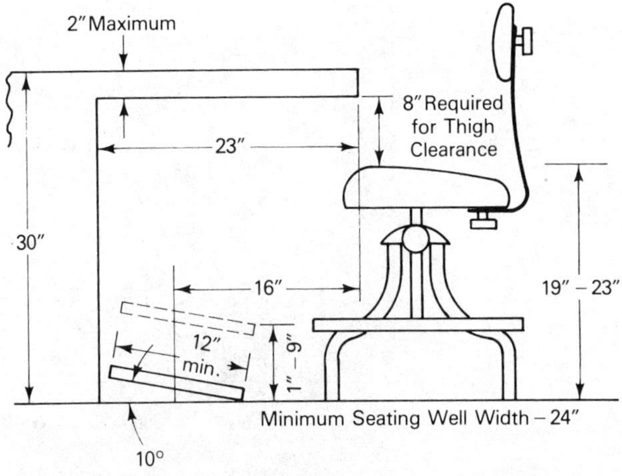

Source: Same as Exhibit XII.1–2, p. 7–98.

XII.2 Energy Expenditure

A. Metabolic Requirements

The human body expends energy to complete any activity. Even when the body is at rest, some energy is being expended. This is referred to as basal metabolism. Also, it takes energy to digest the foods eaten. This is referred to as digestive metabolism. There are individual differences in the amounts of energy required to complete an activity, as well as differences in basal and digestive metabolism. Basal metabolism has been shown to be related to body weight and sex; Konz [1979] suggests basal metabolism rates of 0.018 kilocalories per minute per kilogram (kcal/min/kg) of body weight for men and 0.017 kcal/min/kg for women. He also suggests that digestive metabolism will add about 10 percent to the total energy required for basal metabolism plus energy for activity. The energy expended for a particular activity will depend on body size and conditioning and on individual differences in performing the activity. However, approximate energy costs for various activities have been reported in the literature (see, for example, Katch and McArdle, 1979, for a summary), and illustrative examples are listed in Exhibit XII.2–1. Laboratory equipment is available for more precise estimation of energy cost for particular activities.

B. Rest Requirements

It is physiologically impossible for the body to maintain a rate of energy expenditure that exceeds the rate at which this energy can be replenished by the body. While high levels of energy expenditure are achievable for short periods of time, they must be followed by periods of rest. Exhibit XII.2–2 allows computation of the amounts of rest required for a worker involved in a task requiring a particular energy expenditure level. The amount of rest required for a particular level of energy expenditure depends on how efficient the worker's body is at energy replenishment. While highly conditioned athletes may achieve a replenishment rate of 10 kilocalories per minute (kcal/min), a generally accepted energy standard is 4 kcal/min. Note that these estimates are not corrected for body weight. Exhibit XII.2–2 provides contour lines for 3, 4, 5, and 6 kcal/min rates. Also, note that when the energy cost of work is less than or equal to the energy standard adopted, the chart indicates that no rest is needed. While physiologically this may be true, other factors require that rest periods be provided.

C. Using the Figures

Suppose that analysis of labor requirements for digging a trench with hand labor is being conducted. From Exhibit XII.2–1, we find that workers digging trenches are expected to expend approximately 0.14 kcal/min per kilogram of body weight. Assuming a worker weighs approximately 72 kilograms, the level of energy expenditure is (0.14)(72) = 10 kcal/min. Assuming an energy standard of 4 kcal/min, we use Exhibit XII.2–2 to find that the rest requirement for the workers will be approximately 43 minutes per hour.

References

Katch, F. I. and McArdle, William B., *Nutrition, Weight Control and Exercise*, Houghton Mifflin, Boston, 1977.

Konz, S., *Work Design*, Grid, Inc., Columbus, Ohio, 1979.

EXHIBIT XII.2–1

APPROXIMATE ENERGY COSTS OF VARIOUS ACTIVITIES

Energy Cost, kcal/minute/kilogram	Activity
0.02	Lying at Ease
	Painting, Indoors; Typing with Electric Typewriter
0.04	Shoe Repair
	General Carpentry, Machine Tool Operation
0.06	Clothes Pressing, House Cleaning
	Painting, Outdoors
0.08	Walking, Normal Pace; Hedge Trimming
	Feeding Cattle on Farm; Stacking Firewood
0.10	Scrubbing Floors
	Shoveling Coal
0.12	Tending Furnace in a Steel Mill
	Playing Basketball; Tree Trimming
0.14	Digging Trenches; Hill Climbing with 20 kg Load
	Merchant Mill Rolling, Steel Mill
0.16	Swimming Breast Stroke
	Rapid Chopping with an Ax
0.18	Running at 6 miles/hr (9.7 km/hr)
	Carrying Logs
0.20	Racquetball

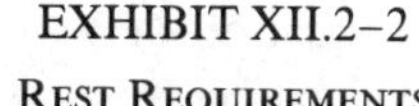

EXHIBIT XII.2–2
REST REQUIREMENTS

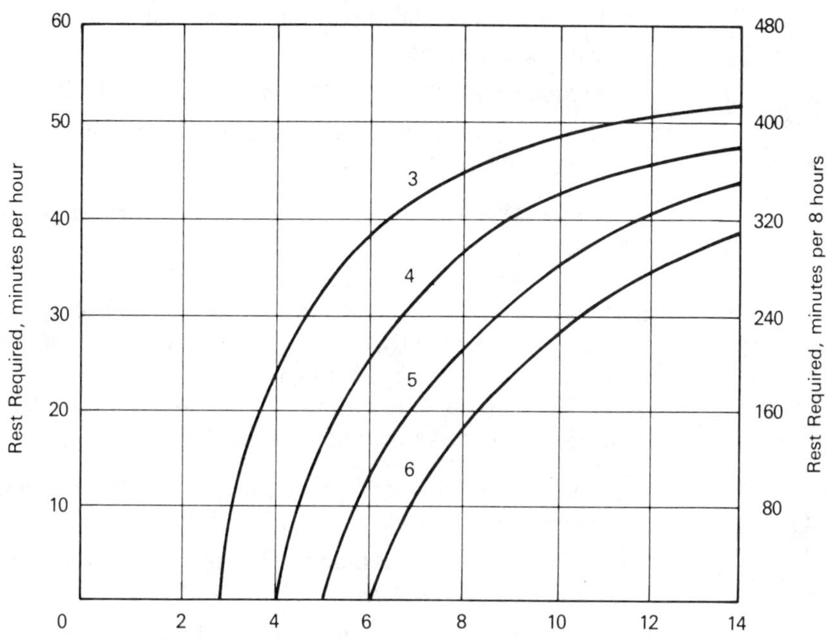

Source: McCormick, E. J., *Human Factors Engineering*, 4th ed., New York: McGraw-Hill Book Co., 1976.

XII.3 Design of Lifting Tasks

A. Introduction

Study of lifting tasks has resulted in extensive tables for strength and recommended loads. The large volume of such tables is due to the number of factors that define a lifting task. The National Institute of Occupational Safety and Health (NIOSH) has published a guide for manual lifting [1981], which lists the following as primary task variables:

1. Object weight (L)—measured in kilograms (pounds)
2. Horizontal location (H)—of the hands at origin of lift measured forward of the body centerline or midpoint between ankles (in centimeters or inches)

3. Vertical location (V)—of the hands at origin of lift measured from floor level (in centimeters or inches)
4. Vertical travel distance (D)—from origin to destination of lift (in centimeters or inches)
5. Frequency of lifting (F)—average number of lifts per minute
6. Duration or period—assumed to be occasional (less than one hour) or continuous (eight hours).

The NIOSH guide provides a procedure for analysis of a lifting task as a function of the above factors. The approach used for task evaluation is to define three regions of weight lifted: (1) acceptable region, (2) administrative controls required region, and (3) hazardous lifting region. The first two regions are separated by the action limit (AL) line, and the last two regions by the maximum permissible limit (MPL) line.

While various criteria were used to establish these lines, properly analyzed lifting tasks may be of three types:

1. Those *above the MPL* should be viewed as unacceptable, and require engineering controls.
2. Those *between the AL and MPL* are unacceptable without administrative or engineering controls.
3. Those *below the AL* are believed to represent nominal risk to most industrial workforces.

To illustrate, the figure on page 265 identifies these regions for a specific task as a function of the horizontal position of the load and the amount lifted. In the illustration, it would be acceptable to lift a 25-pound weight 10 inches in front of the body. However, if the object weighed 50 pounds, administrative controls would be required. Hazardous lifting conditions would exist if this load weighed 100 pounds or more.

B. Analysis of Specific Tasks

Categorization of lifting tasks is accomplished by construction of equations of the lines separating the three catagories. Equations for computing the lines separating the acceptable and controls required regions as the product of four factors are given as

$$\mathrm{AL(kg)} = 40(15/H)(1-0.004|V-75|)(.7+7.5/D)(1-F/F_{\max})$$

for metric units, or

$$\mathrm{AL(lb)} = 90(6/H)(1-0.01|V-30|)(0.7+3/D)(1-F/F_{\max})$$

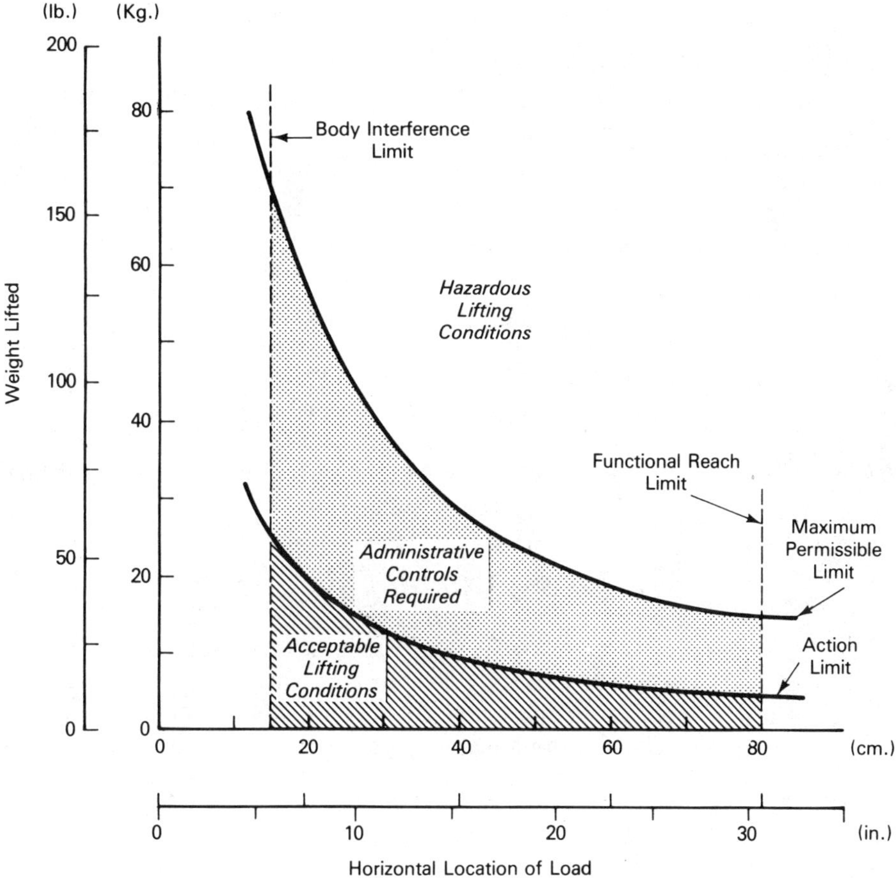

in U.S. customary units, where

H = horizontal location (centimeters or inches) forward of midpoint between ankles at origin of lift

V = vertical location (centimeters or inches) at origin of lift

D = vertical travel distance (centimeters or inches) between origin and destination of lift

F = average frequency of lift (lifts/minute)

F_{max} = maximum frequency that can be sustained (obtained from Exhibit XII.3–1)

The equation of the line separating the controls required region and the hazardous region is

$$\text{MPL} = 3(\text{AL})$$

These variables are assumed to have the following restrictions:

1. H is between 15 cm (6 in) and 80 cm (32 in). Objects cannot, in general, be closer than 15 cm (6 in) without interference with the body. Objects further than 80 cm (32 in) cannot be reached by many people.
2. V is assumed between 0 cm and 175 cm (70 in), representing the range of vertical reach for most people.
3. D is assumed between 25 cm (10 in) and $(200 - V)$ cm $[(80 - V)$ in$]$. For travel less than 25 cm, set $D = 25$.
4. F is assumed to be between 0.2 (one lift every 5 minutes) and F_{max}, which is found in Exhibit XII.3–1. The maximum value allowed is a function of the origin of the lift (V) and the duration of the job. Note that when $V > 75$ cm it is assumed that the worker remains standing when performing the lifting task. When $V \leq 75$ cm, it will be necessary for the worker to bend to pick up the object. For lifting less frequently than once every 5 minutes, set $F = 0$.

C. Using the Model

The following example is adapted from the NIOSH [1981] manual. Consider a punch press operator who, once a shift, must load a 20-kilogram reel of supply stock from the floor onto the machine. Dimensions are shown in the illustration.

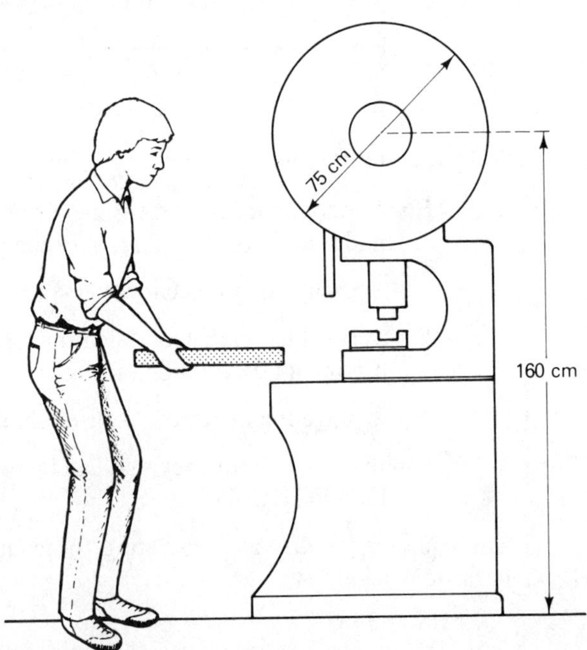

The horizontal location factor was defined earlier with reference to the midpoint between the ankles. As this reference point is somewhat difficult to locate, H is frequently approximated by the distance of the load from the front of the body plus an allowance for the distance from the midpoint between the ankles to the front of the body. A value of 15 cm (6 in) is suggested. Thus, assuming that the operator works from the front of the machine, a reach $75/2 = 37.5$ cm from the front of the body with the load is required, and $H = 37.5 + 15 = 52.5$ cm. The lift starts with the roll sitting on the floor, and assuming the operator stands it on edge before starting the lift, $V = 75/2 = 37.5$ and $D = 160$ cm. Since the lift occurs once per shift, no frequency factor is required, and $F = 0$.

The allowable lift (AL) point for this task is

$$\begin{aligned} \mathrm{AL} &= 40[15/H][1-0.004|V-75|][0.7+7.5/D] \\ &= 40[15/52.5][1-0.004|37.5-75|][0.7+7.5/160] \\ &= 40[0.29][0.85][0.75] = 7.36 \text{ kg} \end{aligned}$$

The maximum permissible limit would be three times this amount, or 22.1 kg. As the actual weight is 20 kg, the task is quite stressful and requires strong administrative controls.

In the above equation for AL, note that the horizontal factor term has the smallest value. By redesigning the task, e.g., by allowing the operator access to the side of the machine, the H factor might be decreased, resulting in a less stressful task.

Reference

National Institute of Occupational Safety and Health, *Work Practices Guide for Manual Lifting*, Publication No. 81-122, 1981.

EXHIBIT XII.3–1

F_{max} VALUES

		Average Vertical Location	
		$V > 75$ cm (30 in)	$V \leq 75$ cm (30 in)
Period	1 hour	18	15
	8 hours	15	12

XII.4 LIGHTING REQUIREMENTS

A. Basic Definitions

The rate at which light is emitted from a source is referred to as *luminous flux*, and is measured in units of *lumens*. The number of lumens per unit of surface area reaching an object determines the *illumination* of that object. The term *foot-candle*, representing one lumen per square foot of surface area, is the measure of illuminance historically used in the United States. In the metric system the unit of measurement is the *lux*, or one lumen per square meter. While the ratio between a square meter and a square foot is 10.764, a conversion factor commonly used is 1 foot-candle equals approximately 10 lux.

The number of lumens emitted by a source depends on its size and intensity. Intensity is measured in units of *candela*, which is referenced to a detailed physical standard.

What the eye sees when looking at an object under a given amount of illumination depends on the surface of the object. The brightness, or *luminance*, of the surface depends on the reflection factor of the surface; in equation form,

$$\text{Illumination} \times \text{Reflection Factor} = \text{Luminance}$$

Since the reflection factor is dimensionless, the units of luminance are the same as those of illumination. However, units of luminance are referred to as *foot-lamberts* to avoid confusion.

B. Lighting Analysis

Detailed procedures for design of lighting systems to achieve specified illuminances have been published. These incorporate information on sources, surroundings, and even the effect of accumulation of dirt.

While people can adapt to a large range of levels for any specified test, it has been shown that visual efficiency improves with increasing illumination. On the other hand, economic considerations may dictate that minimally acceptable levels be used. Exhibit XII.4–1 provides guidelines for these minimal levels by general categories. These groupings and examples are taken from the *IES Lighting Handbook, Application Volume* [1981], which offers an extensive listing of more detailed environments and their recommended minimum levels. As these recommendations are based on the average working population with good eyesight, special considerations may need to be applied in certain instances (e.g., when dealing with the visually impaired or elderly). Since illumination is the quantity measured by the typical light meter, it is well within the capability of plant personnel to ascertain whether each area of their operations meets or exceeds the recommended levels.

Reference

Kaufman, J. E., ed., *IES Lighting Handbook, Application Volume*, Illuminating Engineering Society of North America, New York, 1981.

EXHIBIT XII.4–1

RECOMMENDED LIGHTING LEVELS

Type of Activity	Examples	Illuminance Required, Foot-candles
A. Public space	Building exteriors, parking lots	2–5
B. Simple orientation for short temporary visits	Inactive storage rooms or warehouses	5–10
C. Working spaces where visual tasks are occasionally performed	Elevators, auditoriums, lobbies	10–20
D. Performance of visual tasks of high contrast or large size	Conference rooms, food preparation areas	20–50
E. Performance of visual tasks of medium contrast or small size	Science laboratories, bulletin board areas	50–100
F. Performance of visual tasks of low contrast or very small size	Printing plants, finished lumber grading areas	100–200
G. Performance of visual tasks of low contrast and very small size over a prolonged period	Jewelry and watch manufacturing, fine bench or machine work	200–500
H. Performance of very long prolonged and exacting visual tasks	Dental work on cavities, precision arc welding	500–1000
I. Performance of very special tasks with extremely low contrast and small size	Cloth inspection	1000–5000

Source: Adapted from Kaufman, J. E., ed., *IES Lighting Handbook, Application Volume*, Illuminating Engineering Society of North America, 345 E. 47th St., New York, NY 10017, 1981.

XII.5 Display Design Considerations

A. Description

Displays may be tactual, auditory, visual, or even olfactory. Also, combinations of these display types are used simultaneously, especially when an operator must devote at least one sense heavily to the task at hand. Of all the display types in our industrial environment, visuals are most predominant.

Visual codes are used to convey information in many formats and with varying powers of discrimination. The instrument panel of an automobile uses many of these codes. Pictorial presentations indicate what purpose some displays serve (a thermometer on a blue background, for example, may indicate that an engine is cold). Inclination indicates levels of resources (the fuel gauge). Lights indicate warnings concerning systems operations. (If a door is ajar, a red light indicates this dangerous condition.) Visual numbers provide much information. (The odometer indicates speed, miles driven since resetting the trip meter, and total miles driven.)

B. Comparison of Visual Coding Methods

Exhibit XII.5–1 contains a comparison of various coding methods. The maximum number of coding steps assumes a high level of training and a high use level for the code. Also, at the maximum level, a 5-percent error rate in decoding is to be assumed. The recommended number of code steps assumes operational conditions and a need for high accuracy.

EXHIBIT XII.5–1

Comparison of Coding Methods

Code	Number of Code Steps		Evaluation	Comment
	Maximum	Recommended		
Color				
Lights	10	3	Good	Location time short. Little space required. Good for qualitative coding. Larger alphabets can be achieved by combining saturation and brightness with the color code. Ambient illumination not critical factor.
Surfaces	50	9	Good	Same as above except ambient illumination must be controlled. Has broad application.
Shapes				
Numerals & Letters	Unlimited		—	Location time longer than for color or pictorial shapes. Requires good resolution. Useful for quantitative and qualitative coding. Certain symbols easily confused.
Geometric	15	5	Fair	Memory required to decode. Requires good resolution.
Pictorial	30	10	Good	Allows direct association for decoding. Requires good resolution. Good for qualitative coding only.
Magnitude				
Area	6	3	Fair	Requires large symbol space. Location time good.
Length	6	3	Fair	Requires large symbol space. Good for limited applications.
Brightness	4	2	Poor	Interferes with other signals. Ambient illumination must be controlled.
Visual				
Number	6	4	Fair	Requires large symbol space. Limited application.
Frequency	4	2	Poor	Distracting. Has merit when attention is demanded.
Stereo-depth	4	2	Poor	Limits population of users. Highly limited application. Difficult to instrument.
Inclination	24	12	Good	Good for limited application. Recommended for quantitative code only.
Compound Codes	Unlimited		Good	Provides for large alphabets for complex information. Allows compounding of qualitative and quantitative codes.

Source: Van Cott, Harold P. and Robert G. Kimball, *Human Engineering Guide to Equipment Design* (Revised Ed.), American Institute for Research, Washington, DC, 1970, p. 69.

XIII Conversion Factors

XIII.1 Weights and Measures

A. Description

With two systems of weight and measurement in use in the United States, it is necessary for the industrial engineer and manager to have facility with both. The two systems are called the metric and the U.S. customary. Prior to describing these two systems, it is necessary to define the prefixes that are used in the metric system, as follows:

Symbol	Prefix	Multiple	Equivalent	Symbol	Prefix	Multiple	Equivalent
Exa	E	10^{18}	Quintillion	d	Deci	10^{-1}	Tenth
Peta	P	10^{15}	Quadrillion	c	Centi	10^{-2}	Hundredth
Tera	D	10^{12}	Trillion	m	Milli	10^{-3}	Thousandth
Giga	G	10^{9}	Billion	μ	Micro	10^{-6}	Millionth
Mega	M	10^{6}	Million	n	Nano	10^{-9}	Billionth
Kilo	k	10^{3}	Thousand	p	Pico	10^{-12}	Trillionth
Hecto	h	10^{2}	Hundred	f	Femto	10^{-15}	Quadrillionth
Deka	da	10	Ten	a	Alto	10^{-18}	Quintillionth

Thus, a kilometer is 1,000 meters, and a nanosecond is a billionth of a second.

B. Tables of Selected Metric Weights and Measures

B–1. Linear Measure

10 millimeters (mm) = 1 centimeter (cm)

10 centimeters = 1 decimeter (dm) = 100 millimeters

10 meters = 1 dekameter (dam)

10 dekameters = 1 hectometer (hm) = 100 meters

10 hectometers = 1 kilometer (km) = 100 meters

B–2. Area Measures

100 square millimeters (mm^2) = 1 square centimeter (cm^2)

10,000 square centimeters = 1 square meter (m^2)

100 square meters = 1 are (a)

100 ares = 1 hectare = 10,000 square meters

100 hectares = 1 square kilometer (km^2) = 1,000,000 square meters

B–3. Fluid Volume Measure

10 milliliters = 1 centiliter (cL)

10 centiliters = 1 deciliter (dL) = 100 milliliters

10 deciliters = 1 liter (L) = 1000 milliliters

10 liters = 1 dekaliter (daL)

10 dekaliters = 1 hectoliter (hL) = 100 liters

10 hectoliters = 1 kiloliter (kL) = 1000 liters

B–4. Weight

10 milligrams (mg) = 1 centigram (cg)

10 centigrams = 1 decigram (dg) = 100 milligrams

10 decigrams = 1 gram (g) = 1000 milligrams

10 grams = 1 dekagram (dag)

10 dekagrams = 1 hectogram (hg) = 100 grams

10 hectograms = 1 kilogram (kg) = 1000 grams

1000 kilograms = 1 metric ton (t)

C. Table of Selected Equivalents

Equivalents involving decimal fractions are rounded off to the last decimal place shown, except where they are exact, in which case the exact equivalent is indicated by an E.

C–1. Lengths

$$1 \text{ angstrom (A)} = \begin{cases} 0.1 \text{ nanometer (E)} \\ 3.937 \times 10^{-9} \text{ inch} \end{cases}$$

1 centimeter (cm) = 0.3937 inch

1 decimeter (dm) = 3.937 inches

1 dekameter (dam) = 32.808 feet

1 foot (ft) = 0.3048 meters (E)

1 inch (in) = 2.54 centimeters (E)

1 kilometer (km) = { 0.621 mile; 3281.5 feet

1 meter (m) = { 39.37 inches; 1.094 yards

1 micron (μ) = { 0.001 millimeter (E); 3.937×10^{-5} inches

1 mil = { 0.001 inch (E); 0.0254 millimeter (E)

1 mile = { 5280 feet (E); 1.609 kilometers

1 millimeter (mm) = 0.03937 inch

1 nanometer (nm) = { 0.001 micron (E); 3.937×10^{-8} inch

1 yard = 0.9144 meters (E)

C–2. Areas

1 acre = { 43,560 square feet (E); 4840 square yards (E); 0.405 hectares

1 are (a) = { 119.599 square yards; 0.025 acre

1 hectare (ha) = 2.471 acres

1 square centimeter (cm^2) = 0.155 square inch

1 square decimeter (dm^2) = 15.5 square inches

1 square foot (ft^2) = 929.030 square centimeters

1 square inch (in^2) = 6.4516 centimeters (E)

1 square kilometer (km^2) = { 247.105 acres; 0.386 square mile

$$1 \text{ square meter } (m^2) = \begin{cases} 1.196 \text{ square yards} \\ 10.764 \text{ square feet} \end{cases}$$

1 square mile (mi^2) = 258.999 hectares

1 square yard (yd^2) = 0.836 square meter

C–3. Capacities or Volumes

1 cubic centimeter (cm^3) = 0.061 cubic inch

1 cubic decimeter (dm^3) = 61.024 cubic inches

$$1 \text{ cubic inch } (in^3) = \begin{cases} 0.554 \text{ fluid ounce} \\ 16.387 \text{ cubic centimeters} \end{cases}$$

$$1 \text{ cubic foot } (ft^3) = \begin{cases} 7.481 \text{ gallons} \\ 28.217 \text{ cubic decimeters} \end{cases}$$

1 cubic meter (m^3) = 1.308 cubic yard

1 cubic yard (yd^3) = 0.765 cubic meter

1 dekaliter (daL) = 2.642 gallons

$$1 \text{ gallon (gal)} = \begin{cases} 231 \text{ cubic inches (E)} \\ 3.785 \text{ liters} \\ 128 \text{ fluid ounces (E)} \end{cases}$$

1 hectoliter (hL) = 26.418 gallons

$$1 \text{ liter (L)} = \begin{cases} 1.057 \text{ liquid quarts} \\ 0.908 \text{ dry quarts} \\ 61.025 \text{ cubic inches} \end{cases}$$

$$1 \text{ milliliter} = \begin{cases} 1 \text{ cubic centimeter (E)} \\ 0.061 \text{ cubic inch} \end{cases}$$

$$1 \text{ ounce (oz), liquid} = \begin{cases} 1.805 \text{ cubic inches} \\ 29.573 \text{ milliliters} \end{cases}$$

$$1 \text{ pint (pt), dry} = \begin{cases} 33.600 \text{ cubic inches} \\ 0.551 \text{ liter} \end{cases}$$

$$1 \text{ pint (pt), liquid} = \begin{cases} 28.875 \text{ cubic inches (E)} \\ 0.473 \text{ liter} \end{cases}$$

$$1 \text{ quart (qt), dry} = \begin{cases} 67.201 \text{ cubic inches} \\ 1.101 \text{ liters} \end{cases}$$

$$1 \text{ quart (qt), liquid} = \begin{cases} 57.75 \text{ cubic inches (E)} \\ 0.946 \text{ liter} \end{cases}$$

C–4. Weights or Masses

$$1 \text{ grain} = 64.799 \text{ milligrams}$$

$$1 \text{ gram} = \begin{cases} 15.432 \text{ grains} \\ 0.035 \text{ ounce, avoirdupois} \end{cases}$$

$$\begin{matrix} 1 \text{ hundredweight,} \\ \text{gross or long (gross cwt)} \end{matrix} = \begin{cases} 112 \text{ pounds (E)} \\ 50.802 \text{ kilograms} \end{cases}$$

$$\begin{matrix} 1 \text{ hundredweight,} \\ \text{net or short (net cwt)} \end{matrix} = \begin{cases} 100 \text{ pounds (E)} \\ 45.359 \text{ kilograms} \end{cases}$$

$$1 \text{ kilogram (kg)} = 2.205 \text{ pounds}$$

$$1 \text{ microgram } (\mu\text{g}) = 1 \times 10^{-6} \text{ gram (E)}$$

$$1 \text{ milligram (mg)} = 0.015 \text{ grain}$$

$$1 \text{ ounce, avoirdupois} = \begin{cases} 437.5 \text{ grains (E)} \\ 0.911 \text{ troy ounce} \\ 29.350 \text{ grams} \end{cases}$$

$$1 \text{ ounce, troy (oz t)} = \begin{cases} 480 \text{ grains (E)} \\ 1.097 \text{ avoirdupois ounces} \\ 31.103 \text{ grams} \end{cases}$$

$$1 \text{ pound, avoirdupois} = \begin{cases} 7000 \text{ grains (E)} \\ 1.215 \text{ troy pounds} \\ 453.59237 \text{ grams (E)} \end{cases}$$

$$1 \text{ pound, troy (lb t)} = \begin{cases} 5760 \text{ grains (E)} \\ 0.823 \text{ avoirdupois pounds} \\ 373.242 \text{ grams} \end{cases}$$

$$1 \text{ ton, gross or long} = \begin{cases} 2240 \text{ pounds (E)} \\ 1.12 \text{ net tons (E)} \\ 1.016 \text{ metric tons} \end{cases}$$

$$1 \text{ ton, metric (t)} = \begin{cases} 2204.623 \text{ pounds} \\ 0.984 \text{ gross ton} \\ 1.102 \text{ net tons} \end{cases}$$

$$1 \text{ ton, net or short} = \begin{cases} 2000 \text{ pounds (E)} \\ 0.893 \text{ gross ton} \\ 0.901 \text{ metric ton} \end{cases}$$

C–5. Temperature

To convert Celsius (Centigrade) to Fahrenheit:

$$F° = (9/5)C° + 32°$$

To convert Fahrenheit to Celsius (Centigrade):

$$C° = (5/9)(F° - 32°)$$

XIII.2 Number Formats

A. Description

When we think of numbers, we usually mean decimal numbers, but digital computers don't operate directly in the decimal system. Particularly, digital computers use the binary number system. Representations, or digits, in the binary number system are all zeros and ones, or "bits."

In general, a decimal number is given by

$$a_n 10^n + a_{n-1} 10^{n-1} + \cdots + a_1 10^1 + a_0 10^0$$

where $a_n, a_{n-1}, \ldots, a_1, a_0$ are integers in the range 0 through 9. When we write a decimal number, we delete the powers of ten and the plus signs and write

$$a_n a_{n-1} \ldots a_1 a_0$$

Thus, the decimal number 157 has $a_2 = 1$, $a_1 = 5$, $a_0 = 7$, and can be seen to follow the form

$$1 \times 10^2 + 5 \times 10^1 + 7 \times 10^0$$

The decimal number system has base 10, since each digit is multiplied by a power of ten.

Now, the binary system follows the general form

$$a_n 2^n + a_{n-1} 2^{n-1} + \cdots + a_1 2^1 + a_0 2^0$$

where $a_n, a_{n-1}, \ldots, a_1, a_0$ are one of the integers 0 and 1. Thus, the decimal number 157, in the binary number system (usually, we say "in binary"), is given by

$$1\times2^7+0\times2^6+0\times2^5+1\times2^4+1\times2^3+1\times2^2+0\times2^1+1\times2^0$$

We usually write binary numbers without the powers of two and the plus signs, so that 157 would be written in binary as

10011101

The binary system has base 2, since each digit is multiplied by a power of two. There are two other number systems that frequently appear in computer-related discussions. These are the octal number system, with base 8, and the hexadecimal number system, with base 16. In the octal number system, the decimal number 157 is written as 235. This result can be seen from

$$2\times8^2+3\times8^1+5\times8^0$$

Now, the hexadecimal number system is somewhat more complicated since it has base 16 and there are only ten numeric digits possible. The letters A through F are used to represent the numbers 10 through 15. Thus, decimal number 157 is written 9D in hexadecimal. This result can be seen from

$$9\times16^1+13\times16^0$$

But 13 is written as D, so we write 9D.

B. Reading the Tables

Exhibit XIII.2–1 contains decimal numbers and their corresponding binary, octal, and hexadecimal representations. The tables range from 0 decimal to 256 decimal. The reader can locate decimal number 157 in Exhibit XIII.2–1 and find the results mentioned in Subsection A.

Conversion between the various representations can be accomplished readily by following some straightforward rules. To convert from octal to binary, just convert each octal digit to its binary counterpart in groups of three binary digits, and place the resulting bit accommodations side by side. Thus, the octal number 235 becomes

$$\overbrace{010}^{2}\ \overbrace{011}^{3}\ \overbrace{101}^{5}$$

or 10011101, omitting the leading zero.

Conversion in the other direction, from binary to octal, is accomplished by grouping the bits in threes from the right and converting each group to its octal equivalent. For example, the binary number 11010011 becomes

$$\underbrace{11}_{3}\quad\underbrace{010}_{2}\quad\underbrace{011}_{3}$$

or 323 in octal.

Conversion between binary and hexadecimal numbers is accomplished in a manner similar to the previous, except that grouping is done in fours. Thus, E5 in hexadecimal is converted to

$$\overbrace{1110}^{\mathrm{E}}\,\overbrace{0101}^{5}$$

or 11100101 in binary, and 1101001101 in binary becomes

$$\underbrace{11}_{3}\quad\underbrace{0100}_{4}\,\underbrace{1101}_{\mathrm{D}}$$

or 34D in hexadecimal.

EXHIBIT XIII.2–1

Decimal Numbers and Their Representation in Binary, Octal and Hexadecimal

Decimal Number	Binary	Octal	Hex	Decimal Number	Binary	Octal	Hex
0	0	0	0	45	101101	55	2D
1	1	1	1	46	101110	56	2E
2	10	2	2	47	101111	57	2F
3	11	3	3	48	110000	60	30
4	100	4	4	49	110001	61	31
5	101	5	5	50	110010	62	32
6	110	6	6	51	110011	63	33
7	111	7	7	52	110100	64	34
8	1000	10	8	53	110101	65	35
9	1001	11	9	54	110110	66	36
10	1010	12	A	55	110111	67	37
11	1011	13	B	56	111000	70	38
12	1100	14	C	57	111001	71	39
13	1101	15	D	58	111010	72	3A
14	1110	16	E	59	111011	73	3B
15	1111	17	F	60	111100	74	3C
16	10000	20	10	61	111101	75	3D
17	10001	21	11	62	111110	76	3E
18	10010	22	12	63	111111	77	3F
19	10011	23	13	64	1000000	100	40
20	10100	24	14	65	1000001	101	41
21	10101	25	15	66	1000010	102	42
22	10110	26	16	67	1000011	103	43
23	10111	27	17	68	1000100	104	44
24	11000	30	18	69	1000101	105	45
25	11001	31	19	70	1000110	106	46
26	11010	32	1A	71	1000111	107	47
27	11011	33	1B	72	1001000	110	48
28	11100	34	1C	73	1001001	111	49
29	11101	35	1D	74	1001010	112	4A
30	11110	36	1E	75	1001011	113	4B
31	11111	37	1F	76	1001100	114	4C
32	100000	40	20	77	1001101	115	4D
33	100001	41	21	78	1001110	116	4E
34	100010	42	22	79	1001111	117	4F
35	100011	43	23	80	1010000	120	50
36	100100	44	24	81	1010001	121	51
37	100101	45	25	82	1010010	122	52
38	100110	46	26	83	1010011	123	53
39	100111	47	27	84	1010100	124	54
40	101000	50	28	85	1010101	125	55
41	101001	51	29	86	1010110	126	56
42	101010	52	2A	87	1010111	127	57
43	101011	53	2B	88	1011000	130	58
44	101100	54	2C	89	1011001	131	59

EXHIBIT XIII.2-1—Continued

Decimal Number	Binary	Octal	Hex	Decimal Number	Binary	Octal	Hex
90	1011010	132	5A	135	10000111	207	87
91	1011011	133	5B	136	10001000	210	88
92	1011100	134	5C	137	10001001	211	89
93	1011101	135	5D	138	10001010	212	8A
94	1011110	136	5E	139	10001011	213	8B
95	1011111	137	5F	140	10001100	214	8C
96	1100000	140	60	141	10001101	215	8D
97	1100001	141	61	142	10001110	216	8E
98	1100010	142	62	143	10001111	217	8F
99	1100011	143	63	144	10010000	220	90
100	1100100	144	64	145	10010001	221	91
101	1100101	145	65	146	10010010	222	92
102	1100110	146	66	147	10010011	223	93
103	1100111	147	67	148	10010100	224	94
104	1101000	150	68	149	10010101	225	95
105	1101001	151	69	150	10010110	226	96
106	1101010	152	6A	151	10010111	227	97
107	1101011	153	6B	152	10011000	230	98
108	1101100	154	6C	153	10011001	231	99
109	1101101	155	6D	154	10011010	232	9A
110	1101110	156	6E	155	10011011	233	9B
111	1101111	157	6F	156	10011100	234	9C
112	1110000	160	70	157	10011101	235	9D
113	1110001	161	71	158	10011110	236	9E
114	1110010	162	72	159	10011111	237	9F
115	1110011	163	73	160	10100000	240	A0
116	1110100	164	74	161	10100001	241	A1
117	1110101	165	75	162	10100010	242	A2
118	1110111	166	76	163	10100011	243	A3
119	1110111	167	77	164	10100100	244	A4
120	1111000	170	78	165	10100101	245	A5
121	1111001	171	79	166	10100110	246	A6
122	1111010	172	7A	167	10100111	247	A7
123	1111011	173	7B	168	10101000	250	A8
124	1111100	174	7C	169	10101001	251	A9
125	1111101	175	7D	170	10101010	252	AA
126	1111110	176	7E	171	10101011	253	AB
127	1111111	177	7F	172	10101100	254	AC
128	10000000	200	80	173	10101101	255	AD
129	10000001	201	81	174	10101110	256	AE
130	10000010	202	82	175	10101111	257	AF
131	10000011	203	83	176	10110000	260	B0
132	10000100	204	84	177	10110001	261	B1
133	10000101	205	85	178	10110010	262	B2
134	10000110	206	86	179	10110011	263	B3

EXHIBIT XIII.2-1—CONTINUED

Decimal Number	Binary	Octal	Hex	Decimal Number	Binary	Octal	Hex
180	10110100	264	B4	225	11100001	341	E1
181	10110101	265	B5	226	11100010	342	E2
182	10110110	266	B6	227	11100011	343	E3
183	10110111	267	B7	228	11100100	344	E4
184	10111000	270	B8	229	11100101	345	E5
185	10111001	271	B9	230	11100110	346	E6
186	10111010	272	BA	231	11100111	347	E7
187	10111011	273	BB	232	11101000	350	E8
188	10111100	274	BC	233	11101001	351	E9
189	10111101	275	BD	234	11101010	352	EA
190	10111110	276	BE	235	11101011	353	EB
191	10111111	277	BF	236	11101100	354	EC
192	11000000	300	C0	237	11101101	355	ED
193	11000001	301	C1	238	11101110	356	EE
194	11000010	302	C2	239	11101111	357	EF
195	11000011	303	C3	240	11110000	360	F0
196	11000100	304	C4	241	11110001	361	F1
197	11000101	305	C5	242	11110010	362	F2
198	11000110	306	C6	243	11110011	363	F3
199	11000111	307	C7	244	11110100	364	F4
200	11001000	310	C8	245	11110101	365	F5
201	11001001	311	C9	246	11110110	366	F6
202	11001010	312	CA	247	11110111	367	F7
203	11001011	313	CB	248	11111000	370	F8
204	11001100	314	CC	249	11111001	371	F9
205	11001101	315	CD	250	11111010	372	FA
206	11001110	316	CE	251	11111011	373	FB
207	11001111	317	CF	252	11111100	374	FC
208	11010000	320	D0	253	11111101	375	FD
209	11010001	321	D1	254	11111110	376	FE
210	11010010	322	D2	255	11111111	377	FF
211	11010011	323	D3	256	100000000	400	100
212	11010100	324	D4				
213	11010101	325	D5				
214	11010110	326	D6				
215	11010111	327	D7				
216	11011000	330	D8				
217	11011001	331	D9				
218	11011010	332	DA				
219	11011011	333	DB				
220	11011100	334	DC				
221	11011101	335	DD				
222	11011110	336	DE				
223	11011111	337	DF				
224	11100000	340	E0